John G. Elwood

A MATHEMATICS REFRESHER

(American Edition)

A Mathematics Refresher

AMERICAN EDITION

A. HOOPER, M. A.

NEW YORK
HENRY HOLT AND COMPANY

PREFACE

The original (English) edition of this book, entitled *A Mathematical Refresher*, was written primarily for Royal Air Force candidates who found their mathematics rusty through disuse or who, brought face to face with facts, had to admit that they had not properly grasped the subject at school.

The need for a book of this type was forcibly brought home to the author while coaching R.A.F. men at Scapa Flow who were anxious to qualify as air crew candidates. He therefore brought together MSS and notes compiled during twenty years' teaching, and adapted them to the needs of these young men. Having formed certain very definite views on the necessity for scrapping the old-fashioned methods leading to a grasp of mathematical reasoning, he braved the indignation and scorn of his more orthodox colleagues and boldly set down his own methods of teaching and explanation, which, whatever their mathematical merit, did appear to achieve results. His object is to enable a person of average intelligence to achieve a clear grasp of the essentials of Arithmetic, Algebra, Geometry and Trigonometry with the minimum expenditure of time and effort. The first essential is to break down the barriers, largely artificial, which prevent so many intelligent people from mastering the beautiful simplicity and ordered sequence of mathematical processes. These latter cannot dovetail into each other quickly and naturally if the subject, like Gaul, is divided into three parts. It is possible that separate books on Arithmetic, Algebra and Geometry may be more convenient in school (though the author would contest this); but the fact remains that many boys and girls leave school under the impression that Arithmetic, Algebra and Geometry—to say nothing of such dark mysteries as Trigonometry and Mechanics—are different subjects whose only point in common is their incomprehensibility.

It happened that the author was transferred to Canada immediately after he had completed the MS of the original book (and, luckily for him, before the labor of proofreading could fall on him). In Canada he has been privileged to coach many air crew candidates from Canada and the United States, and quite a number of these young men have admitted that the author's diagnosis of mathematical weakness applies in the New World as well as in the Old. It is at the suggestion of several of these new friends that the author has ventured to revise his original book and produce this American edition.

Being to a great extent freed from the incubus of British currency, weights and measures, this book is naturally even easier than the original "Refresher."

Learned mathematicians, should they chance to light on the book, will doubtless close it with a shudder when they see, for instance, oranges mixed up with Latitude and Longitude. But if the average man finds that an orange helps him to grasp abstract ideas, let him have an orange.

It has been borne in mind throughout the book that many people who discover a need for mathematics after leaving school find they have little or no opportunity of receiving regular instruction by an experienced teacher. Hence, full explanations have been included, such as would be given by a class-room teacher, on those difficulties and pitfalls which experience has shown habitually trip up the unwary.

For the guidance of this class of readers the author ventures to add a few general remarks:

(1) To reason mathematically is like climbing up a mental ladder. One rung leads to the next. Be sure therefore that your feet are firmly on each rung before you attempt to climb higher. Otherwise you will be like the Irishman and tread on the step that isn't there, with unfortunate results. This book has not been thrown together in a haphazard way. Every chapter and every step has been inserted deliberately in a certain order so that the reader, provided he masters every chapter as he goes along, will gain a clear and "dove-tailed" grasp of mathematical processes of reasoning.

(2) You are advised to read through a chapter rapidly and get a rough idea what it is all about. Don't worry about grasping every detail at this first reading of the chapter.

(3) Now take paper and pencil and work steadily through every detail in that chapter and refuse to leave it until you have thoroughly grasped every word in it.

(4) Turn to the exercises on that particular chapter and work at least a selection from them—the answers will be found at the very end of the book.

(5) If you can find a good-natured, long-suffering friend who will bear with you, try now to explain the chapter to him (or, more likely, to her). There is nothing like having to teach a subject to make you understand it thoroughly.

It is hoped that the book may not only prove of help to those anxious to serve their country in the air, but that it may also appeal to that much wider public who so frequently assert they "can't do mathematics." It may possibly help the man who has had a mathematical inferiority complex foisted on him by the kind of teaching that he has had to endure at school to discover that after all he "*can* do mathematics."

A. H.

PORT ALBERT, ONTARIO
June, 1942

CONTENTS

CHAP.   PAGE

1 THE ROMANCE OF NUMBERS 1

2 HOW TO USE DECIMALS 4

3 ANGLES—I 11

4 ANGLES—II. Measurement of Direction 16

5 PLANE AND SOLID FIGURES 25

6 THE METRIC SYSTEM 29

7 ARITHMETIC'S SHORTHAND—ALGEBRA 38

8 SHORTHAND "DIRECTION" IN ALGEBRA 45

9 GEOMETRY WITHOUT TEARS 55

10. SIMPLE GRAPHS 63

11 ALGEBRAIC BINOMIALS: Factors 75

12 FRACTIONS OTHER THAN DECIMAL FRACTIONS 84

13 SIMPLE EQUATIONS 95

14 FORMULAS AND PROBLEMS LEADING TO EQUATIONS . . . 102

15 MORE GEOMETRICAL CONSTRUCTIONS 111

16 PARALLELOGRAMS AND TRIANGLES: Areas 114

17 RATIOS: Proportion, Direct and Inverse; Taxes, Percentage, Simple and Compound Interest 118

18 AVERAGES 140

19 SQUARE ROOT OF ANY NUMBER 146

CONTENTS

CHAP.   PAGE

20 MORE ABOUT SIMILAR FIGURES 149

21 RIGHT-ANGLED TRIANGLES: Theorem of Pythagoras, Trigonometrical Ratios 157

22 SCALE DRAWING: Plans, Direction, Maps and Map-making . 169

23 TIME 181

24 OTHER KINDS OF EQUATIONS: Simultaneous, Quadratic . . 187

25 TWELVE IMPORTANT FACTS ABOUT A CIRCLE 200

26 VELOCITY AND ACCELERATION 204

27 GRAVITY 206

28 RELATIVE VELOCITY AND THE PARALLELOGRAM AND TRIANGLE
   OF VELOCITIES: Application to Air Navigation . . . 209

29 CENTER OF GRAVITY 218

30 LOGARITHMS 225

31 TRIGONOMETRICAL RATIOS: The Solution of Triangles . . 234

32 CALCULATING RELATIVE GROWTH 248

33 RADIANS AND MILS 259

   EXERCISES 261

   TEST PAPERS 312

   ANSWERS 318

   WEIGHTS AND MEASURES 335

   BRITISH MONEY 337

   INDEX 339

   TABLES . . . . i to xvi

CHAPTER 1

THE ROMANCE OF NUMBERS

How the Decimal Scale Arose

Men have ten fingers. Therefore in earliest times they formed the habit of counting things in groups of ten. To help this counting they eventually invented a counting-frame called an Abacus

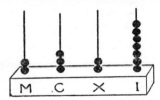

Fig. 1.—Simplest form of Abacus.

(Fig. 1)—still to be seen in our nursery schools. When ten beads have been put on the right-hand wire they are removed and one bead is placed on the next column, to represent the ten taken off the first, and so on.

For centuries no one could think of an easy way in which numbers as shown on the abacus could be written on paper or carved on stone. The Greeks used the letters of their alphabet to represent different numbers, while the Romans used the clumsy signs we still meet with in what are called Roman Numerals.

The number on the abacus sketched in Fig. 1 would have been represented by the Romans as

MMCCCXXVII

This single example shows that it was quite impossible to work even simple calculations which could be performed by a schoolboy to-day with the improved "tools" now at his command.

It also explains how it came about that what we call Arithmetic and Algebra did not—could not indeed—come into existence until a new method of expressing numbers had been invented. By that time the Egyptians and Greeks (and also the Chinese) had discovered many strange and significant facts about lines and figures drawn on a plane or flat surface. The study of such figures arose in order to meet a practical need in Egypt, where the annual flooding of the Nile necessitated the annual marking out of a person's property. The Greeks continued this study of "Geometry" or "Earth-measuring," and men such as THALES (c. 600 B.C.), PYTHAGORAS (c. 550 B.C.), EUCLID (c. 300 B.C.) and ARCHIMEDES OF SYRACUSE (c. 250 B.C.) gave formal expression to this earliest branch of Mathematics. This study of "plane figures" without the aid of other branches of Mathematics involved processes of reasoning which were so difficult to grasp that only those with carefully trained minds could master them thoroughly—as would readily be admitted by generations of unhappy schoolboys forced to study "Euclid" in the way it was taught 300 years before Christ.

In the seventh century A.D. the Arab followers of Mohammed laid the foundations of a great Moslem Empire which stretched from Spain right across North Africa and into Asia. Nordic barbarians were to owe much to this Empire. These Arabs eventually set up Universities—for example at Granada in Spain—where they taught a new and revolutionary method of putting down on paper a "picture" of beads on the abacus, a method they had learned from the Hindus. Like many great inventions, this one was so simple that the marvel is that no one had thought of it before. It consisted first of all of nine signs for each of the numbers "one" to "nine." Later on, a sign for "zero" was added—a most important addition. The all-important thing about this new system was that the position of a digit (as we shall in future speak of the Hindu signs 0, 1, 2, 3, 4, 5, 6, 7, 8, 9) determined its real value, just as the position of a bead on the abacus determines whether it stands for 1 or 10 or 100 or 1000 beads. Thus the number "67" does not stand for 6 added to 7, nor for 6 times 7, but for 6 tens added to 7 units or "ones."

Thanks to this simple invention, Mathematics as we know it today has been built up and has enabled the modern world of science and mechanics to emerge. About 1500 A.D. the principle of the abacus was extended so that fractions of whole numbers could be represented on paper in a very simple fashion.

Thus Fig. 2 represents the number 2327·352 (or 2 thousand, 3 hundred, 2 tens, 7 units and 3 tenths, 5 hundredths and 2 thou-

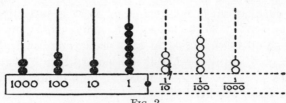

FIG. 2.

sandths). The dot which separates the whole number from the fractional or decimal part is called the decimal point. In Britain it is written as above. In America it is written on the line, thus—2327.352. On the Continent of Europe a comma is used—2327,352.

For all practical purposes decimals may be used to express any fraction, although some fractions cannot be expressed exactly in decimal form. *E.g.* $3\frac{1}{3}$ can only be written, in decimal form, as 3.333333 . . ., the decimal recurring forever. But for all practical purposes (and Mathematics has to deal with practical things) $3.33 is as accurate as is necessary to represent $3\frac{1}{3}$ (see page 9). The important thing to remember is that in representing a fraction like $\frac{1}{3}$ the farther you take the decimal to the right the nearer to $\frac{1}{3}$ it becomes, and you can take it as near as practical needs may require.

CHAPTER 2

HOW TO USE DECIMALS

RULE 1.—**To Read a Decimal.** Remember that decimals must never be read as whole numbers; *e.g.* 25.25 is not "twenty-five point twenty-five." 25.25 means "twenty-five whole numbers and two tenths and five hundredths of a whole number." To avoid such clumsy description we read a decimal figure by figure, thus *"twenty-five point two five."* 435.0035 "four hundred thirty-five point zero zero three five."

RULE 2.—**To Multiply or Divide by 10, 100, 1000.** . . . Look at the picture of the abacus in Fig. 2. You will see at a glance that *every place you move the point to the right increases the value of the whole expression ten times* and that *every place you move it to the left diminishes it ten times.*

Examples. 297.36 × 10   =   2973.6
297.36 × 100   =   29736
297.36 × 1000 = 297360, and so on.

Now you see the value of the invention of the sign 0. It keeps the other digits in their proper abacus places.

297.36 ÷ 10   = 29.736
297.36 ÷ 100   = 2.9736
297.36 ÷ 1000 =   .29736
297.36 ÷ 10000 =   .029736, and so on.

Note that all you do is to move the point as many places as there are 0's in the multiplier or the divisor.

Rule 3.—**To Add or Subtract Decimals.** When writing down the numbers to be added or subtracted, *put the decimal points underneath each other.* Thus:—

Addition   29.37
            5.046   Subtraction
            17.928   239.25   37 *
            237.4103   119.41   17.48
            289.7543←   119.84←   19.52←

* *N.B.*—37 is the same value as 37.00. You may imagine as many 0's on the right-hand side of a decimal as you need.

In adding, combine 1 and 9, 2 and 8, 3 and 7, 4 and 6, 5 and 5 (each sum = 10) whenever possible.

Note on Multiplication

We know that $3 \times 4 = 12$. This is a short way of doing the addition sum:—

            3
            3
            3
            3
           12←

Now let us consider the meaning of $.7 \times 3$. This is another way of indicating that .7 has to be written down 3 times and an addition performed.

            .7
            .7
            .7
           2.1←

We see we could have obtained this result more easily by *multiplying 7 by 3 and putting in a point one place from the right-hand end of answer.*

Now consider $.7 \times 2.5$.   This means .7 added to itself $2\frac{5}{10}$ $(= 2\frac{1}{2})$ times.

$$\begin{array}{r} .7 \\ .7 \\ \hline .35 \\ \hline 1.75 \end{array}$$ *(i.e.* one-half of 70 hundredths)

$1.75\leftarrow$

We see we could have obtained this result more easily by *multiplying 7 by 25 (or 25 by 7) and putting in a point two places from the right-hand end of answer.*

Now consider $.06 \times .01$. This means that .06 must be written down not three times nor two and a half times, but one hundredth of one time, *i.e.* the sum has now become the division sum $.06 \div 100$. Now $.06 \div 100 = .0006$ (moving the point 2 places to the left).

$$\therefore .06 \times .01 = .0006\leftarrow$$

We see we could have obtained this result more easily by *multiplying 6 by 1 and putting in a point four places from the right-hand end of answer.*

RULE 4.—**To Multiply Decimals.**   From the above examples we can deduce the following simple rules for multiplying numbers involving decimals:—

1. *Ignore decimal points until multiplication is finished.*

2. *Count the number of decimal places in multiplicand and multiplier (two top lines) and put a point in your answer that number of places from the right-hand end.*

[*N.B.*—*Remember to begin each line under the figure by which you are multiplying.*]

Thus:

3.052	2.056	3.027
27.6	.0031	2.06
18312	2056	18162
21364	6168	6054
6104	.0063736←	6.23562←
84.2352←		

RULE 5.—**To Divide Decimals by Numbers other than 10, 100, 1000.** . . . *Turn the divisor* (the number by which you are to divide) *into a whole number* if it is not one already by moving the point the necessary number of places to the right. To balance up matters, *move the point in the dividend* (the number to be divided) *the same number of places to the right.* [$8 \div 2 = 4$, and $(8 \times 10) \div (2 \times 10)$ still equals 4, and so on.]

Examples:

(1) **Short division** (when the divisor in whole number form is not more than 12).

$$27 \div 0.3 = 270 \div 3 = 90 \leftarrow$$
$$3 \div 0.4 = \quad 30 \div 4 \text{ (remember } 30 = 30.0)$$
$$= \quad 7.5 \leftarrow$$

(2) **Compound division** (when the divisor can be split into factors * each < 13).†

$$.196 \div 3.2$$
$$= 1.96 \div 32. \quad \text{Now } 32 = 4 \times 8.$$

$$4)\overline{1.96}$$
$$8)\ \overline{.49} \qquad \text{(remember } .49 = .49000)$$
$$= \ \underline{.06125} \leftarrow$$

---

* A *factor* of a number is another number which *goes into it* exactly.
† Shorthand signs to be remembered:—

$<$ "is less than" $(2 < 3)$
$>$ "is greater than" $(3 > 2)$
$\therefore$ "therefore"
$\because$ "because."

(3) **Long division** [when method (1) or (2) cannot be employed].

$.416065 \div .0325$

$= 4160.65 \div 325$

$= 12.802 \leftarrow$

$$325)\overline{4160.65}$$

325

───

910

650

────

2606

2600

────

650

650

────

[In long division it is easier to put your Quotient (answer) *above* the Dividend. Put the point in Quotient above the point in Dividend. Remember that *whenever you bring down a figure* you must *put up a figure* in your answer even if it is only 0.]

To multiply quickly by **25**, move the point two places to the right and divide the answer by 4.

(*i.e.* you first multiply by 100 which is 4 times too large, so you divide that answer by 4.), *e.g.*

$$374.9 \times 25 = \frac{37490}{4}^{*} = 9372.5 \leftarrow$$

To divide quickly by **25**, move the point two places to the left and multiply the answer by 4.

(*i.e.* you first divide by 100 which makes your answer 4 times too small, so you multiply it by 4.), *e.g.*

$$37.49 \div 25 = .3749 \times 4 = 1.4996 \leftarrow$$

To multiply quickly by **125**, move the point three places to the right (*i.e.* multiply by 1000) and divide by 8 $\left(\because 125 = \frac{1000}{8} \right)$.

To divide quickly by **125**, move the point three places to the left (*i.e.* divide by 1000) and multiply by 8.

---

* Note the short way $\left(\frac{37490}{4} \right)$ of writing "$37490 \div 4$."

RULE 6.—**Approximation of Decimals.** If we divide 1 by 3 the answer is .333333 . . . This is called a recurring decimal and is written .3̇. Note that the farther we take .333333 . . . . to the right the closer the value approximates to the exact value of 1 divided by 3.

Now Mathematics deals with real things in everyday life. Suppose we want to find the value of $.3̇. This may be written $.333333 . . . But a little consideration will show that only the first two decimal places mean anything in this case. There are 100 cents in $1, therefore the second decimal place ($\frac{1}{100}$) stands for cents, but all the places to the right of this second place mean nothing. The third place, for instance, stands for $\frac{1}{1000}$ which for practical purposes means nothing to us.

In dealing with large quantities, we sometimes use more than two decimal places, *e.g.*, an author may receive $.3125 per copy on a book. *If a large number are sold* the third and fourth decimal places are important to him.

We often need to write a decimal "correct to (so many) decimal places."

Now .36 is nearer to .4 than to .3 (since 36 hundredths is nearer 40 hundredths than it is to 30 hundredths). So we should write .36 *correct to one decimal place as* .4.

The rule is, *Look at the decimal place that follows the last one required. If it is 5 or more, add 1 to the last place required.*

17.536917 correct to 5 decimal places = 17.53692
    "   "   4   "   "   = 17.5369
    "   "   3   "   "   = 17.537
    "   "   2   "   "   = 17.54
    "   "   1   "   place = 17.5

Sometimes we want to write an expression "correct to (so many) **significant figures.**" *These include the whole numbers in the expression.*

Thus 17.536917 correct to 7 significant figures = 17.53692
" " 6 " " = 17.5369
" " 5 " " = 17.537
" " 4 " " = 17.54
" " 3 " " = 17.5
" " 2 " " = 18
" " 1 " figure = 20

But note that when there are no whole numbers, and the decimal commences with 0 (or 0's) these 0's are not considered as significant.

Thus .004936 correct to 3 significant figures = .00494, but correct to 3 decimal places = .005.

For Exercises see pp. 261–263.

The answer to an **addition** is called the **sum** of the numbers involved.
The answer to a **subtraction** is called the **difference** of the numbers involved.
The answer to a **multiplication** is called the **product** of the numbers involved.
The answer to a **division** is called the **quotient** of the numbers involved.

CHAPTER 3

ANGLES—I

An Angle is an Amount of "Turning"

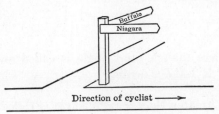

Directions on sign-post seen from above, and angle through which handle-bars are turned.

Fig. 3.—A cyclist approaching Niagara turns off towards Buffalo.

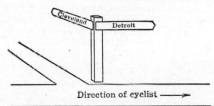

Directions on sign-post seen from above, and angle through which handle-bars are turned.

Fig. 4.—Another cyclist approaching Detroit turns off towards Cleveland.

Note that it makes no difference to the amount of turning you must do whether the arms of the sign-post are long or short. An angle is not measured by the length of its arms, but by the amount of turning between two lines (or directions). Thus:

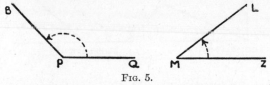

Fig. 5.

* ∠ BPQ is larger than ∠ LMZ.

* Note (1) the shorthand sign for angle, ∠
      (2) In naming an angle put the letter at the point between the other two letters of its arms.

Right Angle. A quarter of a complete turn or revolution is called a *right angle.* (Shorthand: rt. ∠)

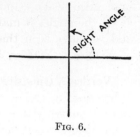

FIG. 6.

Acute Angle. An angle less than a right angle is called an *acute angle.* (Thus, in Fig. 5, ∠ LMZ is acute.)

Obtuse Angle. An angle greater than a right angle is called an *obtuse angle.* (Thus, in Fig. 5, ∠ BPQ is obtuse.)

Reflex Angle. An angle greater than two right angles is called a *reflex angle.*

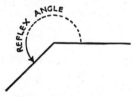

/FIG. 7.

Complements and Supplements. Angles which together make up one right angle are *complementary.* Angles which together make up two right angles are *supplementary.*

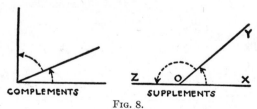

COMPLEMENTS   SUPPLEMENTS

FIG. 8.

Note *that if a line turns round a fixed point through 2 rt. ∠s it lies in exactly the opposite direction and therefore its original and final positions lie in a straight line.* Thus, in Fig. 8, if OX turns round O through 2 rt. ∠s and reaches OZ, then ZOX is a straight line. Also, when a line touches another line (*e.g.* YO touches ZX at O) the angles it makes with that line are called *adjacent* angles, and we have seen that together they make up two rt. ∠s (*e.g.* ∠ YOX + ∠ YOZ = 2 rt. ∠s).

Vertically Opposite Angles. When one line crosses another line it makes two pairs of equal angles which are called *vertically opposite angles.* Thus, in Fig. 9:—

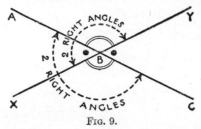

FIG. 9.

∠ ABY = ∠ XBC (vertically opposite ∠ s)
∠ ABX = ∠ YBC ("   "   ")

This can easily be proved from what we have just learned about adjacent angles being supplementary.

Angles connected with Parallel Lines

Parallel lines are lines which will never meet, no matter how far produced (or extended) in either direction.

FIG. 10.

A transverse line or "transversal" (Latin, *trans*, across) is a line cutting two or more parallel lines.

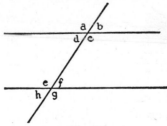

FIG. 11.

For clearness the angles are named by small letters.

ALTERNATE ANGLES

A transverse line makes 2 pairs of *alternate angles,* i.e. *angles inside the parallel lines and on opposite or alternate sides of the transverse line.* Alternate angles are equal. Thus, in Fig. 11:

$$\angle d = \angle f, \quad \text{and} \quad \angle c = \angle e.$$

CORRESPOND- ING ANGLES

A transverse line makes 4 pairs of *corresponding angles,* i.e. *each pair has one angle inside the parallel lines, the other outside the parallel lines, but both are on the same or corresponding side of the transverse line.* Corresponding angles are equal. Thus:

$$\angle a = \angle e, \ \angle d = \angle h, \ \angle b = \angle f, \ \angle c = \angle g.$$

In Fig. 11, therefore, we have:—

$$\angle d = \angle f \quad \text{(alternate)}$$
$$\angle c = \angle e \quad \text{(alternate)}$$

$$\angle a = \angle e \quad \text{(corresponding)}$$
$$\angle d = \angle h \quad \text{(corresponding)}$$
$$\angle b = \angle f \quad \text{(corresponding)}$$
$$\angle c = \angle g \quad \text{(corresponding)}$$

Note also that

$$\angle a + \angle b = 2 \text{ rt. } \angle \text{s} \quad (i.e. \ a \text{ is supplement of } b)$$
$$\angle b + \angle c = 2 \text{ rt. } \angle \text{s} \quad (i.e. \ b \ " \quad " \quad " \ c)$$
$$\angle c + \angle d = 2 \text{ rt. } \angle \text{s} \quad (i.e. \ c \ " \quad " \quad " \ d)$$
$$\angle d + \angle a = 2 \text{ rt. } \angle \text{s} \quad (i.e. \ d \ " \quad " \quad " \ a)$$
$$\angle e + \angle f = 2 \text{ rt. } \angle \text{s} \quad (i.e. \ e \ " \quad " \quad " \ f)$$
$$\text{etc.}$$

Note also that $\begin{cases} \angle\,a = \angle\,c & \text{(vertically opposite)} \\ \angle\,b = \angle\,d & (\quad`` \qquad `` \quad) \\ \angle\,e = \angle\,g & (\quad`` \qquad `` \quad) \\ \angle\,f = \angle\,h & (\quad`` \qquad `` \quad) \end{cases}$

Note also that—

$$\text{Since } \angle\,e = \angle\,c \quad \text{(alternate)}$$

and since $\angle\,f + \angle\,e = 2$ rt. $\angle$ s

$\therefore \quad \angle\,f + \angle\,c = 2$ rt. $\angle$ s.

In the same way $\angle\,d + \angle\,e = 2$ rt. $\angle$ s.

For Exercises see pp. 264–265.

CHAPTER 4

ANGLES—II

Measurement of Direction

For convenience of measurement every right angle is divided into 90 smaller angles called degrees. For very exact measurements the degree is divided into 60 smaller angles called minutes, and each minute into 60 seconds.

$$60 \text{ seconds } ('') = 1 \text{ minute } (')$$
$$60 \text{ minutes } = 1 \text{ degree } (°)$$
$$90° = 1 \text{ right } \angle$$

Angles are measured by a *protractor*. The most useful form of protractor not only shows every degree in two right angles but also has graduations in inches and centimeters and sometimes a diagonal scale marked on it. A typical protractor is shown in Fig. 12.

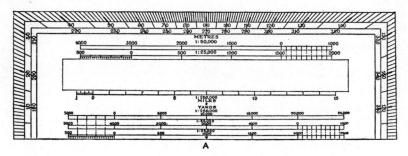

Fig. 12.—Protractor.

Degrees are marked along three edges but only the ends of the angle-arms are shown. The point from which these lines are drawn is marked by an arrow on the bottom edge (marked A in Fig. 12).

There are two sets of figures to these graduations, one set reading from 0° to 180° and another set reading from 180° to 360°.

How to use a Protractor.—Direction in aviation is indicated by the angle between the **North** and the required direction, measured clockwise, and always commencing at the North.

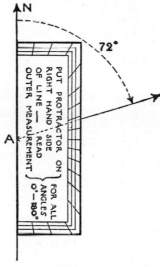

Fig. 13.

EXAMPLE 1.—*Suppose we have to mark on the map a direction 72° from a given spot A.*

(1) Draw a line through A marking the direction North (every map gives this direction).

(2) Place protractor on *right-hand side* of line *for all angles from 0° to 180°.* Put arrow on protractor at A.

(3) Read *outer* angle-measurement on protractor (for all angles *up to 180°*).

(4) Put a dot on map where 72° mark comes.

(5) Remove protractor. Join A to this point and produce line if necessary. All places on this line will be 72° from A.

This particular direction or bearing (72°) is sometimes given as N. 72° E.

EXAMPLE 2.—*To mark a direction 250° from X.*

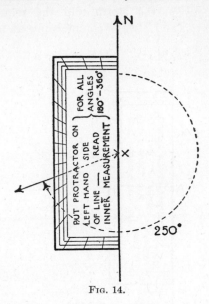

FIG. 14.

(1) As before, draw line through X due North.

(2) Place protractor on *left-hand side* of this line (because the direction is *more than* 180°). Put arrow on protractor at X.

(3) Read *inner* angle-measurement on protractor (for all angles *more than* 180°).

(4) Put a dot on map where 250° mark comes.

(5) Join X to this point and produce line. All places on this line will be 250° from X.

A bearing of 250° is sometimes called S. 70° W.

EXAMPLE 3.—Similarly, 130° from K would mean a direction 130° from North in a clockwise direction (or S. 50° E.).

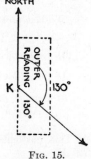

FIG. 15.

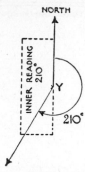

EXAMPLE 4.—Fig. 16 shows a direction 210° from Y (or S. 30° W.).

EXAMPLE 5.—Fig. 17 shows a direction 315° from P [or N.W. (see p. 24), *i.e.* N. 45° W.].

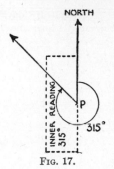

Fig. 17.

Fig. 16.

For Exercises see pp. 265–266.

Two rough but practical methods of finding your way if lost or in a strange country.

(*a*) If stars are visible, find the Great Bear or Plough (visible only N. of Equator).

Draw an imaginary line through Merak and Dubhe, the two end stars known as "Pointers." Continue this line and it will point almost directly to the Pole Star which is always practically due N. of us.

If you walk with the Pole Star directly before you, you will go due North. If you walk with the Pole Star on your left hand, you will go due East. If you walk with the Pole Star on your right hand, you will go due West.

If you walk with the Pole Star behind you, you will go due South.

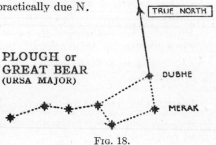

Fig. 18.

(*b*) If the sun is visible hold your watch flat, and point the hour-hand towards the direction of the sun (Fig. 19). *Midway between the hour-hand and the 12 o'clock mark will be the direction South.*

This method only applies North of the Equator. In the Southern Hemisphere, point 12 o'clock mark to the sun, then North lies midway between the 12 o'clock mark and the hour-hand.

NOTE.—If "daylight saving" is in operation remember that your hour-hand is 1 hour ahead of the true or sun time, so allow for this.

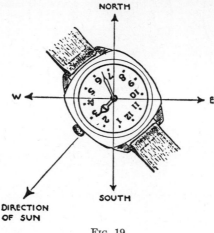

FIG. 19.

This simple knowledge has enabled many prisoners of war to escape and has saved many lives.

Latitude and Longitude

Latitude and Longitude are *angles*.   Their meaning is easily grasped provided a transparent sphere or ball can be visualized. The meaning of certain terms must also be clearly understood. Here they are:—

GREAT CIRCLE.—Any imaginary circle right round the Earth in any direction, provided it cuts the Earth's surface into two equal parts.

MERIDIAN.—Any Great Circle which passes through N. and S. Poles.

EQUATOR.—The Great Circle half-way between N. and S. Poles.

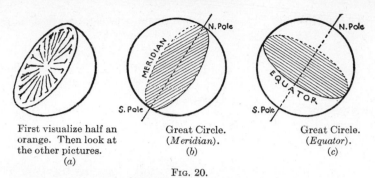

First visualize half an
orange. Then look at
the other pictures.
(a)

Great Circle.
(*Meridian*).
(b)

Great Circle.
(*Equator*).
(c)

Fig. 20.

PLANE.—A flat level surface. The shaded part of Fig. 20*b*
is the Plane of a Meridian.
That in Fig. 20*c* is the Plane of
the Equator. The center of the
Earth lies at the center of the
Plane of every Great Circle.

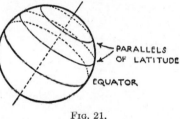

PARALLELS OF LATITUDE
(Fig. 21).—Circles (*not* Great
Circles) parallel to the Equator.

Fig. 21.

The meaning of the statement *Plymouth is Latitude* 50° N.

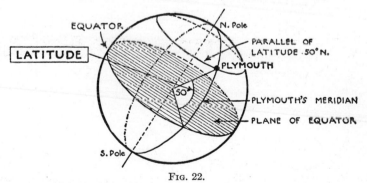

Fig. 22.

If you have difficulty in visualizing this picture, have another
look at the half-orange, Fig. 20(*a*).

The Latitude of Plymouth is the angle between two imaginary lines:—

(1) The line joining Plymouth to the center of the Earth.
(2) The line joining the center of the Earth to the place where Plymouth's Meridian cuts the Equator.

Since this angle is found to be 50° we say that the Latitude of Plymouth (or of any place on this particular Parallel of Latitude) is 50° N., *i.e.* 50° North of the Equator's plane.

The meaning of the statement *Mecca is Longitude* 40° E.

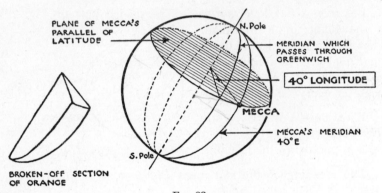

FIG. 23.

The Longitude of Mecca is the angle between the plane of Mecca's Meridian and the plane of the Meridian through Greenwich. Since this angle is found to be 40° to the E. of the Greenwich Meridian the Longitude of Mecca (or of any other place on Mecca's half-Meridian) is said to be 40° E.

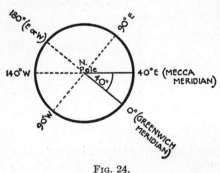

FIG. 24.

The reason why only places on the same *half-*

Meridian Great Circle as Mecca have the same Longitude as Mecca will be apparent if the Earth is viewed from a point directly over the N. Pole (or S. Pole) where all Meridians of Longitude cross each other. (See Fig. 24.)

NOTE CAREFULLY—

(1) All places on the same Parallel of Latitude have the same Latitude.

(2) Only places on the same half-Meridian have the same Longitude.

(3) Distance round Equator = distance round any Meridian G. C. (approximately).

(4) Distances round Parallels of Latitude *decrease* the nearer one approaches N. or S. Poles.

(5) 1° of Latitude measured on the Earth's surface along any Meridian represents $\frac{1}{360}$ of the distance right round the Earth (*i.e.* round any Great Circle). 1° of Latitude on *any* Meridian (or 1° of Longitude on the Equator *only*) therefore represents 69 land miles (approximately), or 60 sea-miles as measured on the Earth's surface.

(6) 1 sea-mile = 6080 feet (Admiralty sea-mile) = 1 nautical mile.

(7) 60 sea-miles = 69 land-miles (approximately). More exactly $\frac{1}{66}$ land-mile = $\frac{1}{76}$ nautical mile.

(8) All places on the same half-Meridian Great Circle have noon simultaneously, since noon at any place is the time when the sun crosses the Meridian of that place. (Britain everywhere takes as "noon" the time when the sun crosses the *Greenwich* Meridian. Hence "Greenwich Mean Time.")

Magnetic North, etc.

NOTE.—A magnetic compass points to the Magnetic North, which is not quite the same as the True North.

The 32 points of the Compass are N., N. by E., N.N.E., N.E. by N., N.E., N.E. by E., E.N.E., E. by N., E., etc. Obviously to turn a ship from N. to E. involves turning through an angle of 90°.

From N. to N. by E. will be a turn of $11\frac{1}{4}°$ (90° ÷ 8) and this angle of $11\frac{1}{4}°$ lies between each point.

These points of the Compass are not needed, as a rule, by air navigators.

Fig. 25.

To learn to "Box the Compass."

    (*a*) First learn the cardinal (chief) points: N. S. E. W.

    (*b*) Then the points mid-way between them: N.E., S.E., S.W., N.W.

    (*c*) Then the points between the latter: N.N.E., E.N.E., E.S.E., S.S.E., S.S.W., W.S.W., W.N.W., N.N.W.

    (*d*) The remaining points are based on (*a*) and (*b*), viz.: On either side of N. we have N. by E., N. by W.; on either side of N.E. we have N.E. by N., N.E. by E.; on either side of E. we have E. by N., E. by S., etc.

    (*e*) Then learn to go round from N. in clockwise direction.

For Exercises see p. 266.

CHAPTER 5

PLANE AND SOLID FIGURES

Notes on Solids, Planes, etc.

If we consider a brick, we find it is a certain amount of matter (*i.e.* baked clay) having six *faces*, each of which is a *plane surface*. (A carpenter's plane turns an uneven surface of wood into a plane surface.)

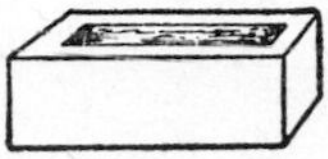

Each edge of the brick is at *right angles* to each of the other edges that touch it.

The opposite sides or edges of each face of a brick are *parallel* to each other.

There are various kinds of plane figures:—

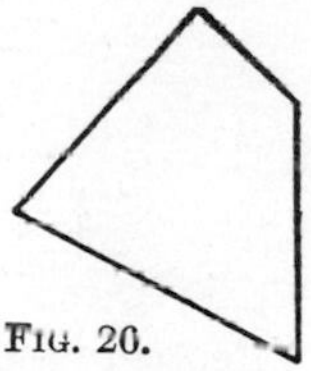

1. QUADRILATERAL: any four-sided plane figure (Fig. 26).

Fig. 26.

2. TRAPEZIUM: a quadrilateral having one pair only of parallel sides (Fig. 27).

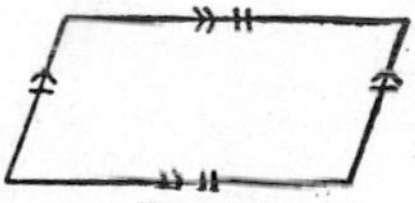

Fig. 27.

3. PARALLELOGRAM: a quadrilateral with its opposite sides parallel (they are also equal).* (Fig. 28.)

Fig. 28.

4. RECTANGLE: a parallelogram whose angles are all right angles. There are two kinds of rectangles: the SQUARE and the OBLONG (Fig. 29).

OBLONG   SQUARE
Fig. 29.

* (Note way of marking equal lines by *strokes*, parallel lines by *arrows*.)

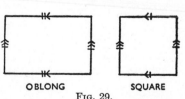

Note that a rectangle is both a parallelogram and a quadrilateral, but a quadrilateral is not necessarily either a parallelogram or a rectangle.

In the same way, a parallelogram is a quadrilateral but not necessarily a rectangle.

Now consider the faces of the solid figure known as a pyramid (Fig. 30).

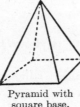 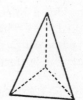

Pyramid with
square base.

Pyramid with
3-sided (triangle) base.

Fig. 30.

A *triangle* is a plane figure with three angles (and of course three sides) only. (The shorthand for triangle is △.)

TRIANGLES NAMED FROM THEIR SIDES.

 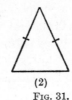 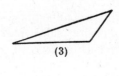

(1)   (2)   (3)

Fig. 31.

(1) *Equilateral triangle*—all three sides equal.
(2) *Isosceles triangle*—only two sides equal.
(3) *Scalene triangle*—no sides equal.

TRIANGLES NAMED FROM THEIR ANGLES.

(1) *Acute-angled triangles*—all three angles acute.

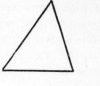

(2) *Obtuse-angled triangles*—one obtuse angle.

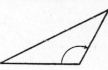

(3) *Right-angled triangle*—one angle a right angle.

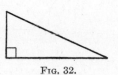

FIG. 32.

[You will find it is impossible to draw any triangle containing more than one obtuse angle or more than one right angle.]

To draw an equilateral triangle.

(1) Draw any line of convenient length. Call it AB.

(2) Take your compasses and with center A and compasses stretched from A to B draw an arc (part of a circle) over the middle of AB.

(3) Do the same from center B. Where the arcs cut will be the point C of equilateral triangle ABC.

To draw an isosceles triangle.

Repeat above, but instead of stretching compasses from A to B stretch them to any distance greater than half the distance from A to B.

This triangle ABC will be an isosceles triangle.

Names of the more common plane figures with *more than four angles* (and therefore more than four sides):—

Pentagon (5 angles, 5 sides).
Hexagon (6 " 6 ").
Octagon (8 " 8 ").

If all the angles are equal (and all the sides) these figures are called *regular* (Regular Pentagons, Regular Hexagons, etc.). Figures with many angles (usually more than four) are all called *Polygons* (Greek, *poly*, many; *gonia*, angles).

When all the angles of a polygon jut out, the polygon is *convex*. When the angles of a polygon do not all jut out, the polygon is *concave* (*i.e.* a concave polygon contains at least one *reflex* angle).

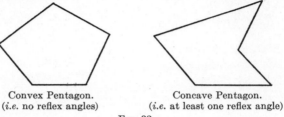

Convex Pentagon.   Concave Pentagon.
(*i.e.* no reflex angles)   (*i.e.* at least one reflex angle)

Fig. 33.

A line has *length* (Long Measure "1st Dimension").
A plane figure has *area* (Square Measure "2nd Dimension").
A solid has *volume* * (Cubic Measure "3rd Dimension").
   A solid also has *weight* or *mass*.†
   A solid also has *density* (mass divided by volume).

For Exercises see p. 266.

* Sometimes called "cubical contents" or "capacity"—more especially when referring to the volume a receptacle (*e.g.* a tank) will contain.
† Strictly speaking, "weight" is the pull of gravitation, "mass" the actual amount of stuff in a thing. Thus, though 1 lb. weight = 1 lb. mass the two things are not really the same. (See Chapter 27.)

CHAPTER 6

THE METRIC SYSTEM

Length, Area, Volume, Weight in the Metric System

One good result of the French Revolution was the introduction into France of a simplified system of weights and measures. This system is used nowadays in practically all European countries and in scientific calculations everywhere.

LENGTH

Unit: **Meter** (one ten-millionth of approximate distance between N. Pole and Equator). For shorter measures the meter is split up into tenths, hundredths, thousandths. Latin prefixes (words placed in front of other words) are used:—

$$\text{deci} = \tfrac{1}{10}$$
$$\text{centi} = \tfrac{1}{100}$$
$$\text{milli} = \tfrac{1}{1000}$$

For larger measures, Greek prefixes are used:—

$$\text{Deka} = 10$$
$$\text{Hecto} = 100$$
$$\text{Kilo} = 1000$$

Thus we get a very simple "long measure":

10 millimeters (mm.)	**= 1 centimeter (cm.)**
10 cm.	**= 1 decimeter (dm.)**
10 dm.	**= 1 meter (m.)**
10 m.	**= 1 Dekameter (Dm.)**
10 Dm.	**= 1 Hectometer (Hm.)**
10 Hm.	**= 1 Kilometer (Km.)**

Utility and Simplicity of Metric System

Since the Metric System is based on the same number (10) as the Abacus number system used by us, the complicated reduction sums involved in our weights and measures are avoided. In reduction sums under the Metric System all we have to do is to insert a decimal point after the measure required (taking care to insert a zero if any unit is omitted).

(Remember, when a whole number stands alone the decimal point is unnecessary, but if inserted it would be on the right of the units column. Thus 57 means 57.)

Example 1. Reduce 5 Km. 3 Hm. 2 m. 3 dm. 7 mm. to meters. If all the units were inserted, this would read:—

$$5 \text{ Km. } 3 \text{ Hm. } 0 \text{ Dm. } 2 \text{ m. } 3 \text{ dm. } 0 \text{ cm. } 7 \text{ mm.}$$

We now insert the decimal point after meters (as meters are asked for) and write our answer thus:—

$$5302.307 \text{ meters} \leftarrow$$

Example 2. Reduce 42165.89 dm. to Km.
(A glance at the table shows us that there are

$$10 \times 10 \times 10 \times 10, \text{ or } 10,000 \text{ dm. in 1 Km.}$$
$$\therefore \text{ we must divide 42165.89 dm. by 10,000.)}$$

Thus, moving the point four places to the left—

$$42165.89 \text{ dm. } = 4.216589 \text{ Km.} \leftarrow$$

Another way of doing this example would be to say:—

The 5 stands for whole dm.
$\therefore$ " 6 " " m.
$\therefore$ " 1 " " Dm.
$\therefore$ " 2 " " Hm.
$\therefore$ " 4 " " Km.
$\therefore$ Put decimal point after the 4 since Km. are asked for.

---

1 inch = 2.5 cm. (approx.)
5 miles = 8 Km.

AREA

The area of a plane figure is the amount of space it occupies on its plane.

The area of a rectangle is found by multiplying its **length** by its **breadth**.

This can be seen from the following figure.

Each small square is 1 cm. by 1 cm., *i.e.* 1 square cm. ∴ by counting we see that *Area of rectangle* = 12 *square centimeters*.

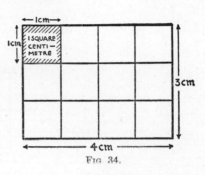

FIG. 34.

The number 12 may be obtained by multiplying length (4) by breadth (3).

When a length is multiplied by a length the answer is always area, *i.e.* square measure.

Consider the area of a square centimeter:

If the sides are divided into millimeters we can draw 100 squares, each with area 1 sq. mm. Therefore—

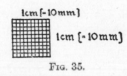

FIG. 35.

> **100 sq. mm. = 1 sq. cm.**
> **100 sq. cm. = 1 sq. dm.**
> and so on.

N.B.—In working in Square Measure under the Metric System move the point *two places* to right or left, instead of one place.

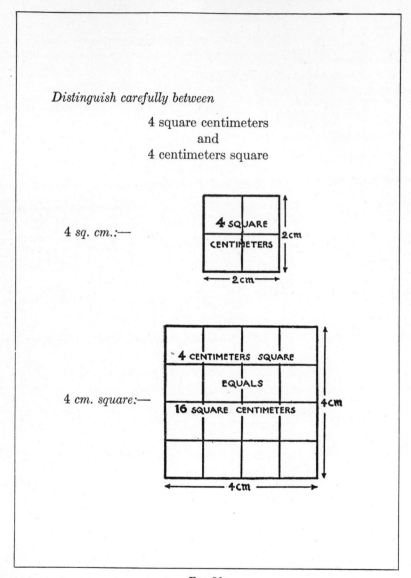

Fig. 36.

VOLUME

The volume ("cubical contents" or "capacity") of a solid is the *amount of space it occupies*. (If a bath is filled to the brim with water and a brick is gently slid into the water, the water which overflows is equal in volume to the volume of the brick.)

The capacity of a jug, bath or other receptacle is the volume (of air, water, etc.) it can contain.

To find the volume of a rectangular solid, multiply **length** by **breadth** by **height.**

Consider the following figures, *e.g.:—*

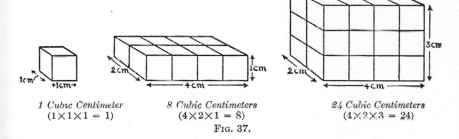

| 1 Cubic Centimeter | 8 Cubic Centimeters | 24 Cubic Centimeters |
| $(1 \times 1 \times 1 = 1)$ | $(4 \times 2 \times 1 = 8)$ | $(4 \times 2 \times 3 = 24)$ |

FIG. 37.

Note that the volumes of these solids could have been found by multiplying **area of base** by **perpendicular height** (*i.e.* height at right angles to base).

Note also that length×length×length gives cubic measure, and that area×length gives cubic measure. Mathematicians call length the 1st dimension, area the 2nd dimension, volume the 3rd dimension.

Therefore:—

1st dimension×1st dimension gives 2nd dimension.
2nd dimension×1st dimension gives 3rd dimension.
3rd dimension÷1st dimension gives 2nd dimension.
3rd dimension÷2nd dimension gives 1st dimension.

We can now build up our table for volume.

1000 (= 10×10×10) cubic millimeters (cu.mm.)
      = 1 cubic centimeter (cu.c.)
1000 c.c.   = 1 cubic decimeter (cu.dm.)
1000 c.dm. = 1 cubic meter (cu.m.)
      i.e. move point three places to right or left.

Another name for 1000 c.c. (= 1 cu. dm.) is 1 *liter*.   Since 1 c.c. of water weighs 1 gram, it follows that 1 *liter of water weighs* 1 *Kg.*

WEIGHT

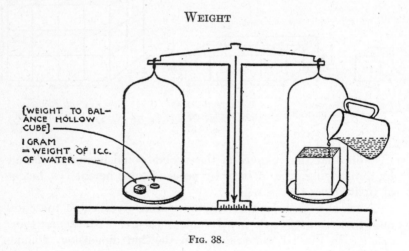

[WEIGHT TO BALANCE HOLLOW CUBE]

I GRAM = WEIGHT OF I.C.C. OF WATER

FIG. 38.

N.B.—Scales and jug are not in proportion to the cube, which has been drawn *full* (actual) *size, i.e.* 1 c.c.

Unit: **Gram.**—The weight of pure water at 4° Centigrade (= just over 39° Fahrenheit) which would be contained in a cube 1 cm. each way, or 1 c.c.

Larger and smaller measures have prefixes as before:

10 milligrams (mg.)	= 1 centigram (cg.)
10 cg.	= 1 decigram (dg.)
10 dg.	= 1 gram (g.)
10 g.	= 1 Dekagram (Dg.)
10 Dg.	= 1 Hectogram (Hg.)
10 Hg.	= 1 Kilogram (Kg.)

Remember, a gram is a *small* weight.

1000 g. = 1 Kg. = $2\frac{1}{5}$ lb. (approx.)
1 ton = 2000 lb. = 907.2 Kg. (approx.)

*Addition, Subtraction, Multiplication and Division
of units of Metric System*

(1) Add together 3.5 m., 175 cm., 2 Dm. 3 dm., giving the
answer in meters.

[We must write down each
quantity in meters, keeping
the points underneath each
other.]

m.
3.5
1.75
20.3
25.55 m.←

(2) A rod is 1.75 m. long; 14.5 cm. are cut off one end. How
many centimeters remain?

cm.
175
14.5
160.5 cm.←

(3) 4560 tins of bully beef are loaded into a
train. If each tin weighs 2500 g. find the
total weight in Kg.
[Work in Kg. 2500 g. = 2.5 Kg. We have
to multiply 2.5 by 4560.   Since 2.5
×4560 is equal to 4560×2.5 we will
choose the latter method as it is shorter.]

$$\begin{array}{r} 4560 \\ 2.5 \\ \hline 2280.0 \\ 9120 \\ \hline 11400.0 \text{ Kg.} \leftarrow \\ \hline \end{array}$$

For Exercises see pp. 267–269.

Decimal Coinage

American	100 cents	= 1 dollar ($) *
French	100 centimes (c.)	= 1 franc (fr.)
Spanish	100 centimos	= 1 peseta (pta.)
Italian	100 centesimi	= 1 lira (*plural* lire)
German	100 pfennig	= 1 mark

To convert from one denomination to the other simply move
the point *two places* to right or left.

*Remember that a single figure labeled, say, "cents" stands for
one hundredth of a dollar and so must go in the* **second** *decimal place
if being expressed in dollars.*

Remember also that 19.7 fr. means, *not* 19 fr. 7 centimes, but
19 fr. 70 centimes, since the first decimal place stands for tenths
of a franc, and seven-tenths of a franc = 70 centimes.

Thus:—

27 francs	= 2700 centimes
2305 centimes	= 23.05 francs (or 23 fr. 5 centimes)
2350 centimes	= 23.5 francs (or 23 fr. 50 centimes)

* The dollar sign ($) is supposed to date from the time of the famous "Pillar
dollar" of Spain, the "piece of eight" (8 reals). The curved position of the sign
was originally the figure 8. The two vertical strokes represented the Pillars of
Hercules (Straits of Gibraltar) which were stamped on the coin itself.

54 lire 5 centesimi = 54.05 lire
54 lire 50 centesimi = 54.5 lire

No new methods for addition, subtraction, multiplication or division are necessary as all calculations come under the decimal system methods.

CHAPTER 7

ARITHMETIC'S SHORTHAND—ALGEBRA

Algebra may be regarded as a "shorthand" and general way of working Arithmetic problems.

Letters are used as well as numbers. In any one sum any particular letter stands for the same value (occasionally, as we shall find, there may be more than one value). Multiplication of letters is much easier than in Arithmetic, for all we have to do is to join the letters together. Thus, xy means the number for which x stands multiplied by the number for which y stands.

Thus:—

$$a \times a \qquad = aa, \qquad \text{which we write for short } a^2$$
$$a \times a \times a \qquad = aaa, \qquad " \qquad " \qquad " \qquad " \quad a^3$$
$$a \times a \times a \times a \times a \times a = aaaaaa, \quad " \qquad " \qquad " \qquad " \quad a^6$$

The little figures are called *indices* (plural of "index"). It must be clearly understood that they are a form of shorthand and that a^6 does not mean 6 times a, but a multiplied by itself six times over (*i.e.* $6 \times a = 6a$, but $a^6 = a \times a \times a \times a \times a \times a$. Thus $2^6 = 2 \times 2 \times 2 \times 2 \times 2 \times 2 = 64$ but $6 \times 2 = 12$).

Now go a step farther and see if we can multiply a^2 by a^3.

$$a^2 \qquad = a \times a, \text{ and}$$
$$a^3 \qquad = a \times a \times a$$
$$\therefore a^2 \times a^3 = a \times a \times a \times a \times a = a^5$$

which gives us a most important law, namely, *to multiply the same kind of letters together we* **add the indices.**

Notice carefully the difference between
$$2a \times 3a \text{ and } a^2 \times a^3$$
To multiply $2a$ by $3a$ we first multiply the numbers in front of the letters ("numerical coefficients") then multiply the letters, *i.e.* $2a \times 3a = 6a^2$.

But, as we have seen, $a^2 \times a^3 = a^5$.

Similarly, $5a^2b \times 4ab^3 = 20a^3b^4$.   (Remember b means b^1, a means a^1.)

Why x^2 is called "x squared."

A square is a rectangle with all four sides equal. Suppose a square has each of its sides x units long.

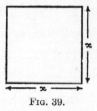

Fig. 39.

Its area (p. 31) is therefore:
$$x \times x \text{ or } x^2 \text{ sq. units.}$$
$\therefore$ we call x^2 "*x squared.*"

We have seen (p. 33) that the volume of a cube whose edges are each x units long will be x^3.

$$\therefore \text{ we call } x^3 \text{ "x cubed."}$$

[Expressions with higher indices are described as follows: x^4, "x to the fourth," "x^5," x to the fifth," x^6, "x to the sixth," x^y, "x to the power y," etc.]

The meaning of "square root."

We have seen that the area of a square comes directly from the length of any one of its sides. The side may therefore be regarded as the root from which the square has grown. We therefore call the length of the side of a square the *square root* of the area of that square. The shorthand for "*square root of*" is $\sqrt{\ }$.

$$\sqrt{1} = 1 \qquad \sqrt{121} = 11$$
$$\sqrt{4} = 2 \qquad \sqrt{144} = 12$$
$$\sqrt{9} = 3 \qquad \sqrt{169} = 13$$
$$\sqrt{16} = 4 \qquad \sqrt{196} = 14$$
$$\sqrt{25} = 5 \qquad \sqrt{225} = 15$$
$$\sqrt{36} = 6 \qquad \sqrt{256} = 16$$
$$\sqrt{49} = 7 \qquad \sqrt{289} = 17$$
$$\sqrt{64} = 8 \qquad \sqrt{324} = 18$$
$$\sqrt{81} = 9 \qquad \sqrt{361} = 19$$
$$\sqrt{100} = 10 \qquad \sqrt{400} = 20$$

It would be worth your while to memorize these.

We shall learn later on how to find the square root of any number.

It is very easy to find the square root when only single algebraic letters are involved.

It is clear from the Law of Indices (p. 38) that—

$$\sqrt{x^2} = x \quad \text{(remember, } x \text{ really means } x^1\text{)}$$
$$\sqrt{x^4} = x^2$$
$$\sqrt{x^6} = x^3$$
$$\sqrt{x^8} = x^4$$
$$\sqrt{x^{20}} = x^{10}$$

So we discover another law:

To find the square root of any power of a letter simply halve the index and this gives you your new index.

We can therefore now say that

$$\sqrt{x^3} = x^{1\frac{1}{2}} \text{ or } x^{\frac{3}{2}}$$
$$\sqrt{x^5} = x^{\frac{5}{2}}$$
$$\sqrt{x^7} = x^{\frac{7}{2}}$$
$$\text{also} \quad \sqrt{x} = x^{\frac{1}{2}}$$

This algebraic knowledge enables us to work out the square roots of many (though not all) numbers.

Example. Find the square root of 1,440,000.

Now 1,440,000 may be split up into prime factors * as follows:

$$
\begin{aligned}
&1{,}440{,}000\\
&= 144 \times 10{,}000\\
&= 12 \times 12 \times 10 \times 10 \times 10 \times 10\\
&= 3 \times 4 \times 3 \times 4 \times 2 \times 5 \times 2 \times 5 \times 2 \times 5 \times 2 \times 5\\
&= 3 \times 2 \times 2 \times 3 \times 2 \times 2 \times 2 \times 5 \times 2 \times 5 \times 2 \times 5 \times 2 \times 5\\
&= 2^8 \times 3^2 \times 5^4
\end{aligned}
$$

$$
\begin{aligned}
\therefore \ \sqrt{1{,}440{,}000} = \sqrt{2^8 \times 3^2 \times 5^4} &= 2^4 \times 3 \times 5^2\\
&= 2 \times 2 \times 5 \times 5 \times 2 \times 2 \times 3\\
&= \quad 100 \quad \times \quad 12\\
&= \quad 1200 \quad \leftarrow
\end{aligned}
$$

Note.—We can only use this method when the number can be split up so that any prime factor appearing occurs an even number of times.

To find a meaning for $x^5 \div x^2$.

First consider the simple arithmetical sum

$$2^5 \div 2^2$$

This may be written

$$
\begin{aligned}
(2\times2\times2\times2\times2) &\div (2\times2)\\
= \quad 32 \quad &\div \quad 4\\
= \quad 8
\end{aligned}
$$

---

* "Prime numbers" are numbers which have no other factors but themselves and 1, *e.g.* 1, 2, 3, 5, 7, 11, 13, 17, 19, 23. . . .
    "Prime factors" are factors which are prime numbers. For definition of "factor" see note on p. 7.

But we see that we could more easily get this result from the line $(2\times2\times2\times2\times2)\div(2\times2)$ if we omitted the divisor factors from left-hand side and multiplied the remaining factors.

Thus: $(2\times2\times2\times2\times2)\div(2\times2)$
$$= 2\times2\times2 \quad \text{(since } (2\times2)\div(2\times2) = 1).$$
$$= 8$$

In the same way,
$$x^5\div x^2 = xxxxx\div xx$$
$$= xxx$$
$$\text{that is,} \quad x^5\div x^2 = x^3$$

which gives us the rule: *for division of the same kind of letters,* **subtract the indices.**

Thus: $x^6 \div x^2 = x^4$
$$x^{10}\div x^3 = x^7$$

Instead of writing the division sign we have a neater method.

$x^6\div x^2$ may be written $\dfrac{x^6}{x^2}$.

Thus: $\dfrac{x^6}{x^2} = x^4; \quad \dfrac{x^{10}}{x^3} = x^7; \quad \dfrac{x^{10}}{x^5} = x^5 \quad (not\ x^2)$

Notice particularly that
$$\frac{x^5}{x^5} = 1$$

(Clearly any number must go into the same number *once.*)

But, applying the rule of division and subtracting the indices, we find that
$$\frac{x^5}{x^5} = x^0$$

$$\therefore \text{since} \quad \frac{x^5}{x^5} = 1 \quad \text{and also} = x^0$$
$$\text{we find that} \quad x^0 = 1$$

This fact is of great importance and will crop up frequently very soon.

By a process of reasoning similar to that in the last section we see that

$$(3\times2\times2\times5)\div(2\times5)$$
$$= 3\times2$$
$$= 6$$

Similarly—

$$abx\div x = ab \qquad \left(\text{or, } \frac{abx}{x} = ab\right)$$

$$abx\div ax = b \qquad \left(\text{or, } \frac{abx}{ax} = b\right)$$

$$abx\div bx = a \qquad \left(\text{or, } \frac{abx}{bx} = a\right)$$

$$abx\div ab = x \qquad \left(\text{or, } \frac{abx}{ab} = x\right)$$

$$abx\div a = bx \qquad \left(\text{or, } \frac{abx}{a} = bx\right)$$

$$abx\div abx = 1 \qquad \left(\text{or, } \frac{abx}{abx} = 1\right)$$

We now see that—

$$\frac{a^5b^2c^4}{a^2bc^2} = a^3bc^2 \leftarrow \qquad \frac{x^2yz}{xy} = xz \leftarrow$$

$$\frac{x^3y^2z^3}{x^3z} = y^2z^2 \leftarrow \qquad \frac{x^2y}{x^3} = \frac{y}{x} \leftarrow$$

$$\frac{12x^4y^3z}{3x^3yz^3} = \frac{4xy^2}{z^2} \leftarrow$$

(Work the division of the numerical coefficients by themselves.)

$$\frac{15x^5y^2z^7}{20x^3y^4z} = \frac{3\times5\times x^5y^2z^7}{4\times5\times x^3y^4z} = \frac{3x^2z^6}{4y^2} \leftarrow$$

$$\frac{38l^3m^2x^3y^4}{57l^2m^2x^2y^3} = \frac{2\times19\times l^3m^2x^3y^4}{3\times19\times l^2m^2x^2y^3} = \frac{2lxy}{3}$$

$$\frac{63a^4b^3x^3y^6z^2}{49ab^5x^4y^3z^4} = \frac{9a^3y^3}{7b^2xz^2}$$

For Exercises see pp. 269–270.

CHAPTER 8

SHORTHAND "DIRECTION" IN ALGEBRA

Algebra has a shorthand way of indicating *direction*. Suppose an automobile starts at A and moves to the right 500 feet to B. It then goes into reverse and backs to the left 200 feet to X. It is now only 300 feet from its starting point A.

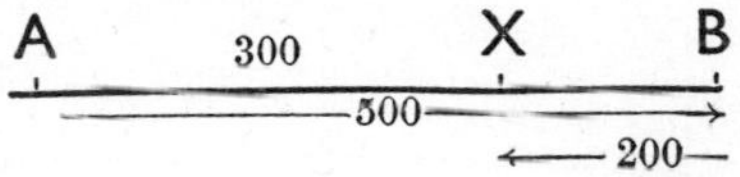

FIG. 40.

All these steps can be shown by algebraic signs called plus (+) and minus (−). Thus:

$$+500 - 200 = +300.$$

Suppose, however, that the car, having reached B, went in reverse for 600 feet to a point Y.

FIG. 41.

All these steps, and also the direction in which Y lies relative to A can be shown thus:

$$+500 - 600 = -100.$$

The same method can be applied for measurements up and down.

Suppose a balloon rises to 2000 feet and is then hauled down 500 feet.

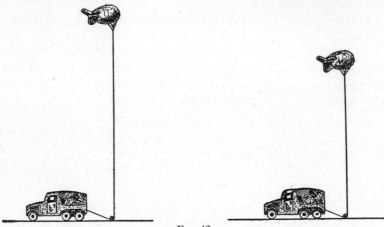

FIG. 42.

Both movements, and the final position of the balloon can be shown on squared paper * if we agree that *direction upwards shall be indicated by +* and *direction downwards by −*.

These movements would be shown algebraically as follows:—

$$+2000-500 = +1500$$

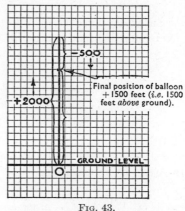

Fig. 43 means that 2000 *up* and 500 *down* equals 1500 *up*.

* Squared paper is only used in mathematics to save the time and labor involved in measuring and marking positions of points.

FIG. 43.

Now apply this rule to a picture of a cage descending the shaft of a coal-mine.

Suppose the cage descends 2000 feet and is then hauled up 1200 feet.

Remember:

direction up, +

direction down, −

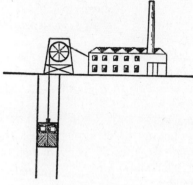

Fig. 44.

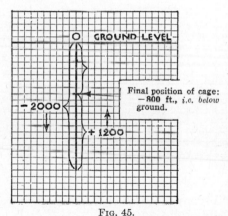

Fig. 45.

Scale: 1 small division to 100 ft.   Pit-head at O.

This would be shown algebraically as follows:—

$$-2000 + 1200 = -800.$$

Remember then that a "minus" quantity represents a direction exactly opposite to the direction of a "plus" quantity. Since + quantities are shown as directions to the *right*, − quantities must be shown to the *left*. Since + quantities are shown *upwards*, − quantities must be shown *downwards*.

More about + and −

Always remember that

> \+ means "*a step in a certain direction.*"
> − means "*a step in the opposite direction.*"

We can apply these + and − signs to questions in which movement (*i.e.* direction) does not appear to enter, *e.g.*: "A man spends $10, then another $2. He then draws $20 salary. What is his final financial position, so far as these transactions are concerned?"

Let us draw a picture of these transactions. We will use squared paper for convenience of measuring, and let each small division stand for $1. Let X be the starting point of these transactions.

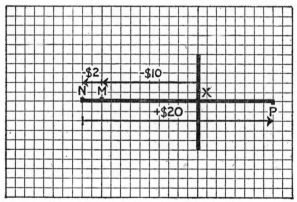

Fig. 46.

Mark off a point M ten divisions *to the left* of X, since spending is a backward step financially. The $2 he then spends "sets him back" another $2, so mark off N, two more divisions *to the left*. He then gets $20 salary, so we count twenty divisions *to the right* of N, the point at which he had arrived, and reach P which we find is eight squares *to the right* of X his starting point. ∴ He is $8 in hand at the end of these transactions.

$$\therefore \ -10-2+20 \ = \ +8.$$

We see that this result could easily be obtained by adding together the − quantities and subtracting the answer from the + quantity.

Now let us "draw a picture" of $-4-12+3+7$.

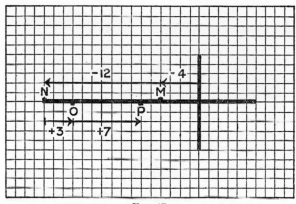

Fig. 47.

Starting at X we mark off—

$$XM = -\ 4$$
$$MN = -12$$
$$NO = +\ 3$$
$$OP = +\ 7$$

and arrive at P which we find is −6 from X.

$$\therefore \ -4-12+3+7 \ = \ -6.$$

We see we could obtain this result easily by adding together the − terms and also the + terms and then striking a balance.

The use of these "direction" signs $+$ and $-$ therefore enables us to work sums which could not be worked by ordinary arithmetic. We used to be taught we could not take 5 from 4. But this *can* be done, the result being:

$$+4-5 = -1.$$

This is obviously the same as saying "take away $+5$ from $+4$." So this gives us an important rule:

To subtract one quantity from another, change the sign of the quantity to be subtracted and strike a balance.

Suppose we try the effect of this rule on a minus quantity *e.g.:* Subtract -5 from 4. We get $4-(-5)$. If the rule works we should get $4+5$ which leaves us with $+9$.

Let us consider what all this means. We have said that $+$ means "a step in a certain direction" and $-$ means "a step in the opposite direction." $\therefore$ $-(-5)$ means "a step in the opposite direction to (-5)," which must mean a step in the $+$ direction.

$$\therefore \; -(-5) \text{ means } +5$$

which not only shows us that our rule for subtraction holds good, but also gives us another most important rule, namely:

Two minus *signs coming together really mean* **plus.**

Reasoning it out on the same lines we find that

$$\begin{aligned}
&\text{(i)} \;\; +(+5) = +5 \\
&\text{(ii)} \;\; +(-5) = -5 \\
&\text{(iii)} \;\; -(+5) = -5
\end{aligned}$$

and we know that   (iv) $-(-5) = +5$

All this can be summed up in the rule:

Like signs give plus.
Unlike signs give minus.

Now let us consider the expression $3(-5)$. When a number or letter touches a bracket (*i.e.* when there is neither $+$ nor $-$

between the number or letter and the bracket) it is understood that everything in the bracket is to be multiplied by the number (or letter) touching it.

∴ $+3(-5)$ means: 3 steps each of 5 units in the same direction as the minus direction.

Similarly, $-3(-5)$ means: 3 steps each of 5 units in the opposite direction to the minus direction, *i.e.* in the plus direction.

Thus we get
$$+3(+5) = +15$$
$$+3(-5) = -15$$
$$-3(+5) = -15$$
$$-3(-5) = +15$$

i.e. *When numbers (or letters) are multiplied together the rule for signs must be applied.* e.g. $-3(a-b) = -3a+3b$.

CAUTION.—Note the difference between

$$+3(-5) \text{ and } +3-5$$

The first expression means 3 steps, each of 5 units, to the left. The second expression means 3 steps to the right and then 5 steps to the left, *i.e.*

$$+3(-5) = -15 \quad \text{but} \quad +3-5 = -2.$$

Example 1.—Simplify $3(a-b)-5(2a-3b)$
Removing the brackets by multiplication and rule of signs, we get

$$3a-3b-10a+15b$$

Combining together a's and b's and remembering that a letter or number (or "term") at the beginning of a line without a sign on its left is understood to have $+$ there, we get

$$-7a+12b\leftarrow$$

We frequently find brackets inside other brackets. The rule is: *Remove the innermost bracket first of all.*

Example 2. $4\{2a-2(3b-3a)-b\}$
$= 4\{2a-6b+6a-b\}$
$= 4\{8a-7b\}$
$= 32a-28b\leftarrow$

Example 3. $2[3x-\{(x+2y)+3(2x+y)\}-2y]$
$= 2[3x-\{x+2y+6x+3y\}-2y]$
$= 2[3x-\{7x+5y\}-2y]$
$= 2[3x-7x-5y-2y]$
$= 2[-4x-7y]$
$= -8x-14y\leftarrow$

It is advisable to check your answers in sums like these by giving any small values to the different letters. Thus in Ex. 1, put $a = 1$, $b = 2$ in original expression and also in your answer. If the two results do not agree you have made a mistake somewhere and must find where it is.

Thus (Ex. 1)   If $a = 1$, $b = 2$.

Expression—
$= 3(a-b)-5(2a-3b)$
$= 3(1-2)-5(2-6)$
$= 3(-1)-5(-4)$
$= -3+20$
$= 17$

Answer—
$= -7a+12b$
$= -(7\times1)+(12\times2)$
$= -7+24$
$= 17$

$\therefore$ our answer was correct.

We can now go a step farther in our understanding of Algebra. We have seen that

$$x^5\div x^3 = x^{5-3} = x^2.$$

We now see that

$$x^3 \div x^5 = x^{3-5} = x^{-2}.$$

What does this x^{-2} mean? Well, let us work the same sum, $x^3 \div x^5$ in another way:

$$x^3 \div x^5 = \frac{x^3}{x^5} = \frac{1}{x^2}$$

$\therefore$ Since $\frac{1}{x^2}$ and x^{-2} are both answers to the same sum, they must mean the same thing.

$\therefore$ x^{-2} is another way of writing the *fraction* $\frac{1}{x^2}$.

Similarly:

$$x^{-3} = \frac{1}{x^3}$$

$$x^{-4} = \frac{1}{x^4}$$

$$x^{-1} = \frac{1}{x}$$

$$10^{-1} = \frac{1}{10} = .1$$

$$10^{-2} = \frac{1}{10^2} = \frac{1}{100} = .01$$

$$10^{-3} = \frac{1}{10^3} = \frac{1}{1000} = .001, \quad \text{and so on.}$$

This will be very important when we come to do Logarithms.

Algebraic Manipulation

Before proceeding farther, make sure you now have a thorough grasp of each of the following algebraic statements which illustrate the various laws of Algebra we have dealt with:

$$x \times x = x^2$$
$$\text{but } x + x = 2x$$
$$x^2 \times x^3 = x^5$$
$$\text{but } 2x \times 3x = 6x^2$$
$$(x^3)^2 = x^3 \times x^3 = x^6$$
$$(x^4)^3 = x^4 \times x^4 \times x^4 = x^{12}$$
$$a \times b = ab$$
$$a \div b = \frac{a}{b}$$
$$\frac{ab}{b} = a$$
$$\frac{ab}{a} = b$$
$$\frac{ab}{ab} = 1$$

3 taken away from 9 is $9 - 3 = +6$
9 taken away from 3 is $3 - 9 = -6$
b taken away from a is $a - b$
a taken away from b is $b - a$
$$+5 + (+3) = 8$$
$$+5 - (-3) = 8$$
$$+5 + (-3) = 2$$
$$+5 - (+3) = 2$$
$$\text{but } +5(-3) = -15$$
$$a(a+b) = a^2 + ab$$
$$a(a-b) = a^2 - ab$$
$$-(a-b) = -a + b$$
$$-(a+b) = -a - b$$

$$\sqrt{x^2} = x$$
$$\sqrt{x^{10}} = x^5$$
$$\sqrt{16x^{16}} = 4x^8$$
$$\sqrt{x} = x^{\frac{1}{2}}$$
$$x^6 \div x^2 = \frac{x^6}{x^2} = x^4$$
$$\text{but } 6x \div 2x = \frac{6x}{2x} = 3$$
$$\frac{x}{x} = 1$$
$$x^0 = 1$$
$$\frac{1}{x} = x^{-1}$$
$$\frac{1}{x^2} = x^{-2}$$
$$.1 = \frac{1}{10} = 10^{-1}$$
$$.01 = \frac{1}{100} = 10^{-2}$$

For Exercises see p. 270.

CHAPTER 9

GEOMETRY WITHOUT TEARS

We shall from time to time use the following terms:—

Circumference of circle.

Arc—part of circumference.

Radius (*plural* "radii") *—distance from center to circumference.

Chord—any straight line across, from circumference to circumference.

Diameter—a chord which passes through the center.

Segment—part of a circle enclosed by an arc and a chord.

Sector—part of a circle enclosed by an arc and two radii.

Semicircle—half a circle (the area enclosed by any diameter and semi-circumference).

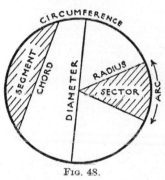

Fig. 48.

The shorthand for circle is ⊙

* Common sense tells you that all radii of the same circle must be equal or the "circle" would be no circle.

How to draw Triangles accurately

A little experimenting will show that to draw a triangle accurately one of the following *sets* of facts must be known:—

(1) The lengths of all three sides.

(2) The lengths of any two sides and the size of the angle between them (*i.e.* "enclosed" or "included" by them).

(3) The length of one side and the size of any two angles (we may have to calculate the third angle).

(4) In the case of a right-angled △, the length of longest side (hypotenuse) and of one other side.

Here are the steps in the construction of any triangle ABC:—

(1) Suppose we are given AB = 4 cm., AC = 3 cm.,

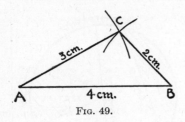

Fig. 49.

BC = 2 cm. Draw a line 4 cm. long. Call it AB (use block letters). With center A and radius equal to AC draw an arc. With center B and radius BC draw another arc cutting the first arc at C.

You will find by experiment that you cannot draw a triangle unless *any two* sides added together are longer than the third side.

(2) Suppose AB = 4 cm., AC = 5 cm., ∠ BAC = 32°. Draw AB = 4 cm. With protractor centered on point A draw an angle of 32°. With compasses at center A, radius = 5 cm., draw an arc cutting the arm of the 32° angle just drawn, at C. Join CB.

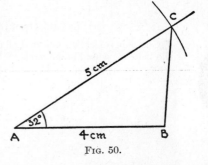

Fig. 50.

(3) (*a*) Suppose we are told AB = 4 cm., ∠ BAC = 40°,
∠ ABC = 70°. (This is the easy case since the
given angles touch the given line.)

Draw AB = 4 cm. With protractor make an angle
of 40° at A, and at B make an angle of 70°. Let
the two lines thus drawn meet at C.

(*b*) If we were given AB = 4
cm. ∠ BAC = 40°
∠ ACB = 110°, we
should first have to
calculate the other
angle, since it is one
of those that touch
the given line. From
the exercises you
worked on page 264
you will have discov-

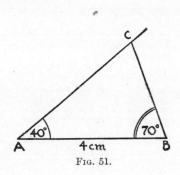

Fig. 51.

ered that the sum of the three angles of any △
always equals 180° or 2 rt. ∠s. ∴ Add together the
two given ∠s and subtract the answer from 180°.
This gives you the remaining angle ABC. You then
proceed as in (3) (*a*).

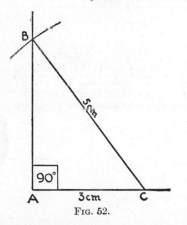

Fig. 52.

(4) Right-angled △.
Given hypotenuse BC (the
longest side, and the
side opposite the rt. ∠)
= 5 cm.,
and AC = 3 cm.

Using protractor draw a
right angle at a point
A. On one of its arms
mark off AC = 3 cm.
With center C, radius 5
cm., draw an arc cutting
the other arm at B.

Geometrical Facts

Angles, Triangles, Polygons

Study and master the facts on this and the opposite page. Become familiar with each figure. Draw the figures without any writing. Then see if you can reproduce the writing without reference to the book. Keep at it until you can do so perfectly.

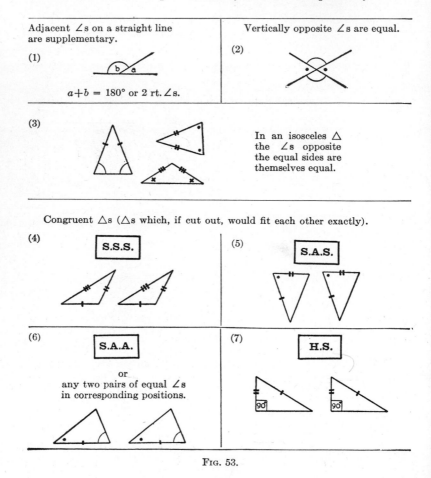

Adjacent ∠s on a straight line are supplementary.

(1)

$a+b = 180°$ or 2 rt. ∠s.

Vertically opposite ∠s are equal.

(2)

(3)

In an isosceles △ the ∠s opposite the equal sides are themselves equal.

Congruent △s (△s which, if cut out, would fit each other exactly).

(4)   **S.S.S.**

(5)   **S.A.S.**

(6)   **S.A.A.**

or
any two pairs of equal ∠s
in corresponding positions.

(7)   **H.S.**

Fig. 53.

Corresponding ∠s are equal

(8)

Alternate ∠s are equal.

(9)

If one side of a △ is produced the exterior ∠ thus formed
equals the sum of the two *opposite* interior ∠s.

(10)

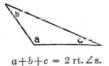

The three ∠s in a △ = 2 rt. ∠s

(11)

The sum of all (any number) ∠s
at a point = 4 rt. ∠s.

(12)

$a+b+c = 2$ rt. ∠s.

(13)   If a polygon has n sides, the sum of its interior ∠s will be
$(2n-4)$ rt. ∠s.

[Find this out by joining corners
to any point O. Find sum of
all the ∠s of all the △s.
Subtract sum of ∠s at O. Do
it first with 5-, 6- and 7-sided
figures. Then n-sided.]

Fɪɢ. 54.

The constructions on pp. 56, 57 are very important and so are the facts given, or data (*Latin*, "things given"). They are summarized in Fig. 53 (4) (5) (6) (7). As we shall often refer to them we will write these four cases in "shorthand" form—

(1) **S.S.S.** (*Three sides*)

(2) **S.A.S.** (*Two sides and enclosed angle*)

(3) **S.A.A.** (*Side and two angles*)

(4) **H.S.**   (*Hypotenuse and one side*)

Commit them to memory.

If one △ can be made to fit exactly on another △ the △s are said to be *congruent*. If you wish to copy a △ exactly you know you must have one of these four sets of data. *Vice versa*, if you know that two △s share any *one* of these four sets of data, you can say they are congruent △s.

The shorthand for "is congruent" is ≡

How to apply the theorems given on pp. 58–59.

Having mastered the theorems, you can use them to discover many facts about various figures. Give brief reasons for your statements when making use of the theorems.

Example 1. State if the triangles in Fig. 55 are congruent. If they are, give sizes of all unmarked sides and angles.

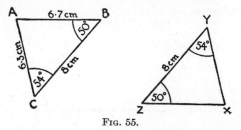

Fig. 55.

$$BC = ZY \text{ (each is 8 cm.)}$$
$$\angle \, ACB = \angle \, XYZ \text{ (each is 54°)} \Big\} \textbf{ S.A.A.}$$
$$\angle \, ABC = \angle \, YZX \text{ (each is 50°)}$$

$$\therefore \; \triangle \, ABC \equiv \triangle \, XYZ \; * \leftarrow$$

$\therefore$ XY (opposite 50° angle) = AC (opp. 50° angle) = 6.3 cm. ←
and XZ (opp. 54° angle) = AB (opp. 54° angle) = 6.7 cm.   ←

$$(\text{Also } \angle \, CAB = \angle \, YXZ)$$

And since the sum of the $\angle$s of any $\triangle$ = 180°

$$\angle \, CAB = \angle \, YXZ = 76°$$

Example 2. In $\triangle$ ABC, (Fig. 56) AB = AC and $\angle$ BAC = 20°. Find $\angle \, x$.

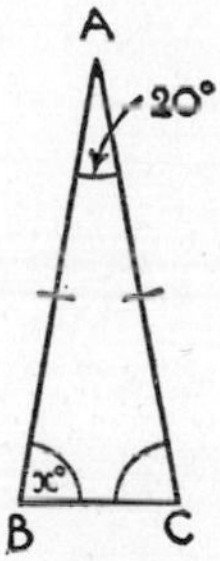

[First mark equal sides and equal $\angle$s.]
AB = AC (given).
$\therefore \triangle$ ABC is isosceles and $\angle$ ABC = $\angle$ ACB. (In an isosceles $\triangle$ the $\angle$s opposite the equal sides are themselves equal.)
Now the sum of all the $\angle$s of $\triangle$ ABC = 180°.
But $\angle$ BAC = 20° (given).
$\therefore$ The other two angles together make up 160°.
But these two angles are equal.

$$\therefore \; \text{each } \angle \text{ is } 80° \qquad \therefore \; \angle x = 80° \leftarrow$$

FIG. 56.

* Note that one $\triangle$ would have to be turned over and twisted round in order to fit the other. If you can't see this in your mind's eye, draw $\triangle$s from the given data, cut out one and see for yourself. Or draw one $\triangle$ on ordinary paper and a second one on transparent (*e.g.* grease-proof) paper and fit the second one on the first. It is well worth while to spend time on doing this, for it will help you to "see" these things mentally.

Example 3. In Fig. 57 AB is parallel to PQ, $\angle$ RPQ = 35°, $\angle$ BPR = 76°. Find $\angle x$.

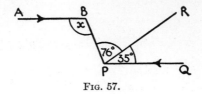

Fig. 57.

$$AB \parallel PQ$$
$$\therefore \quad \angle ABP = \angle BPQ \text{ (alternate)}$$
$$\text{But } \angle BPQ = \angle BPR + \angle RPQ$$
$$= 76° + 35° = 111°$$
$$\therefore \quad \angle x = 111° \leftarrow$$

For Exercises see pp. 271–272.

CHAPTER 10

SIMPLE GRAPHS

Pictures of Growth

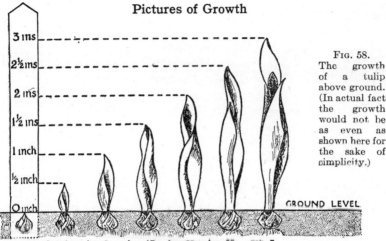

FIG. 58.
The growth of a tulip above ground. (In actual fact the growth would not be as even as shown here for the sake of simplicity.)

Dec. 25   Jan. 1   Jan. 8   Jan. 15   Jan. 22   Jan. 29   Feb. 5
(With acknowledgements to suggestion in Professor Nunn's "Exercises in Algebra" Pt. 1 p. 5.)

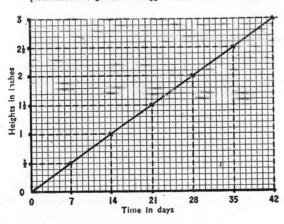

Heights in inches

Time in days

FIG. 59.
Mathematical representation of growth in Fig. 58.

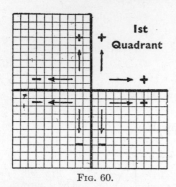

FIG. 60.

A drawing like that in Fig. 59 is called a *Graph*. Each of the lines at right angles is called an *Axis*. The point where they cut each other is called the *Origin*.

The graph in Fig. 59 is really the right-hand top corner of our picture in Fig. 60. As no minus quantities came into this particular problem we needed to draw only the right-hand top corner of that picture (known as the "1st Quadrant").

Now let us draw a graph (Fig. 61) of the average increase in weight of a baby (boy).

Age in months	Weight	Age in months	Weight
0	7½ lb.	15	22½
1	8½	16	23
2	10	17	23½
3	11½	18	24
4	13	19	24½
5	14½	20	25
6	16	21	25½
7	16½	22	26
8	17½	23	26½
9	18½	24	27
10	19½	25	27½
11	20½	26	28
12	21	27	28½
13	21½	28	29
14	22	29	29½

We will represent age along the horizontal axis, weight up the vertical axis. *Always take as large a scale as possible.* We have to

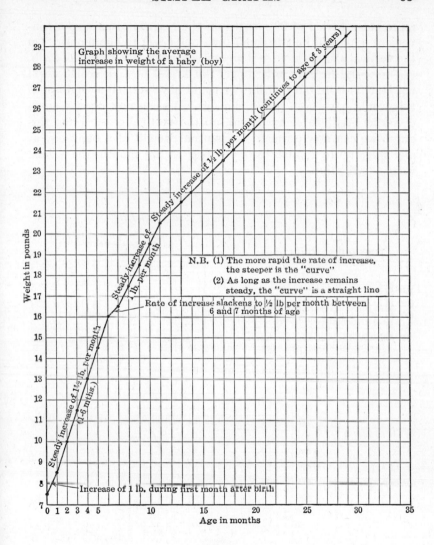

Graph showing the average increase in weight of a baby (boy)

Steady increase of ½ lb. per month (continues to age of 3 years)

Steady increase of 1 lb. per month

N.B. (1) The more rapid the rate of increase, the steeper is the "curve"
(2) As long as the increase remains steady, the "curve" is a straight line

Rate of increase slackens to ½ lb per month between 6 and 7 months of age

Steady increase of 1½ lb. per month (1-6 mths.)

Increase of 1 lb. during first month after birth

Weight in pounds

Age in months

Fig. 61.

represent a period of 29 months on the horizontal axis, so a convenient scale will be two small divisions ($\frac{2}{10}''$) to one month. On the vertical axis we have to represent an increase in weight of 22 lb. ($7\frac{1}{2}$ lb. to $29\frac{1}{2}$ lb.). In order to get the largest possible scale we will not start at 0 lb. but at 7 lb. (we could have started at $7\frac{1}{2}$ lb., but this would have been rather clumsy). We can now allow 4 small divisions ($\frac{4}{10}''$) to every pound, up the vertical axis. From this graph we can now estimate the normal weight of a baby boy at any stage up to 29 months of age (*e.g.* at $22\frac{1}{2}$ months the normal weight is $26\frac{1}{4}$ lb.).

Examples of Graphs in Everyday Life

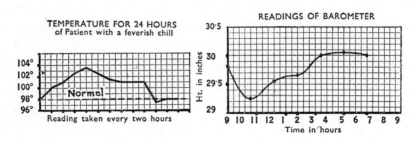

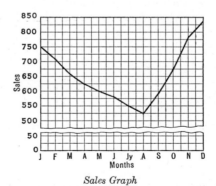

Sales Graph

(By permission from Hill & Linker's "Introduction to College Mathematics.")

Fig. 62.

Speed Graphs

In Figs. 59 and 61 we saw how to link together height or weight and age. We can link together even more easily things which vary in like proportions, *e.g.* distance traveled and time taken to travel that distance. (As we shall see when we come to ratio, speed is found by dividing distance by time taken, *e.g.* 100 miles in 5 hours gives a speed of 20 miles per hour.)

All this can easily be shown on a graph.

Graph of 30 miles per hour

Mark *time* on bottom (horizontal) line, *distance* on upright (vertical) line. (The spaces for hours need not be the same as the spaces for miles. On the scale we have chosen (Fig. 63), each small division on the horizontal axis represents 6 minutes and each small division on the vertical axis represents 5 miles). Now mark with a sharp pencil the spot which connects 30 miles and 1 hour;

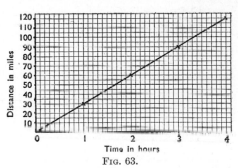

FIG. 63.

then the spot connecting, say, 60 miles and 2 hours. (As graphs of unchanging speed are all straight lines, two points accurately fixed will suffice, but take a third if you like—the spot where 90 miles and 3 hours are connected.)

Join the marks you have made and continue this line right across the page. Every point on this line (or "curve" as it is called, even when it is a straight line) connects together every possible distance between 0 miles and 120 miles and every possible time between 0 hours and 4 hours.

On squared paper draw the graph shown in Fig. 63 and find:—

(*a*) The time taken to go 75 miles at 30 m.p.h.
(*b*) The time taken to go 45 miles at 30 m.p.h.
(*c*) How far one can go in 30 minutes at 30 m.p.h.

Now study Fig. 64, which shows the graphs of speeds of 15, 30, 60 and 120 miles per hour.

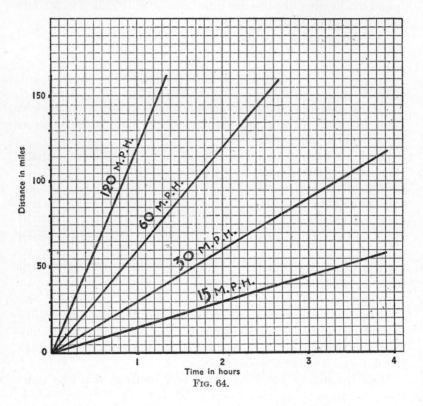

Fig. 64.

You see that the *greater the speed* the *"steeper" the curve*.

The Twenty-four Hour Clock

[*N.B.*—In all military, naval and air operations time is reckoned by the 24-hour clock, thus:

9 A.M. = 0900 hrs.; 9.25 A.M. = 0925 hrs.

12 noon = 1200 hrs.; five minutes past noon = 1205 hrs.

1 P.M. = 1300 hrs.; 2.16 P.M. = 1416 hrs.

Note that 11.5 P.M. is not 235 but 2305. There must be *four digits* every time.

Strictly speaking, midnight is 0000, but in practice one minute before or one minute after it is indicated—2359 or 0001.

In subsequent chapters this method of indicating time will be used.]

An Easy Way of Solving Speed Problems

Example.—A freight train leaves Chicago for the West at mid-day. Its average speed is 40 m.p.h. An express leaves Chicago for the West at 1430 hrs. and averages 60 m.p.h.

(a) How far are the trains apart at 1600 hrs.?

(b) How far are the trains apart at 1800 hrs.?

(o) At what hour does the express overtake the freight train?

(d) How many miles from Chicago does the express overtake the freight train?

This time, as we have to represent larger figures for both distance and time, we shall take smaller scales:

Distance.—One small division to represent 10 miles.

Time.—Five small divisions to represent 1 hour,
    i.e. Each small division on the horizontal axis represents 12 minutes.

We draw the speed graph (Fig. 65) of the freight train from "zero" and call this spot 12.00. Put a mark linking together 40 miles and 1 hour space from zero point. Draw graph of 40 m.p.h. speed.

The express starts at 1430, so we start its speed graph at a point $2\frac{1}{2}$ hours to the right of zero. We now connect together 60 miles and 1 hour space *from* *this $2\frac{1}{2}$-hour point, i.e.* 60 miles and $3\frac{1}{2}$ hours from "zero" on our scale. We now draw graph of 60 m.p.h. speed.

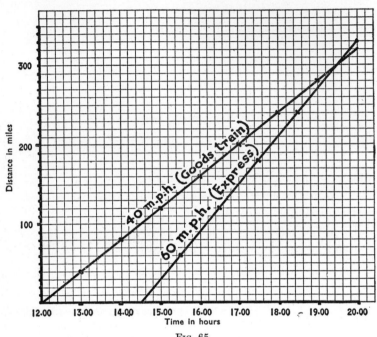

Fɪɢ. 65.

We see the answers at a glance:—

(*a*) Look up 1600 hrs. line. Distance between the "curves" on that line is 7 vertical spaces, *i.e.* 70 miles.←

(*b*) Similarly, at 1800 hrs. distance between curves is 3 spaces, *i.e.* 30 miles.←

(*c*) The express overtakes the freight at 1930 hrs.←

(*d*) The curves cross at a point linking together 300 miles and 1930 hrs.←
∴ Express overtakes freight 300 miles from Chicago.

Picture of a motor journey occupying from mid-day to 1800 hours.

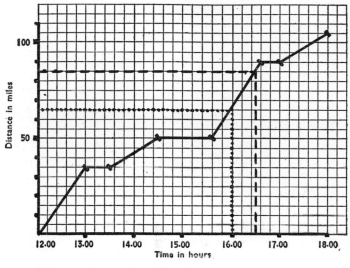

FIG. 66.

Details to observe:

1 small division vertically represents 5 miles.

1 small division horizontally represents $\frac{1}{5}$ of 1 hour or 12 minutes.

∴ $\frac{1}{2}$ a division horizontally represents 6 minutes.

Here is the story told by the graph shown in Fig. 66. A motorist starts out and travels 35 miles (evidently through rural surroundings, as his speed exceeds 30 m.p.h.). It is then 1300 hours and he stops for 30 minutes then sets out again, but more slowly this time, for in the next hour he only covers 15 miles. Probably he has entered the outskirts of a big city. We see that he stops at this point and does not go on until 66 minutes later—possibly he is engaged on some business errand in the city. On leaving at 1536 hrs. he evidently gets into open country once more, for he goes 40 miles in the next hour. It is then 1636 hrs. and he again stops, this time for 24 minutes. He again appears to have entered an urban area, for we see that his speed for the last part of his journey drops to 15 m.p.h. He is then 105 miles from his original starting point, and it is 1800 hrs.

NOTE CAREFULLY.—As speed increases, the graph becomes steeper. Always draw speed graphs with distance marked vertically and time horizontally. You will then see at a glance when the speed increases or decreases.

You can find how far away from his starting point the motorist is at any time between noon and 1800 hrs. You can also find the time he has taken to reach any point on his journey, e.g. at 1630 he is 85 miles from his starting point (trace broken line, starting at 1630); when he has gone 65 miles he has taken almost 4 hours (trace dotted line starting at vertical "distance" 65 miles).

PROPORTION GRAPHS

We can draw graphs showing the connection between any two things when a change in one thing (e.g. distance) involves a proportionate change in the other thing (e.g. time). Thus, we can show a picture of the gasoline consumption of an engine (amount of gasoline used in various periods of time); the various lengths of a spiral spring as various weights are attached; the various times taken for oscillation of pendulums of various lengths at the same place; the load lifted by a certain pull on lifting tackle, etc., etc. All such problems concern things which vary in proportion to each other, so all have regular shapes for their graphs (unlike the temperature chart for a patient in hospital and the other examples on p. 66, which were irregular in shape). The "curve," however, is not always a straight line as it was in speed graphs, but may be a curve in the ordinary sense of the word. In such cases, of course, the curve cannot be drawn until the positions of a large number of points are known.

For instance, the times for a double-swing (one oscillation) for pendulums of various lengths (in latitude $51\frac{1}{2}°$ N.) are as follows:—

Length in feet .	1	2	3	4	5	6
Time in seconds	1.11	1.57	1.92	2.21	2.48	2.71

The graph in Fig. 67 connects length of pendulum (at a spot whose latitude is $51\frac{1}{2}°$ N.) with times for double swing. (*N.B.*—Not a straight line.)

Graph of Oscillation of Pendulum

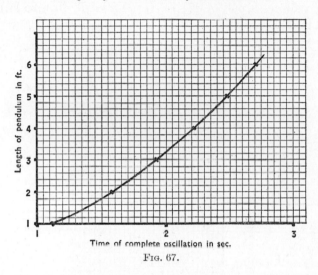

Fig. 67.

A large number of points must be "plotted" if the "curve" is not a straight line. These points must be obtained from particulars given.

Interpreting a Graph

How to interpret a graph such as that in Fig. 68:—

We see by the description of the horizontal and vertical units that it is the graph of some lifting tackle.

We note that a pull of $7\frac{1}{2}$ lb. is required when no load is to be lifted. This indicates the pull necessary to lift the rope, etc., and overcome friction.

So the graph commences at a point representing a 7½-lb. pull on the vertical axis.

We see from the curve that the pull has to be increased by 10 lb. for every 50 lb. load that is added. Thus, to lift a load of 125 lb. requires a pull of 32½ lb. (*i.e.* initial 7½ lb.+25 lb.). See dotted lines on graph.

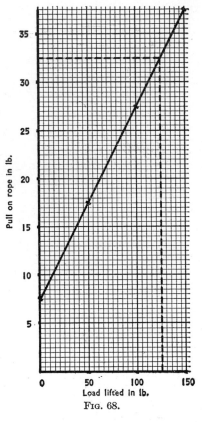

Fig. 68.

For Exercises see pp. 273–277.

CHAPTER 11

ALGEBRAIC BINOMIALS

$(3x+5)$, $(a+b)$, $(5x-y)$ are examples of binomials (Latin *bini*, "two together") or expressions containing two terms.

To multiply binomials:

(1) Multiply one binomial by the first term of the other binomial.
(2) Multiply same binomial by the second term of the other binomial.
(3) Add the results.

[*N.B.* When two brackets are not separated by a $+$ or $-$ sign it means they are to be multiplied together.]

Example 1. $(3x+5)(2x+3)$.
Multiply $(3x+5)$ by $2x = 6x^2+10x$
" $(3x+5)$ by$+3 = \qquad 9x+15$
By addition $(3x+5)(2x+3) = 6x^2+19x+15\leftarrow$

Example 2. $(5x+y)(3x-y) = 15x^2+3xy-5xy-y^2$
$$= 15x^2-2xy-y^2\leftarrow$$

If preferred, multiplication of binomials may be worked as follows:

$$5x+y$$
$$3x-y$$
$$\overline{15x^2+3xy}$$
$$-5xy-y^2$$
$$\overline{15x^2-2xy-y^2}\leftarrow$$

but the first method is better.

To Draw a Picture of $(a+b)(a+b)$ or $(a+b)^2$

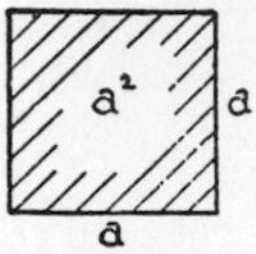

FIG. 69.

We saw that a^2 means the area of the square which has its root (or side) a units long (Fig. 69).

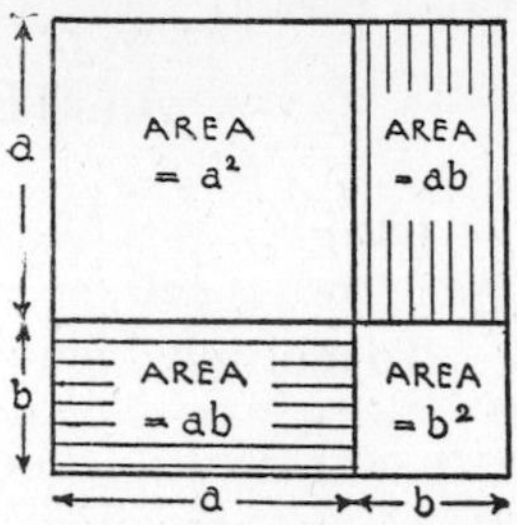

From Fig. 70 we can see that $(a+b)(a+b)$ means the square whose root (or side) is $(a+b)$ units long.

Clearly the total area of the square is $a^2+ab+ab+b^2$ or $a^2+2ab+b^2$.

$$\therefore (a+b)^2 = a^2+2ab+b^2.$$

FIG. 70.

We will now work this by algebraic instead of geometric methods, just to show how unfortunate were the Greek mathematicians in having no Algebra.

$$(a+b)^2 = (a+b)(a+b) = a^2+ab+ab+b^2$$
$$= a^2+2ab+b^2 \leftarrow$$

Now let us work out $(a-b)^2$ by Algebra.

$$(a-b)^2 = (a-b)(a-b) = a^2-ab-ab+b^2$$
$$= a^2-2ab+b^2 \leftarrow$$

Now let us work out $(a+b)(a-b)$

$$(a+b)(a-b) = a^2+ab-ab-b^2$$
$$= a^2-b^2 \leftarrow$$

These last three results are most important and should be committed to memory:—

$$(a+b)^2 = a^2+2ab+b^2$$
$$(a-b)^2 = a^2-2ab+b^2$$
$$(a+b)(a-b) = a^2-b^2$$

After a little practice you can write down the answer to *any* binomial straight away if you bear in mind the following sketch:—

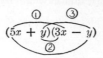

i.e. (1) $5x \times 3x$ gives 1st term of product. . . $= 15x^2$

(2) $(5x \times -y)$ combined with $(y \times 3x)$ gives 2nd
term of product. . . . . $= -2xy$

(3) $+y \times -y$ gives 3rd term of product . . $= -y^2$

The square of any binomial may be written down straight away if the answers to $(a+b)^2$ and $(a-b)^2$ are remembered. *E.g.:*—

(1) To find the value of $(5x+3y)^2$ we have $5x$ instead of a, $3y$ instead of b.

$\therefore$ instead of a^2 we shall have $(5x)^2$ or $25x^2$

instead of $+2ab$ we shall have $+(2 \times 5x \times 3y)$, or $+30xy$

instead of $+b^2$ we shall have $+(3y)^2$ or $+9y^2$.

$$\therefore (5x+3y)^2 = 25x^2+30xy+9y^2 \leftarrow$$

(2) Similarly, $(5x-3y)^2$ gives us $5x$ instead of a, $3y$ instead of b

$\therefore$ instead of a^2 we shall have $(5x)^2$ or $25x^2$

instead of $-2ab$ we shall have $-(2 \times 5x \times 3y)$ or $-30xy$

instead of $+b^2$ we shall have $+(3y)^2$ or $+9y^2$

$$\therefore (5x-3y)^2 = 25x^2-30xy+9y^2$$

We can now manipulate more complicated expressions.

Example 1. Simplify:—

$$x(x+3y)+y(x+2y)$$
$$= x^2+3xy+xy+2y^2$$
$$= x^2+4xy+2y^2 \leftarrow$$

Example 2.   Simplify:—

$$(a+1)(a+3)+(a+2)(a+3)+(a+1)(a+4)$$

(Put a dot under each multiplying term as you deal with it.)

$$= a^2+4a+3 + a^2+5a+6 + a^2+5a+4$$
$$= 3a^2+14a+13\leftarrow$$

Example 3.   Simplify:—

$$(a-b)(a+2b)-(a+2x)(a-x)*-b(a-2b)$$
$$= a^2+ab-2b^2-(a^2+ax-2x^2)-ab+2b^2$$
$$= a^2+ab-2b^2-a^2-ax+2x^2-ab+2b^2$$
$$= 2x^2-ax\leftarrow$$

* Multiply out brackets *then* change all signs on account of − outside.

Remember it is wise to test your answers by putting any small numbers instead of the letters.

Thus, in *Example* 2, put $a = 1$.

Then
$$(a+1)(a+3)+(a+2)(a+3)+(a+1)(a+4)$$
$$= (1+1)(1+3)+(1+2)(1+3)+(1+1)(1+4)$$
$$= \quad (2)(4) \quad + \quad (3)(4) \quad + \quad (2)(5)$$
$$= \quad 8 \quad + \quad 12 \quad + \quad 10 \quad = 30$$

and our answer,
$$3a^2+ \quad 14a \quad +13$$
$$= (3\times1\times1)+(14\times1)+13$$
$$= \quad 3 \quad + \quad 14 \quad +13 = 30$$

which proves that our answer is correct.

Algebraic Factors

$$3\times4 = 12$$

$\therefore$ 3 and 4 are called the factors of 12.

$$x(x+3) = x^2+3x$$

$\therefore$ x and $(x+3)$ are the factors of x^2+3x.

We often have to split up into factors expressions containing several terms. To do this we may employ many methods, the chief ones being:—

    1. The "Common Term" or "Common Bracket" Method.
    2. The "Cross Multiplication" Method.
    3. The "Difference of Two Squares" Method.

1. (a) COMMON TERM.—Find any term which is a factor common to each term in the expression. This gives one of the required factors. To get the other (or others) divide the expression by the factor just found.

Example 1. To find factors of $3x-9$:

    (i.) 3 is a factor of $3x$ and of -9.
    (ii.) Dividing by factor 3, we find the other factor is $(x-3)$.

$$\therefore\ 3x-9 = 3(x-3)\leftarrow$$

Check answer by multiplying factors together and seeing if original expression results.

Example 2.
$$15x^2y - 10xy^2$$
$$= 5xy(3x - 2y)\leftarrow$$

(b) COMMON BRACKET. Find any bracket which is a factor common to the terms of the expression.

Example 3. To find factors of

$$a(x+y)+b(x+y)$$
$$= (x+y)(a+b)\leftarrow$$

$$\boxed{\begin{array}{l} Hint\text{---}\quad a(x+y)\div(x+y) = a \\ \qquad\quad +b(x+y)\div(x+y) = +b \end{array}}$$

Example 4. $a(x+y)-b(x+y)$
                    $= (x+y)(a-b)\leftarrow$

Example 5. $c(y+x)+m(x+y)$
                    $= (x+y)(c+m)\leftarrow$

Since $(y+x)$ is the same as $(x+y)$.

(*c*) Combining "Common Term" and "Common Bracket."

Example 6. $x^2+xy+xz+yz$
                    $= x(x+y)+z(x+y)$
                    $= (x+y)(x+z)\leftarrow$

Example 7. $x^2-xy-xz+yz$
                    $= x(x-y)-z(x-y)$
                    $= (x-y)(x-z)\leftarrow$

Check each line by multiplying out. Be careful of $-$ signs.

Example 8. $x^2+xy-x-y$
                    $= x(x+y)-1(x+y)$
                    $= (x+y)(x-1)\leftarrow$

2. CROSS MULTIPLICATION.
    (*a*) Write down two factors of the first term, one under
        the other.
    (*b*) Write down two factors of the last term, one under
        the other.
    (*c*) Cross multiply and see if results when combined give
        middle term. If they do, write down factors from
        left to right. If they don't, try another set of
        factors.

Example 1. To find the factors of $x^2+14x+33$

$$x+3$$
$$\times \quad (+11x+3x) = 14x = \text{middle term}$$
$$x+11$$

$$\therefore x^2+14x+33 = (x+3)(x+11)\leftarrow$$

Example 2. x^2+6x+8

$$x+8$$
Try $\times \quad +8x+x = 9x$
$$x+1 \quad \text{No good}$$

$$x+4$$
Try $\times \quad +4x+2x =$
$$x+2 \qquad 6x = \text{m.t.}$$

$$\therefore x^2+6x+8 = (x+4)(x+2)\leftarrow$$

Check answers by multiplying factors together.

Example 3. $x^2-2x-35$

$$x+7$$
Try $\times \quad +7x-5x = +2x$
$$x-5 \quad \text{No good (wrong sign)}$$

$$x-7$$
Try $\times \quad +5x-7x = -2x$
$$x+5$$

$$\therefore x^2-2x-35 = (x-7)(x+5)\leftarrow$$

Example 4. x^2-4x+4

$$x+2$$
Try $\times \quad +2x+2x = +4x$
$$x+2 \quad \text{No good}$$

$$x-2$$
Try $\times \quad -2x-2x = -4x$
$$x-2$$

$$\therefore x^2-4x+4 = (x-2)(x-2) \text{ or } (x-2)^2\leftarrow$$

Example 5. $6x^2+11x-10$

$$\underset{2x-1}{\overset{3x+10}{\times}} \quad -3x+20x = +17x \qquad \text{Try} \quad \underset{2x-5}{\overset{3x+2}{\times}} \quad -15x+4x = -11x$$

Try ... No good   Try ... No good

$$\text{Try} \quad \underset{2x+5}{\overset{3x-2}{\times}} \quad +15x-4x = 11x$$

$$\therefore\ 6x^2+11x-10 = (3x-2)(2x+5)\leftarrow$$

[*With practice much of this work can and should be done mentally.*]

3. The Difference of Two Squares.

When two perfect squares are separated by a minus sign the factors are:—

    1st factor: square root of 1st term + square root of second term.

    2nd factor: square root of 1st term − square root of second term.

Example 1. a^2-4
           $= (a+2)(a-2)\leftarrow$

Example 2. $16p^8-25$
           $= (4p^4+5)(4p^4-5)\leftarrow$

Example 3. $(x+y)^2-1$
           $= (x+y+1)(x+y-1)\leftarrow$

Example 4. $(x+y)^2-(a+b)^2$
           $= (x+y+a+b)(x+y-a-b)\leftarrow$

Remember, in the 2nd factor we get "minus the whole of the square root of the 2nd term."

Example 5. $(x+y)^2-(a-b)^2$
$= (x+y+a-b)(x+y-a+b)\leftarrow$

Example 6. $1-x^2+2xy-y^2$
$= 1-(x^2-2xy+y^2)$
$= 1-(x-y)^2$
$= (1+x-y)(1-x+y)\leftarrow$

Example 7. $x^2+6xy+9y^2-a^2+4ab-4b^2$
$= (x^2+6xy+9y^2)-(a^2-4ab+4b^2)$
$= (x+3y)^2-(a-2b)^2$ (by Cross Multiplication)
$= (x+3y+a-2b)(x+3y-a+2b)\leftarrow$

For Exercises see pp. 277–279.

CHAPTER 12

FRACTIONS OTHER THAN DECIMAL FRACTIONS

We have met with fractions like $\frac{1}{10}$, $\frac{1}{100}$, $\frac{1}{1000}$, etc. Now we will consider fractions like $\frac{1}{2}$, $\frac{3}{4}$, $\frac{2}{7}$, $\frac{9}{5}$ which are called "common" fractions.

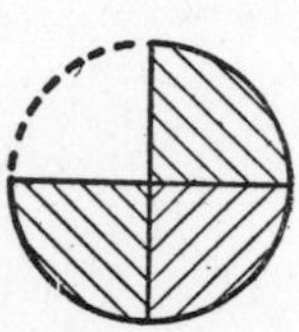

Proper Fractions

The usual and proper meaning of the word "fraction" is "a *part* of a whole."

FIG. 71.

If an apple is cut into four equal parts and three of them (the shaded parts in Fig. 71) are taken, the portion taken is indicated by the fraction $\frac{3}{4}$. We see that this fraction means:

$$\frac{\text{Number of pieces of apple taken (Numerator)}}{\text{Total number of such pieces in one whole apple (Denominator)}}$$

Improper Fractions

Now suppose I say I have $\frac{5}{4}$ apple. This means, from what we have just said, that I have five quarters or fourths of apple. Clearly $\frac{5}{4}$ is not part of a whole apple but represents what is shown in Fig. 72, *i.e.* one whole apple and one fourth-part of another whole apple = $1\frac{1}{4}$. $\frac{5}{4}$, therefore, is not a proper kind of fraction and is called an *Improper Fraction*.

FIG. 72.

Whenever the Numerator of a fraction is greater than the Denominator, the fraction represents more than one whole thing and is therefore called "Improper."

Improper Fractions and Mixed Numbers

We have seen that $\frac{5}{4}$ = one whole apple and $\frac{1}{4}$ of another whole apple, *i.e.* $1\frac{1}{4}$ apples.

An expression like $1\frac{1}{4}$, consisting of a whole number and a fraction, is called a *Mixed Number*.

In the same way $\frac{17}{9} = 1\frac{8}{9}$; $\frac{21}{5} = 4\frac{1}{5}$, and so on. That is:

To change an Improper Fraction to a Mixed Number divide the Numerator by the Denominator. The quotient gives the whole number and the remainder gives the Numerator of the proper fraction (the Denominator being of course the divisor).

Now consider the reverse process. $4\frac{1}{5}$ means 4 whole things and $\frac{1}{5}$ of a whole thing.

The 4 whole things, if all cut up into fifths, would give us 20 fifths. Adding the other $\frac{1}{5}$ we can say that—

$$4\tfrac{1}{5} = \tfrac{21}{5}$$

To change a Mixed Number to an Improper Fraction multiply whole number by Denominator of fraction and add result to Numerator of fraction. Put this answer over Denominator of fraction.

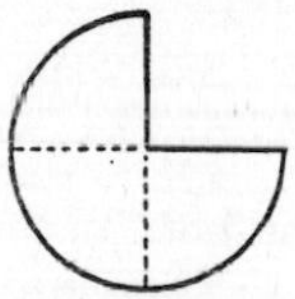

Fig. 73.

Multiplication and Division of Fractions

Suppose (Fig. 73) we have $\frac{3}{4}$ of a cake.

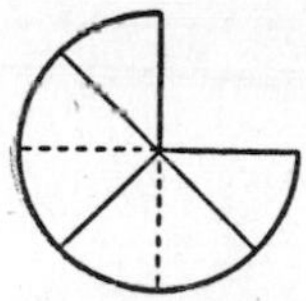

Suppose we then wish to take $\frac{1}{2}$ of this piece.

We will cut each of the original three quarters into two equal parts (Fig. 74). We now have six new pieces, each an eighth-part of the original cake, and if we take half the number of these smaller pieces we shall have 3 of them.

Fig. 74.

$$\therefore \frac{1}{2} \times \frac{3}{4} = \frac{3}{8}$$

∴ The product of two fractions is a new fraction whose numerator is the product of the two numerators, and whose denominator is the product of the two denominators. Thus:

$$\frac{5}{6} \times \frac{7}{11} = \frac{35}{66}$$

Now note that if you multiply (or divide) the top and bottom of a fraction by the same number you do not alter the value of the fraction.

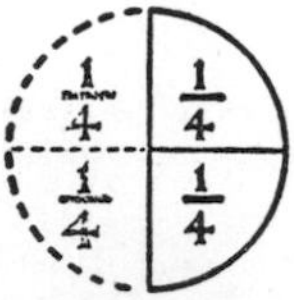

Fig. 75.

Thus: $\frac{1}{2} = \frac{1 \times 2}{2 \times 2}$ since $\frac{1}{2}$ is the same size as $\frac{2}{4}$

Again, $\frac{2}{4} = \frac{2 \div 2}{4 \div 2}$ since $\frac{2}{4}$ is the same size as $\frac{1}{2}$

It often saves labor to divide the top line and the bottom line of a fraction (or fractions) by the same number. This is called "canceling."

Thus: $\dfrac{\overset{2}{\cancel{14}}}{\underset{3}{\cancel{21}}} = \dfrac{2}{3}$

Here we have divided both numerator and denominator by 7, or as we say, "canceled" by 7.

Similarly, $\frac{16}{25} \times \frac{15}{24}$

First we notice that 8 is a factor of 16 on top line and of 24 on bottom line. ∴ we cancel these numbers by 8.

Then we see that 5 is a factor of 15 on top line and of 25 on bottom line. ∴ we cancel these numbers by 5.

$$\overset{2}{\cancel{16}} \times \overset{3}{\cancel{15}}$$
$$\underset{5}{\cancel{25}} \quad \underset{3}{\cancel{24}}$$

We notice that 3 is a factor of two of the numbers we have put down, and as one of them is on top line and one on bottom line we now cancel these numbers by 3.

We then multiply together all the figures that remain uncanceled on top line, and all the figures that remain uncanceled on bottom line.

$$\therefore \dfrac{\overset{2}{\cancel{16}}}{\underset{5}{\cancel{25}}} \times \dfrac{\overset{\overset{1}{\cancel{3}}}{\cancel{15}}}{\underset{\underset{1}{\cancel{3}}}{\cancel{24}}} = \frac{2}{5} \leftarrow$$

Similarly,

$$18 \times \frac{5}{24} = \frac{\overset{3}{\cancel{18}}}{1} \times \frac{5}{\underset{4}{\cancel{24}}} = \frac{15}{4} = 3\tfrac{3}{4} \leftarrow$$

Remember that any whole number may be written as an Improper Fraction simply by putting it on 1.

Thus:

$$6 = \frac{6}{1}$$

Now suppose we have to divide 18 by 6. (We know the answer is 3.)

We could have written this

$$\frac{18}{1} \div \frac{6}{1} = 3$$

Now it is obvious that the same answer would have been obtained had we worked as follows:—

$$\frac{18}{1} \div \frac{6}{1} = \frac{\overset{3}{\cancel{18}}}{1} \times \frac{1}{\cancel{6}_{1}} = 3$$

This gives us an important rule:—

To divide by a fraction invert that fraction and multiply.

Thus:

$$\frac{15}{24} \div \frac{25}{26} = \frac{\overset{\overset{1}{\cancel{3}}}{\cancel{15}}}{\underset{\underset{4}{\cancel{12}}}{\cancel{24}}} \times \frac{\overset{13}{\cancel{26}}}{\underset{5}{\cancel{25}}} = \frac{13}{20} \leftarrow$$

Exactly similar rules apply to multiplication and division of letters. Thus:

Example 1.

$$\frac{a^2b^3c}{x^4y} \times \frac{x^3y^4}{a^3bc} = \frac{a^2b^3cx^3y^4}{a^3bcx^4y} = \frac{b^2y^3}{ax} \leftarrow$$

Example 2.

$$\frac{m^2p}{r^5q} \div \frac{mp^3}{r^2q^2} = \frac{m^2p}{r^5q} \times \frac{r^2q^2}{mp^3} = \frac{m^2pr^2q^2}{mp^3r^5q} = \frac{mq}{p^2r^3} \leftarrow$$

Very Important.—*Remember you can cancel only "top and bottom"; and* **only when multiplying** *can you cancel top of one fraction and bottom of another.*

Thus:

$$\frac{15}{21} \times \frac{14}{20} = \frac{\cancel{15}}{\cancel{21}} \times \frac{\cancel{14}}{\cancel{20}}.$$

This is possible because it is a multiplication sum.

But $\dfrac{15}{21} + \dfrac{14}{20}.$ Here you cannot cancel from one fraction to the other since it is an addition sum. You may, however, cancel top and bottom of $\dfrac{14}{20}\left(= \dfrac{7}{10}\right)$ and top and bottom of $\dfrac{15}{21} = \left(\dfrac{5}{7}\right).$

To multiply mixed numbers, turn into improper fractions, then multiply.

H.C.F. and L.C.M.

At this stage it will be necessary to digress from fractions and deal with H.C.F. and L.C.M.

We saw (p. 7) that a | **Factor** | of a number is another number which | **goes into** | it an exact whole number of times.

Thus:

2 is a factor of 14
3 is a factor of 96
4 is a factor of 28
5 is a factor of 30
6 is a factor of 42
7 is a factor of 84
8 is a factor of 56

Of these factors, 2, 3, 5 and 7 are called Prime Factors (see p. 41).

A | **Common Factor** | of two or more numbers is a number which | **goes into** | each of them an exact number of times.
Thus:

> 2 is a common factor of 4, 6, 8, 10, etc.
> 3 is a common factor of 6, 9, 12, 15, etc.
> 4 is a common factor of 8, 12, 16, 20, etc.
> 5 is a common factor of 10, 15, 20, 25, etc.

The | **Highest Common Factor** | (H.C.F.) of two or more numbers is the highest number which | **goes into** | each of them an exact number of times.

Thus, of all the common factors of 24 and 36, 12 is the highest, so it is called the H.C.F. of 24 and 36.

A | **Multiple** | of a number is another number which | **contains** | it an exact number of times.
Thus:

> 28 is a multiple of 2
> 35 is a multiple of 5
> and so forth.

A | **Common Multiple** | of two or more numbers is another number which | **contains** | each of them an exact number of times.

Thus: 28 is a common multiple of 2, 4, 7 and 14
35 is a common multiple of 5 and 7.

The **Lowest Common Multiple** (L.C.M.) of two or more numbers is the lowest number which **contains** each of them an exact number of times.

Thus, of all the common multiples of 4 and 18, 36 is the L.C.M.

Remember: A Factor "goes into" . . .
A Multiple "contains" . . .

How to Find H.C.F.

Consider the expressions:

$$a^3b^2c \qquad a^2b^4c.$$

They are the "shorthand" forms of

$$aaabbc \qquad aabbbbc.$$

To find the highest expression which will go into each of them (H.C.F.), we have only to find the greatest number of times each letter will divide into *both* given expressions. That is, *aabbc*.

i.e. the H.C.F. of a^3b^2c, a^2b^4c is $a^2b^2c \leftarrow$

We see that we can find any H.C.F. of this kind by taking every letter in turn *which occurs in both given expressions* and writing it with its *smaller* index.

Similarly   (1) the H.C.F. of x^5y^4z and $x^4y^2z^3$ is $x^4y^2z \leftarrow$
                (2) the H.C.F. of a^2bc^4, $a^3b^2c^2$, a^2b^3c is $a^2bc \leftarrow$
                (3) the H.C.F. of a^2bcd, a^2b^3c is $a^2bc \leftarrow$
                    (note that "*d*," not being common to both expressions, cannot come in the H.C.F.)

The H.C.F. of numbers may be found in a similar manner, provided each number is first split into its prime factors. Thus:

Example 1. Find the H.C.F. of 120, 144.

$$120 = 12 \times 10$$
$$= 2 \times 6 \times 2 \times 5$$
$$= 2 \times 3 \times 2 \times 2 \times 5$$
$$= 2^3 \times 3 \times 5$$

$$144 = 12 \times 12$$
$$= 3 \times 4 \times 3 \times 4$$
$$= 3 \times 2 \times 2 \times 3 \times 2 \times 2$$
$$= 2^4 \times 3^2$$

$$\therefore \text{ H.C.F. is } 2^3 \times 3 = 24$$

Example 2. Find the H.C.F. of 378, 630, 882.

$$378 = 2 \times 189$$
$$= 2 \times 3 \times 63$$
$$= 2 \times 3 \times 9 \times 7$$
$$= 2 \times 3^3 \times 7$$

$$630 = 10 \times 63$$
$$= 2 \times 5 \times 9 \times 7$$
$$= 2 \times 3^2 \times 5 \times 7$$

$$882 = 2 \times 441$$
$$= 2 \times 3 \times 147$$
$$= 2 \times 3 \times 7 \times 21$$
$$= 2 \times 3 \times 7 \times 3 \times 7$$
$$= 2 \times 3^2 \times 7^2$$

$$\therefore \text{ H.C.F. is } 2 \times 3^2 \times 7 = 126$$

How to Find L.C.M.

Once more, consider the two expressions:

$$a^3b^2c, \; a^2b^4c^2$$
$$i.e. \; aaabbc, \; aabbbbcc.$$

It is clear that the smallest expression which will contain each of them (L.C.M.) must be *aaabbbbcc*.

i.e. the L.C.M. of a^3b^2c, $a^2b^4c^2$ is $a^3b^4c^2 \leftarrow$

> We see that to find any L.C.M. of this kind, we simply take every letter in turn and write it with its *larger* index.

Similarly (1) the L.C.M. of $a^3b^5c^4d$ and $a^2b^4cd^5$ is $a^3b^5c^4d^5 \leftarrow$
(2) the L.C.M. of x^2y^3z, x^3yz^4, xy^3z^9 is $x^3y^3z^9 \leftarrow$

A similar method may be applied to numbers if they are first split up into their prime factors.

Example. Find the L.C.M. of 12, 30, 42.

$$12 = 2^2 \times 3, \qquad 30 = 3 \times 5 \times 2, \qquad 42 = 3 \times 2 \times 7$$

$$\therefore \text{ L.C.M. is } 2^2 \times 3 \times 5 \times 7 = 420 \leftarrow$$

In cases where letters have numerical coefficients, first split the coefficients into their prime factors. Then proceed as before.

Example. Find the H.C.F. and the L.C.M. of

$$12a^2bc, \quad 8abc^2, \quad 30a^3bc^4$$

$$12a^2bc = 2^2 \times 3a^2bc, \qquad 8abc^2 = 2^3abc^2, \qquad 30a^3bc^4 = 2 \times 3 \times 5a^3bc^4$$

$$\therefore \text{ H.C.F. is } 2abc \leftarrow$$

$$\text{L.C.M. is } 2^3 \times 3 \times 5a^3bc^4 = 120a^3bc^4. \leftarrow$$

Comparison of Fractions

Sometimes we wish to arrange fractions in order ("ascending order" means smallest first rising to largest; "descending order" means the reverse of this).

Suppose we have to arrange $\frac{3}{4}$, $\frac{5}{9}$, $\frac{9}{16}$ in ascending order.

We have seen that if we multiply top and bottom of a fraction by the same number we do not alter the value of the fraction.

We are going to do this to each of the fractions $\frac{3}{4}$, $\frac{5}{9}$, $\frac{9}{16}$, multiplying top and bottom of each fraction by such a number as will leave all the bottom lines alike.

The easiest way to do this is to find the lowest number which contains 4, 9 and 16 (*i.e.* their L.C.M.). This is 144.

We now find by what number the denominator 4 must be multiplied to give this number 144, *i.e.* we *divide* 144 by 4. This gives 36. We now multiply top and bottom of $\frac{3}{4}$ by 36 and arrive at $\dfrac{3 \times 36}{4 \times 36} = \dfrac{108}{144}$.

Repeat this for all the fractions and we get:

$\frac{3}{4}$, $\frac{5}{9}$, $\frac{9}{16}$, are in order the same value as $\frac{108}{144}$, $\frac{80}{144}$, $\frac{81}{144}$.

So, since $80 < 81 < 108$,

$\frac{3}{4}$, $\frac{5}{9}$, $\frac{9}{16}$ in ascending order will be $\frac{5}{9}$, $\frac{9}{16}$, $\frac{3}{4}$.

The quick way to do this is as follows:

Arrange $\frac{3}{4}$, $\frac{5}{9}$, $\frac{9}{16}$ in ascending order.

L.C.M. of 4, 9, 16 = 144.

Now write 144 once only, as it will be the common Denominator for all three fractions:

$$\overline{\hspace{3cm}}$$
$$144$$

Now proceed as follows:

$144 \div 4 = 36 \quad 3 \times 36 = 108$. Put up 108 in Numerator—

$$\frac{108,\hspace{2cm}}{144}$$

$144 \div 9 = 16 \quad 5 \times 16 = 80$. Put up 80 in Numerator—

$$\frac{108,\ 80,\hspace{1.5cm}}{144}$$

$144 \div 16 = 9 \quad 9 \times 9 = 81$. Put up 81 in Numerator and we get—

$$\frac{108,\ 80,\ 81}{144}$$

(Remember this is a short way of writing $\frac{108}{144}$, $\frac{80}{144}$, $\frac{81}{144}$).

$\therefore$ $\frac{3}{4}$, $\frac{5}{9}$, $\frac{9}{16}$ in ascending order will be $\frac{5}{9}$, $\frac{9}{16}$, $\frac{3}{4}$ ←

Addition and Subtraction of Fractions

Proceed as we did in comparison of fractions, *i.e.* find the Lowest Common Measure of the Denominators concerned. Thus:—

Example 1.

$$\frac{5}{18} + \frac{4}{15} \text{ (L.C.M. of 18 and 15 = 90)} = \frac{25+24}{90} = \frac{49}{90} \leftarrow$$

Example 2. $\qquad \frac{5}{18} - \frac{4}{15} = \frac{25-24}{90} = \frac{1}{90} \leftarrow$

Example 3. $\qquad \frac{a}{bd} + \frac{c}{bg} = \frac{ag+cd}{bdg} \leftarrow$

Note: To add *mixed numbers*, add whole numbers first, then fractions.

A question involving fractions may contain some or all of the following:—
(1) Brackets, (2) the word "of," (3) the signs $\times$ and $\div$, and (4) the signs $+$ and $-$.

The steps of the working must be taken strictly in this order:

(1) Whatever is contained within brackets must first be simplified into one quantity.

(2) Two fractions connected by "of" must be simplified into one quantity.

(3) Multiplication and division must be done before addition and subtraction.

The following examples will illustrate these rules:

(i) $\dfrac{1}{2} + \dfrac{1}{3} \times \dfrac{1}{4} = \dfrac{1}{2} + \left(\dfrac{1}{3} \times \dfrac{1}{4}\right) = \dfrac{1}{2} + \dfrac{1}{12} = \dfrac{7}{12}$ [multiplication before addition]

(ii) $\left(\dfrac{1}{2} + \dfrac{1}{3}\right) \times \dfrac{1}{4} = \dfrac{5}{6} \times \dfrac{1}{4} = \dfrac{5}{24}$ [brackets before multiplication]

(iii) $\dfrac{1}{2} \div \dfrac{1}{4}$ of $12 = \dfrac{1}{2} \div \left(\dfrac{1}{4}\text{ of }12\right) = \dfrac{1}{2} \div 3 = \dfrac{1}{6}$ ["of" before division]

(iv) $\dfrac{1}{2} \div \dfrac{1}{4} \times 12 = \dfrac{1}{2} \times \dfrac{4}{1} \times 12 = 24$ [Work out $\div$ and $\times$ from left to right]

(v) $\dfrac{1}{3} + \dfrac{1}{2} \times \dfrac{1}{4}$ of $12 = \dfrac{1}{3} + \dfrac{1}{2} \times 3 = \dfrac{1}{3} + 1\dfrac{1}{2} = 1\dfrac{5}{6}$

["of" first,   "$\times$" second,   "$+$" third]

To turn a fraction into a decimal

Divide Numerator by Denominator

$\dfrac{1}{2} = .5$, since $\quad 2\overline{\smash{)}1.0}$ $\underline{0.5}$ $\dfrac{3}{5} = .6$, since $\quad 5\overline{\smash{)}3.0}$ $\underline{0.6}$

To turn a decimal into a fraction

The decimal figures (without the point) become the Numerator. The Denominator is 1 with as many zeros as there are figures *after* the point.

Thus:

$$.307 = \frac{307}{1000} \qquad .0017 = \frac{17}{10000} \qquad 17.9421 = 17\frac{9421}{10000}$$

For Exercises see pp. 279–280.

CHAPTER 13

SIMPLE EQUATIONS

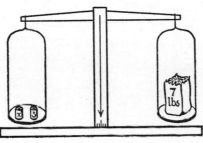

FIG. 76.

In the left-hand pan in Fig. 76 we have two weights balancing 7 lb. of sugar in the other pan. One weight is marked x, the other 3 lb. What number of lb. does x stand for? Omitting the sign "lb." we may set down the facts as follows:

$$x+3 = 7$$

This is called an "equation," *i.e.* a statement about certain things which balance each other.

Suppose we take away the 3 lb. from the left-hand pan.

To preserve the balance we must do the same on the other side, *i.e.* take away 3 lb. from the 7 lb. of sugar. As the balance will still be preserved we can put down

$$x+3-3 = 7-3$$
$$i.e.\ x = 4\leftarrow$$

Let us set out the equation and its solution more neatly:

$$x+3 = 7$$
$$\therefore \; x = 7-3$$
$$\therefore \; x = 4 \leftarrow$$

> Note that all we have done is to move $+3$ to
> right-hand side and change its sign.

Now imagine the pans balanced with the weights shown in Fig. 77.

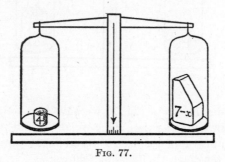

Fig. 77.

On the right-hand pan was originally a slab of butter weighing 7 lb. A piece of butter weighing x lb. has been cut off the slab, which now weighs $(7-x)$ lb. and balances when 4 lb. is on the left-hand pan.

We get $\qquad\qquad 4 = 7-x$

Now add x to each side

$$\therefore \; 4+x = 7-x+x$$
$$\therefore \; 4+x = 7$$

Now take away 4 from each side

$$\therefore \; x = 7-4$$
$$\therefore \; x = 3$$

Writing down the equation and its solution more neatly we get:—

$$4 = 7 - x$$
$$\therefore \ x = 7 - 4$$
$$\therefore \ x = 3 \leftarrow$$

Note that all we need do is—
(1) Get all terms containing x on one side of the $=$ sign, all terms without x on the other side.
(2) Change the signs of any terms we have to take across to the other side.

From Fig. 76 we see that we can do what we like to one side of an equation *provided we do the same to the other side.* (This applies equally well to multiplication and division as to addition and subtraction.)

How to test your Answer to an Equation

Take the above example

$$4 = 7 - x$$

If $x = 3$ (the answer that we hope is correct),
Then left-hand side $= 4$,
and right-hand side $(= 7 - x) = 7 - 3 = 4$ also

$$\therefore \ x = 3 \quad \text{satisfies the equation.}$$

Now suppose we have to solve the equation

$$5x - 4 = 7 + 4x$$

Arrange terms containing x on left-hand side, *all other* terms on right-hand side.

Example 1. Solve: $\quad 5x - 4 = 7 + 4x$
$$\therefore \ 5x - 4x = 7 + 4$$
$$\therefore \quad x = 11 \leftarrow$$

Test. If $x = 11$

Then left-hand side of equation:	and right-hand side of equation:
$5x-4 = 5\times11-4$	$7+4x = 7+4\times11$
$\quad = 55-4$	$\quad = 7+44$
$\quad = 51$	$\quad = 51$

$$\therefore \ x = 11 \quad \text{satisfies the equation.}$$

Sometimes another step (division) comes in:—

Example 2. Solve:
$$7x-5 = 5x+7$$
$$\therefore \ 7x-5x = 7+5$$
$$\therefore \ 2x = 12$$

Now divide each side by 2

$$\therefore \ x = 6\leftarrow$$

Test. If $x = 6$

Then left-hand side:	and right-hand side:
$7x-5 = 7\times6-5$	$5x+7 = 5\times6+7$
$\quad = 42-5$	$\quad = 30+7$
$\quad = 37$	$\quad = 37$

$$\therefore \ x = 6 \quad \text{satisfies the equation.}$$

Note carefully the difference between—

$$2x = 12 \qquad 2+x = 12$$
$$\therefore \ x = 6 \quad \text{and} \quad \therefore \ x = 10$$

Equations involving Fractions and/or Brackets

Example 3. Solve:
$$\frac{3x}{4} - \frac{5x}{12} = 3 - \frac{x}{3}$$

(1) Turn any whole numbers into fractions.

$$\therefore \ \frac{3x}{4} - \frac{5x}{12} = \frac{3}{1} - \frac{x}{3}$$

(2) Find L.C.M. of all the denominators and then proceed to arrange each side of equation on this new denominator, as we did in addition or subtraction of fractions. Note, however, that we need not write down this common denominator in working equations, since if a fraction of one quantity equals the same fraction of another quantity the quantities themselves must be equal. Thus, if one-twelfth of a = one-twelfth of b, $a = b$.

$$\left[\text{So, if } \quad \frac{3x}{4} - \frac{5x}{12} = \frac{3}{1} - \frac{x}{3} \right.$$

$$\left. \therefore \frac{9x - 5x}{12} = \frac{36 - 4x}{12} \right]$$

and it follows that

$$9x - 5x = 36 - 4x$$

$$\therefore 9x - 5x + 4x = 36$$

$$\therefore 8x = 36$$

$$\therefore x = \frac{36}{8} = 4\tfrac{1}{2} \leftarrow$$

Test for Accuracy. If $x = 4\tfrac{1}{2}$

Left-hand side:
$$\frac{3x}{4} - \frac{5x}{12} = \frac{3 \times 4\tfrac{1}{2}}{4} - \frac{5 \times 4\tfrac{1}{2}}{12}$$
$$= \frac{3 \times 9}{4 \times 2} - \frac{5 \times 9}{12 \times 2}$$
$$= \frac{27}{8} - \frac{15}{8} = \frac{12}{8} = 1\tfrac{1}{2}$$

Right-hand side:
$$3 - \frac{x}{3} = 3 - \frac{4\tfrac{1}{2}}{3}$$
$$= 3 - 1\tfrac{1}{2} = 1\tfrac{1}{2}$$

$$\therefore x = 4\tfrac{1}{2} \quad \text{satisfies the equation.}$$

It may be necessary to remove brackets first of all.

Example 4. Solve:
$$3(x-5) = 7(x+2)$$
$$\therefore\ 3x-15 = 7x+14$$
$$\therefore\ 3x-7x = 14+15$$
$$\therefore\ -4x = 29$$

$$\therefore\ x = -\frac{29}{4} = -7\tfrac{1}{4} \leftarrow$$

N.B.—Always give your answer in the form $+x = \ldots$

Test. If $x = -7\tfrac{1}{4}$

Left-hand side:
$$3(x-5) = 3(-7\tfrac{1}{4}-5)$$
$$= 3(-12\tfrac{1}{4})$$
$$= -36\tfrac{3}{4}$$

Right-hand side:
$$7(x+2) = 7(-7\tfrac{1}{4}+2)$$
$$= 7(-5\tfrac{1}{4})$$
$$= -36\tfrac{3}{4}$$

$$\therefore\ x = -7\tfrac{1}{4}\ \text{satisfies the equation.}$$

In solving an equation always remember to begin every line of your working with the shorthand sign $\therefore$ Never begin with an $=$ sign.

Equations involving Decimals

$$\text{Solve:}\quad .3x-.05 = 4-.2x$$

Hints.—
(1) Look at the term containing the largest number of decimal places. (In this case .05.)
(2) Move the point in this term sufficient places to the right to turn it into a whole number.
(3) Balance by moving the point in each other term (throughout the equation) the same number of places to the right.
    All decimals will now have disappeared.

Caution.—Remember $.3x$ means $.3 \times x$ so $.3x$ only contains 1 decimal place, not 2 places. Compare this with $.25$ which contains 2 decimal places.

Example.

$$.3x - .05 = 4 - .2x$$
$$\therefore \ 30x - 5 = 400 - 20x$$
$$\therefore \ 30x + 20x = 400 + 5$$
$$\therefore \ 50x = 405$$

$$\therefore \ x = \frac{40.5}{5} \text{ (first dividing each side by 10)}$$

$$\therefore \ x = 8.1 \leftarrow$$

N.B.—Always give the answer in decimals if the sum is set in decimals.

Test. If $x = 8.1$

Then left-hand side:
$$.3x - .05 = .3 \times 8.1 - .05$$
$$= 2.43 - .05$$
$$= 2.38$$

and right-hand side:
$$4 - .2x = 4 - .2 \times 8.1$$
$$= 4 - 1.62$$
$$= 2.38$$

$$\therefore \ x = 8.1 \quad \text{satisfies the equation.}$$

For Exercises see p. 281.

CHAPTER 14

FORMULAS AND PROBLEMS

As formulas play a very important part in scientific and mechanical problems of everyday life it is important that a thorough grasp of their evolution and working should be obtained. Formulas are sometimes very complicated in appearance but their application is quite simple.

In Algebra, *letters* are used to represent *numbers*. Thus x may stand for the number 2, or 3, or 4 . . .

A *quantity* means a *number of things*, not merely a number. A letter alone cannot therefore represent a quantity or *number of things*, but must have the *kind of thing* written after it before it is used in a formula. Thus "x bananas" stands for "2 bananas" or "3 bananas" or . . . *Never say "Let x be the bananas." Say "Let x be the number of bananas."* This distinction may appear trivial, but failure to observe it leads to confusion and muddled thinking and consequent failure in solving problems.

A *formula* is an algebraic expression linking together certain mathematical facts about different quantities.

How to evolve Formulas

Example 1. A rule for making tea is "1 teaspoonful for each person and 1 for the pot." Find a formula for the amount of tea required for various numbers of people.

Let s oz. be the weight of a teaspoonful of tea.
Let N be the number of people.
Let A oz. be the amount of tea required for N people.
Then the formula is

$$A = Ns + s \ [\text{or } A = s(N+1)]$$

Example 2. The area of a rectangle is found by multiplying its base by its height, and the area of a triangle is found by multiplying half its base by its perpendicular height. Write these statements as formulas.

Let A_1 sq. in. = area of rectangle.
Let A_2 sq. in. = area of triangle.
Let b_1 in.   = base of rectangle.
Let b_2 in.   = base of triangle.
Let h_1 in.   = height of rectangle.
Let h_2 in.   = perpendicular height of triangle.

Then $A_1 = b_1 h_1$ and $A_2 = \frac{1}{2} b_2 h_2$ are the required formulas.

Remember that A_2 is only a way of distinguishing from A_1. It has nothing to do with "A squared."

Example 3. The circumference of a circle is π times * its own diameter. Write (*a*) a formula showing this and (*b*) another showing the connection between a radius and its circumference.

(*a*) Let c in. — circumference of circle.
    Let d in. = diameter of circle.
      Then first formula is $c = \pi d$.
(*b*) Let r in. = radius of circle.
    Since every diameter is twice as long as the radius of its circle we have only to substitute † $2r$ for d in the formula already found.
∴ Second formula is $c = 2r\pi$, or as it is usually written:
$$c = 2\pi r.$$

* The Greek letter π (pronounced "pie") stands for the number of times any diameter goes into its own circumference. As this number contains a decimal which never ends, we use the symbol π for it. The value of π is 3.14159 . . . but we usually call it $\frac{22}{7}$ or 3.14.

† When you substitute one letter for another, *don't forget to remove the original.*

Example 4. The area of a circle is π times the square of its own radius. Express this as a formula.

> Let r in.   = radius
> Let A sq. in. = Area of circle
>> Then A = πr^2 is the required formula.

Example 5. The volume of a cylinder (Fig. 78) is found by multiplying the area of any cross-section (*e.g.* base) by the height of the cylinder. Express this as a formula.

N.B.—The cross-section is circular in shape.

> Let V cu. in. = vol. of cylinder
> Let r in.   = radius of cross-section
> Let h in.   = height of cylinder
> Now area of cross-section = πr^2 (see *Example* 4).

Fɪɢ. 78. $\therefore$ V = $\pi r^2 h$ is the required formula.

Example 6. The volume of a cone (Fig. 79) is one-third the volume of a cylinder on equal base. Find a formula for the volume of a cone.

> Let V cu. in. = volume of cone
> Let r in.   = radius of base
> Let h in.   = height of cone

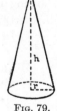

Fɪɢ. 79.

Volume of cylinder on same base = $\pi r^2 h$ (*Example* 5).

$\therefore$ V = $\frac{1}{3}\pi r^2 h$ is required formula.

In all these formulas we can substitute English for Metric measures and *vice versa,* provided we keep units corresponding, *e.g.* cu. in. go with sq. in. and in.; cu. ft. with sq. ft. and ft.; cu. cm. with sq. cm. and cm., etc.

Example 7. Write a formula for finding the depth of water in any rectangular tank after various quantities of water have been pumped into it (Fig. 80).

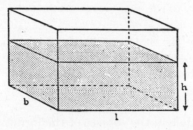

Fɪɢ. 80.

N.B.—"Shape" of water in tank is same shape as tank, *i.e.* cuboid (brick-shape).

    Let V c.c. be volume of water pumped in.
    Let l cm. be internal length of tank.
    Let b cm. be internal breadth of tank.
    Let h cm. be height of water in tank.
Now the volume of a cuboid is length × breadth × height.

$$\therefore V = lbh$$

$$\therefore \text{Required formula is} \quad h = \frac{V}{lb} \leftarrow$$

If you have difficulty in "seeing" this last step consider these easy examples of similar manipulation:

$12 = 6h$	$12 = 3 \times 2h$
$\therefore h = \dfrac{12}{6}(= 2)$	$\therefore h = \dfrac{12}{3 \times 2}(= 2)$

Note that there is a "limiting value" to h in this particular problem, namely the height of the tank. h can have any values up to but not above this height.

"Change of Subject" in a Formula

In the last example we had a "change of subject" when we changed $V = lbh$ to $h = \dfrac{V}{lb}$

We should use the first formula if we wished to find the volume of water, the second if we wished to find the height of water.

To "change the subject" in a formula merely needs an understanding of how to manipulate an equation.

Example 8. Make u the subject of the formula $V - u = at$.

$V - u = at$	Now leave only u term on left-hand side.
$\therefore \ -u = at - V$	Now make subject $+$.
$\therefore \ u = -at + V$	Now rewrite with $+V$ first on right-hand side because it is neater to put $+$ term before $-$ term.

i.e. $u = V - at \leftarrow$

Example 9. Make a the subject of the formula $V - u = at$.

$V - u = at$	Now get term containing a on left-hand side.
$\therefore \ at = V - u$	Now divide both sides by co-efficient of a.
$\therefore \ a = \dfrac{V - u}{t} \leftarrow$	

Similarly, we could get—

$$V = at + u \qquad \text{and} \qquad t = \dfrac{V - u}{a}$$

Example 10. Make "a" the subject of:—

$$s = ut + \tfrac{1}{2}at^2$$

Get rid of fraction. (Here multiply throughout by 2. If more than one fraction, multiply throughout by L.C.M. of all denominators.)

$$2s = 2ut + at^2$$
$$\therefore at^2 = 2s - 2ut$$

$$\therefore a = \frac{2s - 2ut}{t^2} \leftarrow$$

Making Use of Formulas

If we know, or can find out, the values of all the letters save one in a formula, it is an easy matter to find the value of that one letter.

The formula for the volume of metal in a pipe (*i.e.* a hollow cylinder (Fig. 81)) is: $V = \pi l(R+r)(R-r)$ *

where l cm. = length of pipe.
        R cm. = outer radius of pipe.
        r cm. = inner radius of pipe.
        V c.c. = volume of metal in pipe.

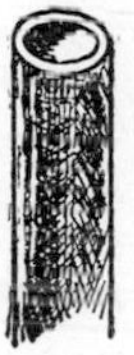

Fig. 81

* This formula is obtained by multiplying the area of the cross-section of metal in the pipe by the length of pipe (compare example of solid cylinder on p. 104). The product is then factored.
Area of cross-section of metal = area of outer circle − area of inner circle
$$= \pi R^2 - \pi r^2$$
Volume of metal $= l(\pi R^2 - \pi r^2)$
$$= l\pi(R^2 - r^2)$$
$$= \pi l(R+r)(R-r)$$

Example 11. Find what length of pipe 10 cm. in diameter and made of metal 5 mm. thick can be made from 1 cu. m. of metal. (Take $\pi = 3.14$.)

We must first of all find R and r in cm. and then reduce 1 cu. m. to c.c.

If diameter of pipe = 10 cm., R = 5 cm.

Since metal is 5 mm. (= .5 cm.) thick, $r = 4.5$ cm.

1 cu. m. = 1000 cu. dm. = 1,000,000 cc.

Now change the subject of the formula from V to l.

$$V = \pi l(R+r)(R-r)$$

$$\therefore l = \frac{V}{\pi(R+r)(R-r)} = \frac{1000000}{3.14(9.5)(.5)} = 67047 \text{ cm. (approx.)}$$

$$= 6.7047 \text{ Hm. (approx.)} \leftarrow$$

Solving Problems by Making Equations

Having grasped the principle of translating words into Algebra in Exercises on pp. 281–282, you are in a position to tackle problems.

Hints.—

(1) Read the question very carefully.

(2) Write down what you are given statement by statement. (At first write down the words as well as their Algebra translation. After a time you will be able to omit the words.)

(3) Link up your "Algebra translations" into an equation.

(4) Check your answer *from the problem* (not from your equation which may itself be incorrect).

Example 1. A certain number is multiplied by 4, and 6 is then taken away from the result. If 14 remains, what was the number?

Let x be the number

Words.	Algebra Translation.
"The number multiplied by 4" .	$4x$
"Take away 6"	-6
"The result is 14". . . .	$= 14$

$$\therefore 4x - 6 = 14 \qquad \therefore 4x = 20 \qquad \therefore x = 5\leftarrow$$

[*Check* (from the *problem*)—
If I multiply 5 by 4 I get 20.   If I then take away 6 I get 14.
$$\therefore 5 \text{ is correct answer.}]$$

Example 2. The sum of three consecutive even numbers is 72. Find the numbers.

[In Algebra the letter x (or any other letter) stands for any number, odd or even, *but $2x$ must be even* since twice any number, be it odd or even, gives us an even number (*e.g.* $2\times5 = 10$, $2\times6 = 12$, $2\times7 = 14 \ldots$). So whenever we have to represent an even number in Algebra we put $2x$. The next even numbers above and below $2x$ must be $(2x+2)$ and $(2x-2)$. For an odd number we put either $2x+1$ or $2x-1$. Think this out before proceeding farther.]

Let $2x$ be the first of the three even numbers

Words.	Algebra.
The first of the three numbers .	$2x$
The next even number . . .	$(2x+2)$
The next even number . . .	$(2x+4)$
The sum of these three numbers .	$2x+(2x+2)+(2x+4)$
"is 72"	$= 72$

$$\therefore 2x+2x+2+2x+4 = 72$$
$$\therefore 2x+2x+2x = 72-2-4$$
$$\therefore 6x = 66$$
$$\therefore x = 11$$
$$\therefore 2x = 22, \qquad 2x+2 = 24, \qquad 2x+4 = 26$$
$\therefore$ the numbers are 22, 24, 26← [Check as before.]

Example 3. What is the next higher number to x?

"Little Sum": What is the next higher number to 4? Answer 5. How can I get that answer from the number 4? Add 1. *i.e.* the answer is $4+1$.

$$\therefore \text{our answer is } x+1\leftarrow$$

Example 4. Write down 5 consecutive numbers of which x is middle one.

"Little Sum": What are the 5 consecutive numbers of which 7 is the middle one? Answer 5, 6, 7, 8, 9. How can I get these, using the given number 7?

$$(7-2),\ (7-1),\ 7,\ (7+1),\ (7+2),$$

$\therefore$ our answer is $(x-2),\ (x-1),\ x,\ (x+1),\ (x+2)$ ←

Example 5. A man is x years old. How old will he be in y years?

"Little Sum": A man is 30 years old. How old will he be in 10 years? Answer 40. How can we get that answer from our given number? Add 30 and 10.

$$\therefore \text{ our answer is } (x+y) \text{ years} \leftarrow$$

Example 6. A cistern was found to be three-fourths full of water. After running off 220 gallons it was found to be one-fifth full. Find the capacity of the cistern.

Let x gallons = the capacity of the cistern. The cistern had in it $\frac{3x}{4}$ gallons, from which 220 gallons were drawn off. This left $\left(\frac{3x}{4} - 220\right)$ gallons. But as we are told that the cistern was then a fifth full $\therefore$ $\left(\frac{3x}{4} - 220\right)$ gallons must be the same as $\frac{x}{5}$ gallons.

$$\therefore \frac{3x}{4} - 220 = \frac{x}{5} \qquad\qquad \therefore \frac{3x}{4} - \frac{x}{5} = 220$$

$$\therefore \frac{15x-4x}{20} = 220 \therefore \frac{11x}{20} = 220 \therefore 11x = 4400$$

$$\therefore x = 400$$

Hence the cistern held 400 gallons ←

For Exercises see pp. 283–285.

CHAPTER 15

MORE GEOMETRICAL CONSTRUCTIONS

Review definitions on p. 55.

(1) *To bisect a straight line.*
Let AB be the line.

> *Make all construction lines as thin as possible.*

Fig. 82.

With center A and any radius $> \frac{1}{2}$AB draw an arc.

With center B and same radius, draw another arc cutting the former at P, Q.

Join PQ, cutting AB at X.
Then AB *is bisected at* X (*i.e.* AX = XB).

(2) *To bisect an angle.*
Let ABC be the angle.

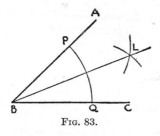
Fig. 83.

With center B and any convenient radius, draw an arc cutting AB at P and BC at Q.

With center P and any convenient radius, draw an arc inside the ∠ ABC.

With center Q and the same radius, draw an arc cutting the last arc at L. Join LB.

Then LB *bisects* ∠ ABC (*i.e.* ∠ ABL = ∠ LBC).

(3) *To draw an angle equal to a given angle.*
Let ABC be the angle to be copied.

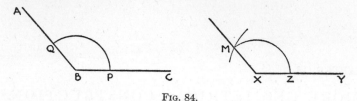

Fig. 84.

Draw any line XY.

With center B, any radius, draw an arc cutting BC at P and BA at Q.

With center X and same radius, draw an arc cutting XY at Z.

Measure (with compasses) the distance PQ.

With center Z and this radius cut the arc at M. Join MX.

Then ∠ MXY = ∠ ABC.

Perpendiculars

(4) We often need to draw a line perpendicular (*i.e.* at right angles) to another line—(*a*) from a point *on* that line, (*b*) from a point *outside* that line.

(*a*) Let AB be the line, P the point on AB.

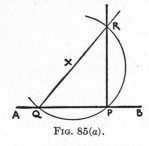

Fig. 85(*a*).

Take any point X *off* the line.

With center X, radius XP, draw an arc cutting the line AP at P and Q.

Join QX and produce to cut arc at R. Join RP.

Then RP *is perpendicular to* AB.

[The "shorthand" for "is perpendicular to" is ⊥.]

(*b*) Let AB be the line, P the point outside AB.

Take any point *on* the line. (It is useful to get accustomed to taking A or B, for you will often have to drop a per-

pendicular from one corner of a △ to
the opposite side and you may consider
PA as one side of a possible △ PAB.)

Join that point to P. Bisect line at
O [Constrn. (1) p. 111]. With center
O, radius OP, draw an arc cutting AB
at S. Join PS.

Then PS *is perpendicular to* AB.

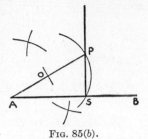

FIG. 85(b).

(5) *To divide a line into a given number of equal parts.*

Let AB be the line to be divided into, say, 5 equal parts.

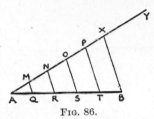

FIG. 86.

At any acute angle to AB draw
AY any length. Mark off on it AM
a suitable short length and then MN,
NO, OP, PX, each equal to AM.

Join XB. Draw PT, OS, NR, MQ,
all ‖ XB.

Then AB will be divided into 5
equal parts at Q, R, S, and T.

A quick way to draw parallel lines.
Put protractor up against XB as
   shown in Fig. 87.
Put ruler by protractor as shown.
Keep ruler still.
Slide protractor down ruler to P,
   O, N, etc.

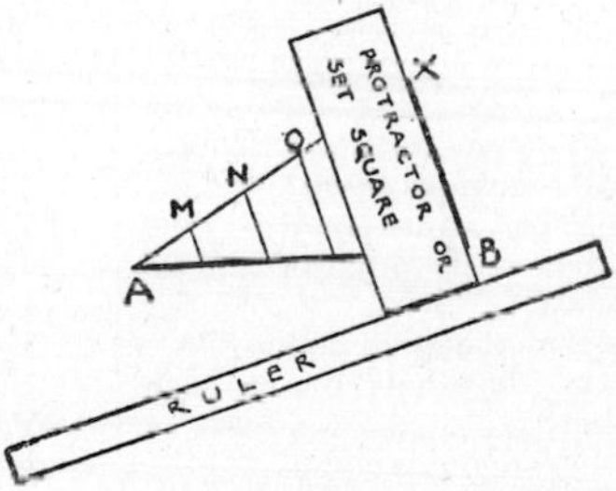

FIG. 87.

For Exercises see pp. 285–286.

CHAPTER 16

PARALLELOGRAMS AND TRIANGLES

We have seen (p. 25) *that a parallelogram is a quadrilateral with opposite sides parallel.*

Consider the four ⊡s in Fig. 88. Test the facts given by actual measurement and, if you are curious about these things, prove these facts by using theorems you already know.

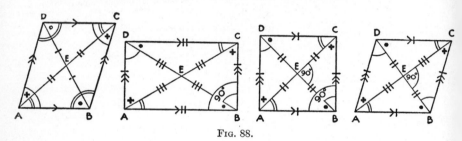

Fɪɢ. 88.

	Any ⊡.	Square.	Oblong.	Rhombus.
Are all four sides equal? . .	No	Yes	No	Yes
Are opposite sides equal? . .	Yes	Yes	Yes	Yes
Are diagonally opposite angles equal?	Yes	Yes	Yes	Yes
Does each diagonal bisect ⊡? .	Yes	Yes	Yes	Yes
Do the diagonals bisect each other?	Yes	Yes	Yes	Yes
Are the diagonals equal? . .	No	Yes	Yes	No
Are the diagonals at rt. ∠s? .	No	Yes	No	Yes
What is the sum of the 2 ∠s at ends of each side? . . .	2 rt. ∠s	2 rt. ∠s	2 rt. ∠s	2 rt. ∠s

Nᴏᴛᴇ—The shorthand for parallelogram is ⊡. A line joining opposite corners across a ⊡ is called a diagonal.

The Area of any Parallelogram = Base×Perpendicular Height

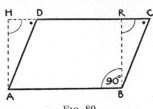

FIG. 89.

It is easy to prove △ HAD ≡ △ RBC (SAA)

∴ △ HAD = △ RBC in area.

∴ Figure ABCH − △ HAD = Figure ABCH − △ RBC in area.

i.e. ▱ ABCD = rectangle ABRH in area.

∴ Area of ▱ ABCD = Area of rectangle ABRH

= AB×BR.

∴ Area of any Parallelogram = Base×Perpendicular Height.

Parallelograms on the same base (or equal bases) and of the same perpendicular height (or between the same parallel lines) are equal in area.

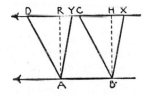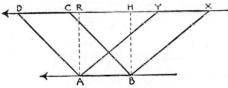

FIG. 90.

This is obvious since—

the area of ▱ ABCD = rect. ABHR.

and the area of ▱ ABXY = rect. ABHR.

i.e. ▱ ABCD = ▱ ABXY (in both cases in Fig. 90).

Area of a Triangle

By drawing two parallel lines you will find you can build up a □ from any △.

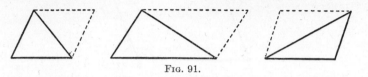

Fig. 91.

Since we know that a diagonal bisects its parallelogram it is clear that each △ is half the area of its "own" parallelogram.

Now the area of any □ = base×perpendicular height.

∴ *the area of any* △ = $\frac{1}{2}$ *base×perpendicular height.*

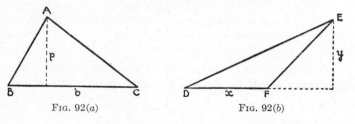

Fig. 92(*a*)   Fig. 92(*b*)

Area of △ ABC = $\frac{1}{2}$ *bp*.   Area of △ DEF = $\frac{1}{2}$ *xy*.

If the △ is obtuse-angled, as in Fig. 92(*b*), produce base and measure perpendicular height *y* above base line (or turn △ round in imagination and call DE base, dropping a line from F at right ∠s to DE to get a different height).

Triangles on the same base (or on equal bases) and between the same parallel lines (or of equal height) are equal in area.

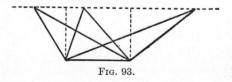

Fig. 93.

This is obvious, since each △ = half the area of the rectangle on same base and between the same parallel lines.

Note that the area of any △ may be found in more than one way.

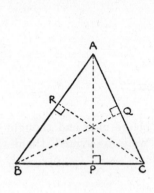

Fig. 94.

Area of △ ABC
= ½ BC×AP
or ½ AC×BQ
or ½ AB×CR

Area of △ XYZ
= ½ XY×ZF
or ½ YZ×XG
or ½ XZ×EY

[*Note that the perpendiculars from the corners of a △ to the opposite sides (or sides produced) meet at the same point.*]

Area of a Right-Angled Triangle

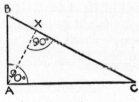

Fig. 95.

Area of △ ABC = ½ AC×AB
or ½ BC×AX

For Exercises see pp. 287–289.

CHAPTER 17

RATIOS

Shadows of Poles, etc.

In the infancy of mathematics, long before men had thought out Arithmetic or Algebra, certain facts were discovered, thanks to the clear-cut shadows cast by the brilliant sun of Egypt.

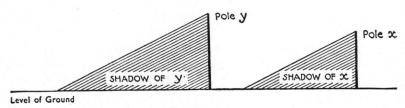

FIG. 96.

It was noticed that if two unequal poles were set upright on level ground, the longer pole was just the same part of its shadow as the shorter pole was of *its* shadow. (When the sun was very high in the sky the poles might be longer than their shadows. In such a case the longer pole would be the same number of times as great as its shadow as was the shorter pole as great as its own shadow.)

Look carefully at the "shadow triangles" in Fig. 96. If the poles were 4 meters and 3 meters long respectively, and if the shadow cast by the longer pole was found to be 8 meters long, then the shadow cast by the shorter pole would be 6 meters long. The Egyptian wise men would know this without having to measure the shorter shadow.

With our advantage in knowing something about Arithmetic we can see at a glance that

$$\text{if } \frac{4}{8} = \frac{3}{x} \quad \text{then} \quad x = 6$$

$\frac{4}{8}$ may be written $4 : 8$ (read, "four is to eight") and $\frac{4}{8} = \frac{3}{6}$ may be written $4 : 8 = 3 : 6$ ("4 is to 8 as 3 is to 6").

The fraction $\frac{4}{8}$ is sometimes called the "ratio of 4 to 8," and

when we get two ratios that are equal, the numbers constituting those ratios are said to be "in proportion."

Thus, since $\frac{4}{8} = \frac{3}{6}$, 4, 8, 3, 6 are said to be "in proportion." In the same way, 1, 2, 2, 4 are in proportion as will be seen at once if we put them in fraction form: $\frac{1}{2} = \frac{2}{4}$.

Again, since $\dfrac{\text{length of pole } y}{\text{shadow of pole } y} = \dfrac{\text{length of pole } x}{\text{shadow of pole } x}$

each fraction is the ratio of length of a pole to the length of its own shadow.

Moreover, since both ratios are equal, all four things are in proportion. By measurement we can also find out that the ratio of any pair of sides in the one $\triangle$ is equal to the ratio of the correspondingly situated sides in the other $\triangle$.

The two "shadow triangles" in our picture are clearly the same *shape* though not the same *size*. Figures which are the same *shape* are called "similar figures."

We shall meet with them later on.

Remember.—An enlargement of a man's photograph must obviously be *similar in shape* to the original photograph or we should not recognize who the man was. It is not the same size, *i.e.* it will not *fit* the original photograph, but it is the same or *similar shape*.

Here we have in Fig. 97 a portrait of Donald Duck and an enlargement. Now if in the original portrait the length from the tip of the toe on the left to the tip of the toe on the right is ⅔ of the total height of Donald Duck, then you will find the same fraction or ratio in the corresponding parts in the enlargement.

FIG. 97.

Ratios

As we have seen, *the ratio of one thing to another simply means the size of the one thing compared with the size of another thing, i.e.* the number of times one thing (*e.g.* a pole) is as great as the other thing (*e.g.* the shadow of that pole). Thus, every fraction is the ratio of its Numerator to its Denominator, and every ratio may therefore be written as a fraction.

Thus: 3 : 4 ("three is to four") may be written $\frac{3}{4}$

$a : b$ ("*a* is to *b*") may be written $\frac{a}{b}$

Some things which are really ratios are disguised through being expressed as whole numbers. *Speed, for instance, is a ratio, as it includes two things, distance and time.* We are all familiar with this form of ratio; when we say that an airplane can travel 1200 miles in 6 hours we say its speed is 200 m.p.h. This is a short way of saying:

Distance covered : *time taken as* 200 : 1

which ratio may also be expressed as $\frac{200}{1}$

[For this reason we shall find that the average of two speeds, say 20 m.p.h. and 30 m.p.h. is not necessarily 25 m.p.h. It depends on total distance covered and total time taken. You cannot average speed in the way you average ordinary numbers because speed is a *ratio* between distance and time.]

A ball player's batting average is another example of a ratio, since it includes two things: total number of hits made and total number of times at bat, i.e. it may be written in the form $\dfrac{\text{number of hits}}{\text{times at bat}}$. (This is the reason for a fact known to all baseball fans, but possibly not understood by everyone, namely, that if a player's batting average for June is .240 and for July .360 it is very unlikely that his average for the two months is .300, *i.e.* $\left(\dfrac{.240 + .360}{2}\right)$. He may have made 24 hits in 100 times at bat in June and 18 hits in 50 times at bat in July—giving him an average of .280 for the two months.)

All ratios, being fractions, may be expressed in innumerable ways without altering the actual ratio, *e.g.*:

the ratio $2 : 4$ may be written $\dfrac{2}{4}$ which is clearly the same ratio as:

$$\frac{3}{6}, \frac{4}{8}, \frac{5}{10} \cdot \cdot \cdot \text{ each ratio being equal to } \frac{1}{2}$$

(*i.e.* Numerator : Denominator as $1 : 2$).

Sometimes we have to find the ratio between two expressions of the same kind but containing different units (*e.g.* tons : lb.). We must first reduce the two expressions to the same units, then put them in fraction form and reduce to lowest terms.

Example 1. Find the ratio between $1\frac{1}{4}$ hours and 45 minutes.

$$1\tfrac{1}{4} \text{ hours } = 75 \text{ minutes.}$$

$$\therefore \text{ ratio is } \frac{75}{45} \text{ or } \frac{5}{3} \quad or \quad 5 : 3 \leftarrow$$

Example 2. Express in the form $a:1$ the following ratio: $8.50 to $6.

Reduce each expression to the lowest unit in either (*i.e.* cents).

$$\therefore \text{ ratio is } \frac{850}{600} = \frac{17}{12} = 1\tfrac{5}{12} = \frac{1\tfrac{5}{12}}{1} = 1\tfrac{5}{12}:1\leftarrow$$

Example 3. A photograph measuring 9 in. by 5 in. is enlarged so that the larger side becomes 18 in. In what ratio is the area increased?

Graph showing at a glance the length and breadth of every possible photograph whose sides are in the ratio 5 : 9.

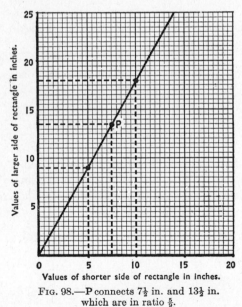

Values of larger side of rectangle in inches.

Values of shorter side of rectangle in inches.

Fig. 98.—P connects 7½ in. and 13½ in. which are in ratio ⅚.

The shorter side obviously becomes 10 in.

Now, area of original photograph = (9×5) sq. in. and

area of enlarged photograph = (18×10) sq. in.

∴ ratio in which area is increased

$$=\frac{10\times18}{9\times5}=\frac{4}{1} \text{ (or } 4:1)\leftarrow$$

Note this result carefully. *If we double each side of any rectangle we quadruple (multiply by 4) its area.*

Proportion

Problems of proportion gave Greek mathematicians immense difficulty, as you will agree if you turn to a book of Euclid. You will there see how difficult—nowadays unnecessarily difficult—it is to grasp the meaning of proportion in geometrical language— the only mathematics of Euclid's day.

As we have seen, when two ratios (or fractions) are equal, the four quantities involved in the ratios are "in proportion."

If $\dfrac{3}{4} = \dfrac{6}{8}$ then   3, 4, 6, 8 are "in proportion."

So if $\dfrac{a}{b} = \dfrac{c}{d}$ a, b, c, d are "in proportion."

We know that if we multiply each side of any equation by the same thing we do not destroy the balance. So we will multiply each side of the equation $\dfrac{a}{b} = \dfrac{c}{d}$ by $\left(\dfrac{b}{c}\right)$

$$\frac{a}{b} = \frac{c}{d} \quad \therefore \frac{a}{b} \times \frac{b}{c} = \frac{c}{d} \times \frac{b}{c}$$

$$\therefore \text{ by canceling } \quad \frac{a}{c} = \frac{b}{d}$$

i.e. Since $\qquad \dfrac{3}{4} = \dfrac{6}{8}$ or, $3 : 4 = 6 : 8$

we can say that $\dfrac{3}{6} = \dfrac{4}{8}$ or, $3 : 6 = 4 : 8$

In the same way, if

$$\frac{a}{b} = \frac{c}{d} \quad \therefore 1 \div \frac{a}{b} = 1 \div \frac{c}{d} \quad \therefore 1 \times \frac{b}{a} = 1 \times \frac{d}{c} \quad \therefore \frac{b}{a} = \frac{d}{c}$$

Now multiply each side of the equation $\frac{a}{b} = \frac{c}{d}$ by $\frac{bd}{1}$.

$$\frac{a}{b} \times \frac{bd}{1} = \frac{c}{d} \times \frac{bd}{1}$$

∴ by canceling $\quad ad = bc$

We could get this result straight away by multiplying diagonally ("corner to corner")

This time-saving device is most valuable and important.

Thus, to solve the equation $\frac{x}{8} = \frac{3}{4}$

we multiply diagonally and get $4x = 24$.

$$\therefore \ x = 6 \leftarrow$$

Caution: You may only multiply diagonally like this when each side of the equation consists of a solitary fraction, *i.e.* when you have four quantities which are in proportion.

Remember that, since any whole number may be written as an improper fraction by standing it on 1, we can multiply diagonally in cases like $\frac{x}{4} = 5$ by writing the equation thus:

$$\frac{x}{4} = \frac{5}{1} \quad \therefore \ x = 20 \leftarrow$$

Now see how to tackle problems involving Proportion.

Example 1. If 10 eggs cost 30¢ how many may be bought for 48¢?

Ratio of number of eggs to cost of those eggs $= \dfrac{10}{30}$ (working in cents).

∴ Since the number of eggs which can be bought for 48¢ will be in the same ratio we get

$$\frac{x}{48} = \frac{10}{30}$$

$$\therefore \ 30x = 10 \times 48$$

$$\therefore \ x = \frac{10 \times 48}{30} = 16 \leftarrow$$

∴ 16 eggs can be bought for 48¢.

For those who may find this quick method of working proportion sums difficult to grasp, another method is available called the Unitary Method. The rules are:—

(1) Ask yourself "what *kind of thing* have I to find?"

(2) Write down *what you are told* (*not* what you are asked) with this *kind of thing* at the end of the sentence.

(3) Then reduce to 1 (or unity) as shown on p. 126. Ask yourself as you come to each fresh line, "Will the result be *more* or *less* than the preceding line?" If more, you multiply (*i.e.* put the number on the top line) if less, you divide (*i.e.* put the number on the bottom line).

Those who prefer this more clumsy method are advised to learn these **rules** by heart.

Example 1. *By Unitary Method:*

(1) Kind of thing: "eggs."

(2)   30 cents buys 10 eggs

(3) ∴ 1 cent buys $\dfrac{10}{30}$ eggs (impossible in practice but theoretically sound)

∴ 48 cents buys $\dfrac{10 \times 48}{30}$ eggs = 16 eggs←

Graph connecting number and price of eggs at the rate of 10 for 30¢

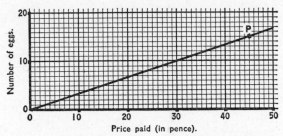

FIG. 99.—P connects together 45 cents and 15 eggs.

Example 2. A car goes 75 miles on 3 gallons of gasoline. How many gallons will be needed for a journey of 200 miles in this car?

Ratio of distance to gallons used $= \dfrac{75}{3} \therefore \dfrac{75}{3} = \dfrac{200}{x}$

$\therefore x = 8$ gals.←

By Unitary Method:

(1) Kind of thing we have to find: "gallons."

(2) 75 miles require 3 gallons

(3) ∴ 1 mile requires $\dfrac{3}{75}$ gallons

∴ 200 miles require $\dfrac{3 \times 200}{75}$ gallons = 8 gallons←

Graph showing petrol consumption at rate of 3 *gallons for* 75 *miles*

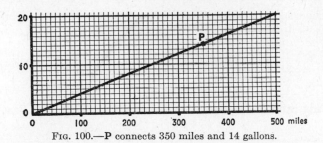

FIG. 100.—P connects 350 miles and 14 gallons.

Ratios of Kilometers, Statute miles, Nautical miles.

$$\frac{1}{41} \text{ Km.} = \frac{1}{66} \text{ statute mile} = \frac{1}{76} \text{ Nautical mile.}$$

Example 1. Express 82 statute miles as Kilometers.

$$\frac{1}{66} \text{ statute mile} = \frac{1}{41} \text{ Km.}$$

$$\therefore \quad 1 \quad \text{``} \qquad \text{``} \quad = \frac{66}{41} \quad \text{``}$$

$$\therefore \quad 82 \quad \text{``} \qquad \text{``} \quad = \frac{66}{41} \times \frac{82}{1} = 132 \text{ Km.} \leftarrow$$

Example 2. Express 90 Nautical miles as statute miles.

$$\frac{1}{76} \text{ Naut. mile} = \frac{1}{66} \text{ stat. mile}$$

$$\therefore \quad 1 \quad \text{``} \qquad \text{``} \quad = \frac{76}{66} \quad \text{``} \qquad \text{``}$$

$$\therefore \quad 90 \quad \text{``} \qquad \text{``} \quad = \frac{76}{66} \times \frac{90}{1} = 103\tfrac{7}{11} \text{ stat. miles} \leftarrow$$

Scales

> The scale of a map or plan is an example of ratio. Thus, if a map is drawn to the scale 1 inch to 1 mile this ratio is
>
> $$\frac{1 \text{ inch}}{1 \text{ mile}} = \frac{1 \text{ inch}}{(5280 \times 12) \text{ inches}} = \frac{1}{63360}$$
>
> *i.e. the scale of the map is* 1 : 63360.
>
> **This ratio or fraction is called the Representative Fraction (R.F.)**

Example 3. A plan is drawn to the scale of 6 in. to 1 mile. Find the area of an airport which is represented on this plan as having an area of 42 sq. in.

Now our scale tells us that if we draw a square on the plan with sides 6 in., this square will have an area of 6^2 or 36 sq. in. on the plan and will represent an area of 1 sq. mile or 640 acres on the Earth.

Let x acres = area of airport.

Ratio of area on plan to area on Earth $= \dfrac{36 \text{ sq. in.}}{640 \text{ acres}}$

$\therefore \dfrac{36 \text{ sq. in.}}{640 \text{ acres}} = \dfrac{42 \text{ sq. in.}}{x \text{ acres}}$ $\therefore 36x = 640 \times 42$

$\therefore x = 746\frac{2}{3}$ acres.

(We need not reduce the 640 acres and x acres to sq. in. here, since all the multiplying factors would cancel each other out.)

By Unitary Method:

36 sq. in. on plan represent 640 acres

$\therefore$ 1 sq. in. on plan represents $\dfrac{640}{36}$ acres

$\therefore$ 42 sq. in. on plan represent $\dfrac{640 \times 42}{36}$ acres $= 746\frac{2}{3}$ acres.

Example 4. The scale of a map is 1 : 15840. Find the distance between two factories which are 14 in. apart on the map.

The ratio between map distance and Earth distance is $\dfrac{1}{15840}$

$$\therefore \ \frac{1}{15840} = \frac{14}{x}$$

$$\therefore \ x = 14 \times 15840 \text{ in.} = \frac{14 \times 15840}{5280 \times 12} \text{ miles}$$

$$= 3\tfrac{1}{2} \text{ miles} \leftarrow$$

By Unitary Method:

1 in. on map represents 15840 in. on Earth
$\therefore$ 14 in. on map represent 15840 × 14 in. on Earth

$$= \frac{15840 \times 14}{5280 \times 12} \text{ miles} = 3\tfrac{1}{2} \text{ miles} \leftarrow$$

So far every example we have considered has been a case of what is known as *Direct Variation, i.e.* as one quantity in a ratio increases the other also increases (number of eggs, price of those eggs; distance gone by car, gasoline used for that distance; distance or area on map, distance or area on Earth represented by that distance or area).

We will now consider another type of proportion problems in which as one quantity *increases* the other quantity *decreases*.

Such quantities are said to *"vary inversely."* Most of such problems deal with *speed-and-time* or *work-and-time.* Be on your guard in such proportion sums.

Suppose an aircraft has to fly 200 *miles. If its average speed is* 100 *m.p.h. it will take* 2 *hours. If its average speed is* 200 *m.p.h. it will take* 1 *hour, i.e.:*

As speed *increases*, time taken *decreases*.

We see that the ratio of the two speeds above is $\frac{1}{2}$ and that the corresponding ratio of the times is $\frac{2}{1}$, *i.e.* one is the "inverse" of the other.

When doing inverse proportion keep this simple example in mind. It will keep you straight.

Example 5. A train traveling at 48 m.p.h. takes 50 minutes for a certain journey. At what rate must it run to do the journey in 40 minutes?

$$\text{Ratio of speeds} = \frac{48}{x}$$

$$\text{Inverse ratio of time taken} = \frac{40}{50}$$

$$\therefore \ \frac{48}{x} = \frac{40}{50}$$

$$\therefore \ x = \frac{48 \times 50}{40} = 60 \text{ m.p.h.} \leftarrow$$

By Unitary Method:

Train takes 50 minutes if its speed is 48 m.p.h.
Train takes 1 minute if its speed is (48 × 50) m.p.h.
Train takes 40 minutes if its speed is $\frac{48 \times 50}{40}$ m.p.h.

$$= 60 \text{ m.p.h.} \leftarrow$$

Graphs representing speeds of 48 *m.p.h.* (A) *and* 60 *m.p.h.* (B)

P is point on A which shows that this train goes 40 miles in 50 min.

Q is point on B which shows that this train can do that journey in 40 minutes.

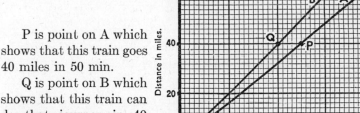

FIG. 101.

Example 6. If 6 men can dig a trench in 8 hours, how long will 9 men take to do it, working at the same rate per man?

A little thought will show you that this also is an example of Inverse Variation. As the number of men increases, the time they take decreases— or at least it does in theory. In practice there comes a point when too many may hinder a job in various ways. But we are concerned here with theory. Ratio of numbers of men $= \dfrac{6}{9}$. Inverse ratio of time taken $= \dfrac{x}{8}$

$$\therefore \ \frac{6}{9} = \frac{x}{8} \ \therefore \ 9x = 48 \ \therefore \ x = 5\tfrac{1}{3} \text{ hours} \leftarrow$$

By Unitary Method:

6 men dig trench in 8 hours

$\therefore$ 1 man digs trench in 8×6 hours

$\therefore$ 9 men dig trench in $\dfrac{8 \times 6}{9}$ hours $= 5\tfrac{1}{3}$ hours$\leftarrow$

Compound Proportion

Sometimes we have to deal with units that have to be multiplied together.

Example 7. The Royal Hotel puts up a party of 20 guests for 7 days and another party of 24 guests for 10 days.

(1) Find the ratio of the two hotel bills.
(2) If the smaller bill were $350 what would the larger bill be?
(3) If the larger bill were $672 what would the smaller be?

To feed and house 20 guests for 7 days is (in theory) equivalent to feeding and housing 1 guest for 20×7 days; while 24 guests for 10 days is equivalent to 1 guest for 24×10 days.

(1) $\therefore$ The ratio between the hotel bills will be

$$\frac{20 \times 7}{24 \times 10} \text{ or } \frac{7}{12} \leftarrow$$

(2) $\therefore$ The smaller bill is $\frac{7}{12}$ of the larger;

and the larger bill $\frac{12}{7}$ of the smaller.

$\therefore$ If the smaller bill is $350 the larger bill is

$$\frac{12}{7} \text{ of } \$350 = \$600 \leftarrow$$

(3) In this case the smaller bill would be

$$\frac{7}{12} \text{ of } \$672 = \$392 \leftarrow$$

By Unitary Method:

(1) As before.

(2) 20 guests are fed for 7 days for $350

∴ 1 guest is fed for 7 days for $350 ÷ 20

∴ 1 guest is fed for 1 day for $350 ÷ (20×7)

∴ 24 guests are fed for 1 day for $350×24 ÷ (20×7)

∴ 24 guests are fed for 10 days for $\dfrac{\$350 \times 24 \times 10}{20 \times 7} = \$600 \leftarrow$

(3) 24 guests are fed for 10 days for $672

∴ 1 guest is fed . . . etc., etc.

Some very Familiar Ratios in Everyday Life

Speed. As we have seen, speed is a *ratio* because it combines two things, *distance* and *time, i.e.*

$$\text{speed} = \text{distance} : \text{time}$$

$$\text{or, speed} = \frac{\text{distance}}{\text{time}}$$

If the distance is in miles and the time in hours, the speed is "so many miles per hour."

If the distance is in feet and the time in seconds, the speed is "so many feet per second," and so on.

Thus, | **60 m.p.h. = 88 ft. per sec.**

∴ 30 m.p.h. = 44 ft. per sec. (by division)

∴ 15 m.p.h. = 22 ft. per sec. (by division)

∴ 45 m.p.h. = 66 ft. per sec. (by addition)

Remember these.

Rates of Pay, Wages, Salaries, Rent, Income Tax, etc. All these are ratios, for they each embrace two things, *payment* and *period to which payment refers* (or in the case of Taxes *sum on which payment is based*), *e.g.* $30 per *week;* $3 per *day;* $2000 a *year;* Income tax at so much on the dollar.

Percentage is a most important form of ratio which is constantly used for convenience in comparing the sizes of two quantities. (The "shorthand" for "per cent" is %.) In percentage the ratio one quantity bears to another is converted into an equal ratio containing the number 100.

Thus every percentage is a proportion sum, since two equal ratios are involved.

A few examples will make this clear:—

Example 9. A candidate gets 15 marks out of a possible 20. What is his percentage? (This is another way of asking what would he have got had 100 been the possible.)

$$\frac{\text{Marks obtained}}{\text{Maximum possible}} = \frac{15}{20} = \frac{x}{100} \quad \therefore \ x = 75$$

Answer, 75%

Note: The Unitary Method may be used in percentage if preferred.

The simplest and therefore quickest and best way of dealing with percentages is to use the **fractional** *form of ratios.*

Thus, in the above example, we could have said:

$$\text{Fraction of marks obtained} = \frac{15}{20}$$

$$\text{This fraction of } 100 = \frac{15}{20} \times \frac{100}{1} = 75\% \leftarrow$$

Example 10. To pass an examination a candidate must obtain 60% of the maximum marks. If this maximum is 175, what is the least number of marks which will allow him to pass?

The fraction of marks required $= \dfrac{60}{100}$

This fraction of 175 $= \dfrac{60}{100} \times \dfrac{175}{1} = 105$ marks←

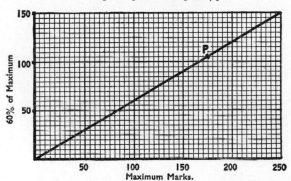

Graph representing 60%

FIG. 102.—Point **P** shows that if maximum is 175, 60% of 175, or marks necessary to pass, will be 105, and so on.

To find what percentage one quantity is of another quantity.—

(1) Write down the ratio between the two quantities *in fraction form*. Reduce top and bottom lines to lowest kind of unit in either.

(2) Take this fraction of 100.

Example 11. Express \$3.50 as a percentage of \$40.

In fraction form, ratio is $\dfrac{\$3.50}{\$40.00} = \dfrac{350}{4000}$

$$\therefore \% \text{ is } \dfrac{350}{4000} \times \dfrac{100}{1} = 8\tfrac{3}{4}\%\leftarrow$$

Example 12. A line is drawn 6.8 cm. long, whereas it should have been 7 cm. long. What is the error per cent?

[*N.B.* Error per cent will be based on the *true length*.]

Error on true length = 7 cm. − 6.8 cm. = 0.2 cm.

Fractional error of true length = $\dfrac{0.2}{7}$ $\left(\text{or } \dfrac{2}{70}\right)$

∴ Percentage error = $\dfrac{2}{70} \times \dfrac{100}{1}\% = \dfrac{20}{7}\%$

$= 2.857\% \leftarrow$ (correct to three decimal places)

Example 13. A tailor allows 5% discount for cash payment. A customer pays him \$200 cash. What was the original bill (to nearest dollar)?

The ratio of a bill of \$100 to cash paid is 100 : 95 or $\dfrac{100}{95}$

∴ The bill was $\dfrac{100}{95} \times \$200 = \$210.53$

Caution. Keep clearly in mind the differences between the following three questions:—

    (1) What fraction of \$40 is \$3.50?
    (2) What decimal of \$40 is \$3.50?
    (3) What percentage of \$40 is \$3.50?

Answer to (1) is $\dfrac{3.50}{40.00} = \dfrac{7}{80}$

Answer to (2) is $\dfrac{7}{80} = .0875\leftarrow$ (To turn fraction into decimal see Ch. 12)

Answer to (3) is $\dfrac{7}{80} \times \dfrac{100}{1}\% = 8\frac{3}{4}\%\leftarrow$

Percentage Profit and Loss. Percentage profit or loss is always reckoned on the *Cost Price.*

Caution. A small percentage profit (or loss) may involve a large sum of money.

Similarly, a large percentage profit (or loss) may only involve a small sum of money.

This will be seen from the examples which follow.

Example 14. A shopkeeper buys a ruler for 4¢ and sells it for 6¢. What is (*a*) his actual profit in cash and (*b*) his profit per cent?

[C.P. = Cost Price; S.P. = Selling Price; Pr. = Profit.]

C.P. = 4¢; S.P. = 6¢; ∴ Actual cash profit = 2¢ ← (*a*)

$$\% \text{ Pr.} = \frac{2}{4} \times \frac{100}{1} = 50\% \leftarrow (b)$$

Example 15. A firm contracts to build a battleship for \$34,000,-000. The work costs them \$33,000,000. What is (*a*) their actual cash profit and (*b*) their percentage profit?

$$\text{C.P.} = \$33,000,000$$
$$\text{S.P.} = \$34,000,000$$

∴ Actual cash Pr. = \$1,000,000 ← (*a*)

$$\% \text{ Pr.} = \frac{1,000,000}{33,000,000} \times \frac{100}{1} = 3\% \leftarrow (b)$$

These last two examples show that *percentage is the ratio between actual profit and cost price if that cost price were 100 units.*

Example 16. I sold my car for $700 thereby losing 35%. What did I pay for it? (Nearest dollar.)

$$\text{Ratio of C.P. to S.P.} = 100 : 65 \text{ or } \frac{100}{65}$$

$$\therefore \text{ C.P.} = \frac{100}{65} \times \frac{\$700}{1} = \$1077 \leftarrow$$

NOTE: Use Unitary Method, if preferred, for all Profit and Loss sums.

Simple Interest

Money lent or borrowed is called the *Principal*. The charge made for its use is called the *Interest*. The charge made every year for the use of each $100 borrowed is called the *Rate*.

The sum of money lent (Principal)+Interest is called the *Amount*.

Simple Interest is merely a form of proportion sum. To save time, the following formula should be memorized as it enables you to work out any Simple Interest sum very easily:

$$I = \frac{PRT}{100} \left(\text{or } P = \frac{100\,I}{RT}, \text{ etc. } \begin{array}{l} \text{(See "Change of} \\ \text{Subject")} \end{array} \right)$$

where I = Simple Interest
        P = Principal
        R = Rate
        T = Number of years (or fraction of 1 year).

Example 1. Find the Simple Interest on $656 for 3 years at 4% per annum.

$$I = \frac{PRT}{100} = \frac{656 \times 4 \times 3}{100} = \$78.72 \leftarrow$$

Example 2. At what rate of Simple Interest must $600 be borrowed for $2\frac{1}{2}$ years if it is to amount to $645?

"Amount" = Principal+Interest, *i.e.* 645 = 600+interest.

$$\therefore \text{ Interest} = \$45. \text{ Now I} = \frac{PRT}{100}$$

$$\therefore R = \frac{100\ I}{PT} = \frac{100\times45}{600\times2\frac12} = 3\%\leftarrow$$

Compound Interest means that each year's interest is added to the princi- pal and the following year's interest is on new principal (*i.e.* old princi- pal *plus* inter- est). Instead of spending labo- rious hours in working Com- pound Interest by Arithmetic, spend the time in mastering logarithms. You will then be able to do Com- pound Interest easily and quickly. In passing, how- ever, study the two graphs on this page and you will see the great difference between Simple and Compound Interest after the expiration of a few years.

4%
Simple Interest

Fig. 103.—Show- ing Amount of $1 at end of any period up to 35 years—*i.e.* $1 doubles itself at 4% Simple Interest in 25 years, and trebles itself in 50 years. (Not shown on this small graph.)

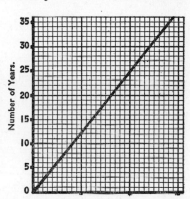

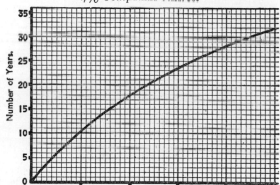

4% Compound Interest

Fig. 104.—Showing Amount of $1 at end of any period up to 35 years—*i.e.* $1 doubles itself at 4% Compound Interest in less than 18 years and trebles itself in a little over 28 years.

For Exercises see pp. 290–294.

CHAPTER 18

AVERAGES

Averages fall under two classes, (*a*) averages of simple numbers, (*b*) averages of ratios, such as speed, etc.

To average ordinary numbers, money, time, etc., all we do is to divide the total by the number of things concerned. Thus:—

Example 1. A garage finds that cars were booked for the following runs: 6 miles, 8 miles, 49 miles, 3 miles, 104 miles, 17 miles, 5 miles. What is the average run?

Total mileage = 192 miles. Number of runs = 7

$$\therefore \text{ Average run } = \frac{192}{7} \text{ miles } = 27\tfrac{3}{7} \text{ miles} \leftarrow$$

Note.—In dealing with large numbers the following short cut may be possible:—

Example 2. School attendances in a certain city in one week were as follows. Find the average daily attendance.

Monday	139,476
Tuesday . . .	139,217
* Wednesday . .	138,954
Thursday . . .	139,549
Friday . . .	139,498

Here we note that the lowest figure was *more than* 138,000 (Wednesday), so we need only calculate average attendance *above that figure*, viz.:—

1476, 1217, 954, 1549, 1498
Total = 6694

Average above 138,000 = $\dfrac{6694}{5}$ = 1339   (to nearest whole number).

∴ Average attendance was 138,000+1339 = 139,339‹

Example 3. The weights of a racing crew are as follows. Find the average weight (*a*) including coxswain, (*b*) without coxswain.

lb.
114
186   Total weight (including coxswain) = 1463 lb.
174   ∴ (*a*) Average weight $\dfrac{1463 \text{ lb.}}{9}$ = 163 lb.←
159   (to nearest lb.)   =
183
143   Weight without coxswain = 1349 lb.
146   ∴ (*b*) Average weight $\dfrac{1349 \text{ lb.}}{8}$
161   (to nearest lb.)   =
197   = 169 lb.←
1463

Example 4. A man's wages for 6 weeks are as follows: $32, $26, $39.50, $31, $37.50, $29. What is his average wage for these 6 weeks?

Total received = $195. Number of weeks = 6.

∴ Average = $\dfrac{\$195}{6}$ = $32.50←

Example 5. A train takes the following times to travel between various stations:—

A to B   .   .   .   45 minutes
B to C   .   .   .   1 hour, 5 minutes
C to D   .   .   .   48 minutes
D to E   .   .   .   35 minutes

What is the average duration of its non-stop runs?
We must divide total time by number of non-stop runs.

$$\textit{i.e. } 193 \text{ minutes} \div 4 = 48\tfrac{1}{4} \text{ minutes} \leftarrow$$

We now come to consider the average of **ratios**.

Contrast very carefully Example 5 with the one that follows.

Example 6. A train climbs a steep gradient 8 miles long at 20 m.p.h., then goes 80 miles on level ground at 50 m.p.h. What is its average speed?

$$\left[\text{Note carefully that it is } \textit{not } \frac{50+20}{2} \text{ or } 35 \text{ m.p.h.}\right]$$

Speed is a *ratio*, and as we have seen, every ratio includes two things.

Therefore, to average ratios we must divide the total of one kind of thing by the total of the other kind of thing, not merely divide the sum of the ratios by 2. Thus, in our problem:

$$\text{Total mileage} = 8+80 = 88$$

$$\text{Time going up gradient} = \frac{8}{20} \text{ hr.} = \frac{2}{5} \text{ hr.}$$

$$\text{Time going along level} = \frac{80}{50} \text{ hr.} = \frac{8}{5} \text{ hr.}$$

$$\therefore \text{ Total time} = 2 \text{ hr.}$$

$$\therefore \text{ Average speed} = \frac{\text{Total distance}}{\text{Total time}} = \frac{88}{2} = 44 \text{ m.p.h.} \leftarrow$$

Example 7. Two ships leave Liverpool for New York at the same time. One steams at 20 knots and returns at 20 knots. The other steams to New York at 30 knots and returns at 10 knots owing to a defect in her engines. Which gets back first? (Assume they both stay 20 hours at New York.)

Graphical Illustration of "Catch Problem"

The broken line indicates the *average* speed of the second ship (= 15 knots).

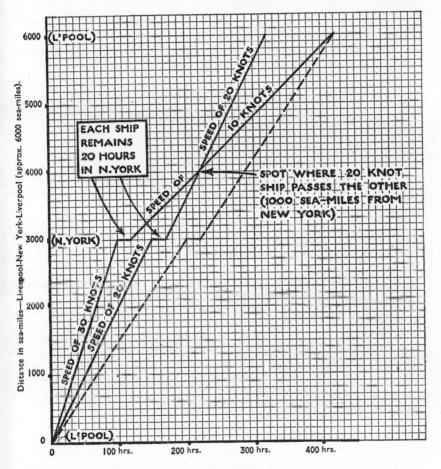

FIG. 105.

In making speed-graphs, keep distance vertical and time horizontal. You will then see at a glance whether speed is increasing or decreasing by the steepness of the graph.

This is a well-known catch and many have fallen to it and said that both ships get back together, because the average of the *numbers* 20 and 20 is the same as the average of the *numbers* 10 and 30.

We must however in each case divide *total distance* by *total time*, as the numbers 20, 30 and 10 are really *ratios*. The distance to New York is roughly 3000 sea miles. So the total distance there and back is roughly 6000 sea miles.

∴ One ship takes 150 hours out and 150 hours back

∴ its average speed is $\dfrac{6000}{300}$ or 20 knots.

The other takes 100 hours out and 300 hours back

∴ its average speed is $\dfrac{6000}{400}$ or 15 knots.

∴ *The ship steaming at* 20 *knots gets back first.*

[This is shown graphically in Fig. 105 (p. 143). A study of the figure will convince you of the great amount of information revealed by a graph.

E.g.—Dotted line shows an average speed of 15 knots. Had one ship gone at this speed there and back, the two ships would not have crossed each other. Notice how this fact is clearly shown on the graph.]

To Find the Total, given the Average

With ordinary numbers (not ratios) simply multiply the average by the number of things involved.

Example 8. The average quantity of gasoline sold by a garage is $5\frac{1}{2}$ gallons per car that calls. If 860 cars call in a certain week, how many gallons of gasoline are sold?

$$5\tfrac{1}{2} \times 860 = 4730 = \text{number of gallons sold} \leftarrow$$

But, once again, beware of ratio averages!

Example 9. A man pays income tax one year on $2400 at the rate of 25¢ on the $. The next year he pays on $3200 at 35¢ on the $. How much does he pay altogether?

[Beware the common mistake of arguing: "Average rate of tax = 30¢ on the $. Total income $5600. ∴ He pays (5600 × 30¢) or $1680." He doesn't get off so lightly!]

Tax paid on 1st year's income = 2400×25¢ = $600
Tax paid on 2nd year's income = 3200×35¢ = $1120
∴ Total tax paid = $1720←

Example 10. An automobile dealer sells 13 cars, each costing him $320, at an average profit of 20%, and 12 other cars, each costing him $380, at an average profit of 30%. Find the total profit.

Average profit on 13 cars = 20% of $320 = $64
∴ Total profit on 13 cars = 13×$64 = $832

Average profit on 12 cars = 30% of $380 = $114
∴ Total profit on 12 cars = 12×$114 = $1368

∴ Total profit on 25 cars = $2200←

For Exercises see p. 295.

CHAPTER 19

SQUARE ROOT OF ANY NUMBER

We have seen (p. 39) how to find the square root of certain numbers. Here is a mechanical way of finding the square root of *any* number.

Example 1. $\sqrt{1398.76}$, *i.e.* with an *even* number of figures to the left of the decimal point.

$$
\begin{array}{r}
3\quad 7\quad .4 \\
\overline{3\,|13/98/.76/} \\
3\,|\ 9 \\
\hline
67\,|498 \\
7\,|469 \\
\hline
744\,|2976 \\
|2976 \\
\end{array}
$$

$$\therefore\ \sqrt{1398.76} = 37.4\leftarrow$$

Steps in Working

(1) Starting from the decimal point, mark off the figures two at a time, so that you have 13, 98, 76.

(2) Get the square root of 13, or of the perfect square below it, *i.e.* 3.

(3) Put this 3 in the answer and also in the divisor and proceed as in ordinary division; $3\times3 = 9$.

(4) Now make a new dividend and a new divisor. Subtract 9 from $13 = 4$ and bring down the next pair of figures, 98, thus making the new dividend 498.

Add the last figure in the answer, 3, to the last divisor, 3, $= 6$.

(5) Now your new divisor will be sixty something, the "something" being the same number both in the answer and in the divisor. Try 8; $8\times68 = 544$ is too great, 7 will do. 7 is the next figure in the divisor and the answer.

(6) $67\times7 = 469$ from 498 leaves 29, and so 2976 becomes new dividend.

(7) Add 7, the last figure in the answer, to the last figure in the divisor, $67 = 74$.

(8) Get your last figure in the answer, 4, as in step (5).

Example 2. $\sqrt{660.49}$, *i.e.* with an *odd* number of figures to the left of the decimal point. Here we start by getting the square root of 6 and then proceed as in Example 1.

$$
\begin{array}{r|l}
\multicolumn{2}{c}{2\ 5\ .7} \\
\hline
2 & 6\,'60\,'.49\,' \\
2 & 4 \\
\hline
45 & 260 \\
5 & 225 \\
\hline
507 & 3549 \\
 & 3549 \\
\end{array}
$$

$$\therefore\ \sqrt{660.49} = 25.7\leftarrow$$

Note carefully the position of the decimal point in the square root.

Example 3. $\sqrt{164.8}$. Here is an example of a number whose square root does not work out exactly. Add as many noughts as are necessary.

$$
\begin{array}{r|l}
\multicolumn{2}{c}{1\ 2\ .8\ 3} \\
\hline
1 & 1\,'64\,'.80\,'00\,' \\
1 & 1 \\
\hline
22 & 64 \\
2 & 44 \\
\hline
248 & 2080 \\
8 & 1984 \\
\hline
2563 & 9600 \\
 & 7689 \\
\end{array}
$$

$$\therefore\ \sqrt{164.8} = 12.83\leftarrow$$

For approximate calculations of square root, a graph saves much time and labor. (See Fig. 106, p. 148.)

A Home-made Ready reckoner.   Square-root graph for all numbers between 0 and 100.

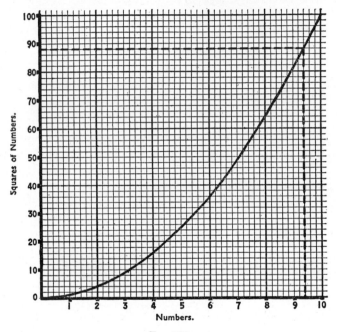

Fig. 106.

$\sqrt{88}$ is shown on this graph as being 9.4. This is not quite accurate (as one would expect) but it is approximately correct, the real root being 9.381.

For Exercises see p. 295.

CHAPTER 20

MORE ABOUT SIMILAR FIGURES

Consider once more two "shadow triangles" (p. 118) like those in Fig. 107.

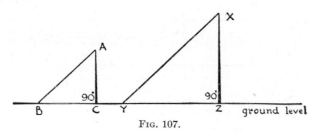

FIG. 107.

AB and XY are rays of the sun. As seen on the Earth these are parallel, *i.e.* AB||XY.

Now the ground, being level, is represented by the straight line BCYZ.

$$\therefore \ \angle \text{ B} = \angle \text{ Y (corresponding)}.$$

Also $\angle$ C = $\angle$ Z (both are rt. $\angle$s $\because$ poles are upright)

$\therefore$ Remaining $\angle$ A = Remaining $\angle$ X (sum of $\angle$s of any $\triangle$ = 180°)

$$\therefore \ \triangle \text{ ABC is equiangular to } \triangle \text{ XYZ.}$$

This is true, not only of right angled similar $\triangle$s, as in this case, but of similar $\triangle$s of any shape.

We have then a most important fact:—
  Similar $\triangle$s are equiangular.
Or conversely:
  $\triangle$s which are equiangular are similar.

All map-making other than aerial photography map-making depends on this fact. A piece of land of any shape can be split up into △s whose angles can be measured. Since the size of an angle does not depend on the length of its arms, angles of the same size as those of the "land" triangle can be drawn on paper and a "miniature" of the piece of land emerges. The map-maker first measures (on the land) a base line, using great care to get the exact measurement. He then measures the angles made by a prominent landmark as viewed from either end of the base line. He then draws a line on paper to represent his base line on the land (this fixes the scale or ratio of the map) and then draws lines at the angles he has observed. The point where these lines cut gives him the position of the landmark. (See p. 178.)

We saw that in the two "shadow triangles" in Fig. 96

$$\frac{\text{Length of shadow of shorter pole}}{\text{Length of shorter pole}} = \frac{\text{Length of shadow of longer pole}}{\text{Length of longer pole}}$$

So, in Fig. 108,
$$\frac{a}{b} = \frac{x}{y}$$

 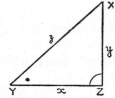

Fig. 108.

For ease of reference we name sides of △s by *small* letters corresponding to the *capitals* of opposite corners.

Note that we need not mark all three pairs of equal ∠s. If two pairs are equal the remaining pair must be equal.

Not only so, but *the ratio of any pair of sides in △ ABC equals the ratio of the corresponding sides in similar △ XYZ. This is true for all kinds of similar △s.*

i.e. $\frac{a}{b} = \frac{x}{y}$ and reciprocals (*i.e.* "upside down" ratios) $\frac{b}{a} = \frac{y}{x}$

$\frac{c}{a} = \frac{z}{x}$ and reciprocals; $\frac{c}{b} = \frac{z}{y}$ and reciprocals.

Sometimes it is difficult to pick out sides which are correspondingly placed in the other △, *e.g.* when one △ is twisted round.

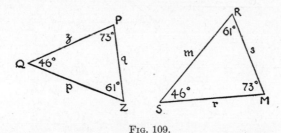

FIG. 109.

The difficulty disappears if the following method is used:

In △ PQZ $\dfrac{q}{z} = \dfrac{\text{side opposite } \angle\ 46°}{\text{side opposite } \angle\ 61°} = \dfrac{s}{r}$ in △ MSR.

In △ PQZ $\dfrac{p}{z} = \dfrac{\text{side opposite } \angle\ 73°}{\text{side opposite } \angle\ 61°} = \dfrac{m}{r}$ in △ MSR.

and so on.

Before proceeding farther it is essential that the meaning of these facts should be clearly grasped. A study of the numerical examples that follow will make the meaning clear.

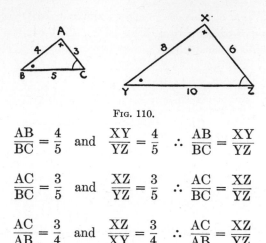

FIG. 110.

$$\frac{AB}{BC} = \frac{4}{5} \quad \text{and} \quad \frac{XY}{YZ} = \frac{4}{5} \quad \therefore \frac{AB}{BC} = \frac{XY}{YZ}$$

$$\frac{AC}{BC} = \frac{3}{5} \quad \text{and} \quad \frac{XZ}{YZ} = \frac{3}{5} \quad \therefore \frac{AC}{BC} = \frac{XZ}{YZ}$$

$$\frac{AC}{AB} = \frac{3}{4} \quad \text{and} \quad \frac{XZ}{XY} = \frac{3}{4} \quad \therefore \frac{AC}{AB} = \frac{XZ}{YZ}$$

Note that you *cannot* say:

$$\frac{AB}{BC} = \frac{AC}{AB}, \text{ etc. } \left(\frac{4}{5} \text{ does not equal } \frac{3}{4}\right)$$

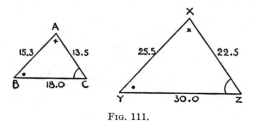

FIG. 111.

$$\frac{AB}{BC} = \frac{15.3}{18} = \frac{17}{20} \quad \text{and} \quad \frac{XY}{YZ} = \frac{25.5}{30} = \frac{17}{20} \quad \therefore \frac{AB}{BC} = \frac{XY}{YZ}$$

$$\frac{AC}{BC} = \frac{13.5}{18} = \frac{3}{4} \quad \text{and} \quad \frac{XZ}{YZ} = \frac{22.5}{30} = \frac{3}{4} \quad \therefore \frac{AC}{BC} = \frac{XZ}{YZ}$$

$$\frac{AC}{AB} = \frac{13.5}{15.3} = \frac{15}{17} \quad \text{and} \quad \frac{XZ}{XY} = \frac{22.5}{25.5} = \frac{15}{17} \quad \therefore \frac{AC}{AB} = \frac{XZ}{XY}$$

Now use the numerical examples above to discover another important set of equal ratios.

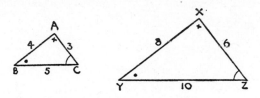

Fig. 110. (Repeat.)

$$\frac{AB}{XY} = \frac{4}{8} = \frac{1}{2} \qquad \frac{AC}{XZ} = \frac{3}{6} = \frac{1}{2} \qquad \frac{BC}{YZ} = \frac{5}{10} = \frac{1}{2}$$

$$\therefore \frac{AB}{XY} = \frac{AC}{XZ} = \frac{BC}{YZ}.$$

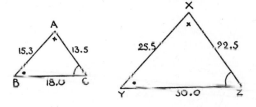

Fig. 111. (Repeat.)

$$\frac{AB}{XY} = \frac{15.3}{25.5} = \frac{3}{5} \qquad \frac{AC}{XZ} = \frac{13.5}{22.5} = \frac{3}{5} \qquad \frac{BC}{YZ} = \frac{18}{30} = \frac{3}{5}$$

$$\therefore \frac{AB}{XY} = \frac{AC}{XZ} = \frac{BC}{YZ}$$

i.e. when two △s are similar, the ratio between any side of one △ and the corresponding side of the other △ is always the same.

Now let us see what results follow when we place the smaller △ in one corner of its similar △ so that angle A fits angle X, as in Fig. 112.

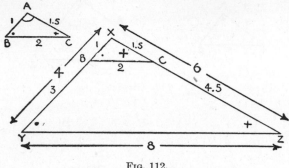

Fig. 112.

(i) We see at a glance (by the equal ∠s) that BC ∥ YZ.

(ii) We know (and can see from the numbers) that:

$$\frac{XB}{BY} = \frac{XC}{CZ} = \frac{1}{3}$$

(iii) We see that $\dfrac{XB}{XY} = \dfrac{1}{4}$ $\dfrac{XC}{XZ} = \dfrac{1}{4}$ and $\dfrac{BC}{YZ} = \dfrac{1}{4}$

$$\therefore \frac{XB}{XY} = \frac{XC}{XZ} \doteq \frac{BC}{YZ}$$

Hence we get the following most important facts:—

(a) **Any interior line drawn parallel to one side of a triangle divides the other two sides in the same ratio.**

(b) **The ratio between the parallel lines equals the ratio between any other pair of corresponding sides of the two similar △s.**

How to apply this knowledge

Example 1. In Fig. 113 find x and y.

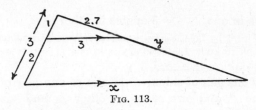

FIG. 113.

From (*b*) p. 154, $\dfrac{3}{x} = \dfrac{1}{3}$ $\therefore\; x = 9 \leftarrow$

From (*a*) p. 154, $\dfrac{2.7}{y} = \dfrac{1}{2}$ $\therefore\; y = 5.4 \leftarrow$

Example 2. In Fig. 114 find x.

From (*a*) p. 154,   we see that AR = RC.

From (*b*) p. 154, $\dfrac{x}{1.4} = \dfrac{1.5}{3.0}$

$\therefore\; x = .7 \leftarrow$

In this case, of course, we could say:

$$AR = \tfrac{1}{2}\,AC \text{ and}$$
$$AP = \tfrac{1}{2}\,AB$$
$$\therefore\; PR = \tfrac{1}{2}\,BC$$
$$= .7$$

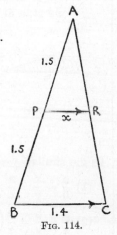

FIG. 114.

The facts disclosed in *Example* 2 are most important.

(1) *Any line drawn from the mid-point of one side of a △ and parallel to a second side, bisects the third side.*

(2) *Any line joining the mid-points of two sides of a △ is parallel to the third side and equal to half of it.*

Summary of Facts about Similar Triangles

Two triangles are similar in shape if we know the following
data:—

(1) 3 angles in one △ = 3 angles in other △.

> (This is by far the most important case. As we have seen it is
> enough to know that two angles in one △ = two angles in the
> other △)

(2) Ratio of one pair of sides in one △ and size of included ∠ $\Big\}$ = $\Big\{$ **Ratio of one pair of sides in other △ and size of included ∠**

(3) Ratio of one side to each of the other sides in one △ $\Big\}$ = $\Big\{$ **Ratio of one side to each of the other sides in other △**

(4) *Right-∠d △s.*
Ratio of hypotenuse to one side in one △ $\Big\}$ = $\Big\{$ **Ratio of hypotenuse to one side in other △**

Compare these data with the data for congruent △s on p. 60.

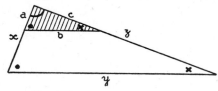

Fig. 115.

In the **similar** △s, in Fig. 115,

(1) $\dfrac{a}{b} = \dfrac{x}{y}$ $\dfrac{a}{c} = \dfrac{x}{z}$ $\dfrac{b}{c} = \dfrac{y}{z}$ $\left(\text{and } \dfrac{b}{a} = \dfrac{y}{x}, \text{ etc.} \right)$

(2) $\dfrac{a}{x} = \dfrac{b}{y} = \dfrac{c}{z}$ $\left(\text{and } \dfrac{x}{a} = \dfrac{y}{b} = \dfrac{z}{c} \right).$

(3) **Line b ∥ line y.**

For Exercises see pp. 296–297.

CHAPTER 21

RIGHT–ANGLED TRIANGLES

For convenience of reference we shall sometimes name **angles** by Greek letters, such as θ ("theta") and ϕ ("phi").

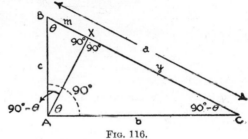

Study the angles in Fig. 116. If we start by calling $\angle$ B, $\theta°$ we see that $\angle$ BAX = $90° - \theta°$ (since the sum of the angles of any $\triangle$ = $180°$).

Also, in $\triangle$ AXC, $\angle$ XAC = $\theta°$ (since it is the complement of $\angle$ BAX), and $\angle$ ACX = $90° - \theta°$.

FIG. 116.

Here we have three triangles, $\triangle$ ABC, $\triangle$ ABX, $\triangle$ AXC.
The angles of $\triangle$ ABC are $90°$, $\theta°$, $(90° - \theta°)$.
The angles of $\triangle$ ABX are $90°$, $\theta°$, $(90° - \theta°)$.
The angles of $\triangle$ AXC are $90°$, $\theta°$, $(90° - \theta°)$.

$\therefore$ *All three triangles are similar to one another.*

$$\frac{\text{side opposite } (90° - \theta°)}{\text{side opposite } 90°} = \frac{c}{a} \text{ in } \triangle \text{ ABC} = \frac{m}{c} \text{ in } \triangle \text{ ABX}$$

$$\therefore c^2 = am.$$

$$\frac{\text{side opposite } \theta°}{\text{side opposite } 90°} = \frac{b}{a} \text{ in } \triangle \text{ ABC} = \frac{y}{b} \text{ in } \triangle \text{ AXC}$$

$$\therefore b^2 = ay$$

$$\therefore c^2 + b^2 = am + ay = a(m + y) = a(a) = a^2$$

$$\therefore \mathbf{c^2 + b^2 = a^2}$$

This fact is of enormous importance. Let us see what it means.

To draw a picture of $c^2 + b^2 = a^2$

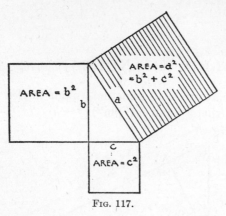

Clearly c^2 means the square whose side is c units long.

b^2 means the square whose side is b units long.

a^2 means the square whose side is a units long.

FIG. 117.

We see, then, that in any right-angled triangle the square on the hypotenuse is equal to the sum of the squares on the other two sides.

This surprising fact was first discovered by Pythagoras in the sixth century B.C. It is therefore known as the "Theorem of Pythagoras."

Examples of the Usefulness of the Theorem of Pythagoras

Example 1. In Fig. 118 find the length of AB.

$(AB)^2 = (AC)^2 + (BC)^2$ (Theorem of Pythagoras)

$\quad = 4^2 + 3^2$

$\quad = 16 + 9$

$\therefore$ AB $= \sqrt{25} = 5$ cm. $\leftarrow$

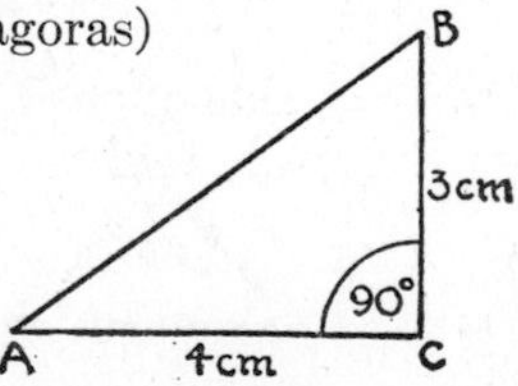

FIG. 118.

Now see Fig. 119.

Make use of *Example* 1 if you have to set out a large figure with right ∠s in it (*e.g.* tennis-court, foundations of hut, etc.). It was the method employed by the ancient Egyptians and Babylonians centuries before Pythagoras.

You can see in Fig. 119 that these Egyptians have tied four knots in a cord so that there are gaps of 3, 4 and 5 equal units of length respectively between the knots, as shown at the side of the figure.

Then they have pegged the cord on the ground of the courtyard to form a triangle which you can see contains a right angle.

Fig. 119.

Example 2. In Fig. 120 find x.

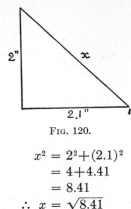

Fig. 120.

$$x^2 = 2^2 + (2.1)^2$$
$$= 4 + 4.41$$
$$= 8.41$$
$$\therefore \; x = \sqrt{8.41}$$
$$= 2.9'' \leftarrow$$

Example 3. In Fig. 121, find x.

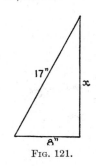

Fig. 121.

$$(17)^2 = x^2 + 8^2$$
$$\therefore \; x^2 = (17)^2 - 8^2$$
$$= (17+8)(17-8) \; *$$
$$= (25)(9)$$
$$\therefore \; x = (5)(3) = 15'' \leftarrow$$

* Since $a^2 - b^2 = (a+b)(a-b)$, always make use of factors whenever possible (*e.g.* when, as here, you get the difference of two squares (see Chapter 11)). It saves time and labor.

Example 4. Find the area of the isosceles △ ABC in Fig. 122.

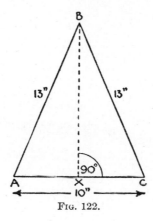

Fig. 122.

We must find the perpendicular height (see Chapter 16).
Draw BX perpendicular to AC.
We must now calculate AX.

△ AXB and △ CXB are rt.-∠d △s with hypotenuse and one side (BX) in each equal. ∴ △ AXB ≡ △ CXB.

$$\therefore \text{AX} = \text{XC}. \quad \therefore \text{AX} = \tfrac{1}{2}\text{AC} = 5''$$

From rt.-∠d △ AXB
$$(13)^2 = (\text{BX})^2 + (\text{AX})^2$$
$$\therefore \ (13)^2 = (\text{BX})^2 + 5^2$$
$$\therefore \ (\text{BX})^2 = (13)^2 - 5^2$$
$$= (13 + 5)(13 - 5)$$
$$= 18 \times 8$$
$$= 144$$
$$\therefore \ \text{BX} = 12''$$

Area of △ ABC = ½ base × perpendicular height
$$= 5 \times 12 \text{ sq. in.}$$
$$= 60 \text{ sq. in.} \leftarrow$$

Example 5. Find the distance * from the center of a circle to a chord † 12 in. long if the circle has radius 10 in.

AB (chord) = 12″

OA, OB (radii) = 10″

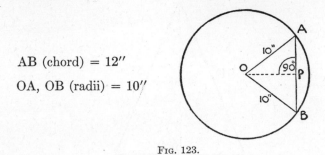

FIG. 123.

Since the two △s are rt.-∠d and have equal hypotenuses and one side (OP) the same in both.

Then △ OPA ≡ △ OPB
∴ AP = PB = ½AB = 6″

Now from rt.-∠d △ OPA

$$(OA)^2 = (AP)^2 + (OP)^2$$
$$\therefore \ (10)^2 = 6^2 + (OP)^2$$
$$\therefore \ (OP)^2 = (10)^2 - 6^2$$
$$= (10+6)(10-6)$$
$$= (16)(4)$$
$$\therefore \ OP = (4)(2) = 8'' \leftarrow$$

* By "distance of a line from a point or another line" we mean perpendicular distance.
† For definition of chord, radius, etc., see p. 55.

Practise making drawings of cubes and cuboids (bricks). Draw two rectangles thus:—

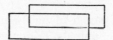

making upper rectangle slightly smaller than lower one. Join corners and underline edges that would be visible. Learn to "see" which ∠s are rt. ∠s (though they will not be rt. ∠s in your figure, as it will be in "perspective," *e.g.* ∠ EAC in Fig. 124).

Example 6. In Fig. 124 calculate EC.

Method:

First calculate AC from right-∠d △ ABC.
Then calculate EC from right-∠d △ EAC.

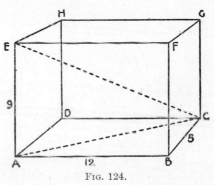

Fig. 124.

In △ ABC, $(AC)^2 = (AB)^2 + (BC)^2 = 144 + 25 = 169$
          $\therefore AC = \sqrt{169} = 13.$

In △ EAC, since EAC is a right angle,
   $(EC)^2 = (EA)^2 + (AC)^2 = 9^2 + (13)^2 = 81 + 169 = 250$
          $\therefore EC = \sqrt{250} = 15.8$ approx.

For Exercises see pp. 298–299.

Trigonometry

The Meaning of sin, cos, tan

A most important branch of mathematics took its rise from the right-angled triangle, namely Trigonometry, the science of the relationship between the sides and angles of a triangle. All trigonometry is based on the ratios of the sides of a right-angled triangle. These ratios occur so often that they are known by special names.

$$\begin{aligned}
&\text{Sine, written } \mathbf{sin,} \quad \text{pronounced ``sign.''}\\
&\text{Cosine, written } \mathbf{cos,} \quad \text{pronounced ``cos.''}\\
&\text{Tangent, written } \mathbf{tan,} \quad \text{pronounced ``tan.''}
\end{aligned}$$

They connect each of the acute angles of a right-angled triangle with the sides of that triangle.

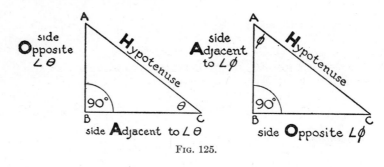

FIG. 125.

$\sin \theta$ is the ratio $\dfrac{AB}{AC}$ $\sin \phi$ is the ratio $\dfrac{BC}{AC}$

$\cos \theta$ is the ratio $\dfrac{BC}{AC}$ $\cos \phi$ is the ratio $\dfrac{AB}{AC}$

$\tan \theta$ is the ratio $\dfrac{AB}{BC}$ $\tan \phi$ is the ratio $\dfrac{BC}{AB}$

All this is very confusing to beginners, but thanks to a mnemonic borrowed from Professor P. T. Nunn (*The Teaching of Algebra*) the ratios can be mastered in a very few minutes.

First, remember the order in which the ratios have been written down, *sin, cos, tan.*

Now suppose a friend says, "A bomb smashed all my windows yesterday."

Your exclamation on first hearing such news is **OH!**

Suppose, however, your friend met you again, and again told you his sad news—your surprise would be less and you would probably exclaim **AH!**

You meet your friend again. Again he insists on telling you his misfortune. You are bored by now and say **Oh, Ah!**

First ratio, $\sin \theta = \dfrac{O}{H} = \dfrac{AB}{AC}$ $\sin \phi = \dfrac{O}{H} = \dfrac{BC}{AC}$

Second ratio, $\cos \theta = \dfrac{A}{H} = \dfrac{BC}{AC}$ $\cos \phi = \dfrac{A}{H} = \dfrac{AB}{AC}$

Third ratio, $\tan \theta = \dfrac{O}{A} = \dfrac{AB}{BC}$ $\tan \phi = \dfrac{O}{A} = \dfrac{BC}{AB}$

Remember:

    O means the side opposite the angle concerned.
    A means the side adjacent to the angle concerned.
    H means the hypotenuse.

It will be a great help to you if you memorize these trigonometric ratios so that you know them as well as you do the multiplication table.

The Values of the Trigonometrical Ratios of 30° *and* 60°

Draw an equilateral triangle ABC side 2″.

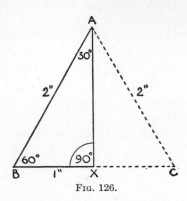

FIG. 126.

Bisect ∠ BAC by a line cutting BC in X.

It is easy to prove △ AXB ≡ △ AXC   [**SAS**]
∴ BX = XC = 1″ and ∠ AXB = 90°

Also,   ∠ B = 60° (∠ in equilateral △)
and   ∠ BAX = 30°.

Now find the length of AX.

$$(AB)^2 = (AX)^2 + (BX)^2 \text{ (Pythagoras)}$$
$$\therefore 4 = (AX)^2 + 1$$
$$\therefore (AX)^2 = 3$$
$$\therefore AX = \sqrt{3}$$

(We cannot work this out exactly, so we will leave it in this form.)

We now get △ ABX in Fig. 126 with the dimensions as shown in Fig. 127.

∴ Using the mnemonic on p. 165 we see that:

$$\sin 30° = \frac{1}{2} \qquad \sin 60° = \frac{\sqrt{3}}{2}$$

$$\cos 30° = \frac{\sqrt{3}}{2} \qquad \cos 60° = \frac{1}{2}$$

$$\tan 30° = \frac{1}{\sqrt{3}} \qquad \tan 60° = \sqrt{3}$$

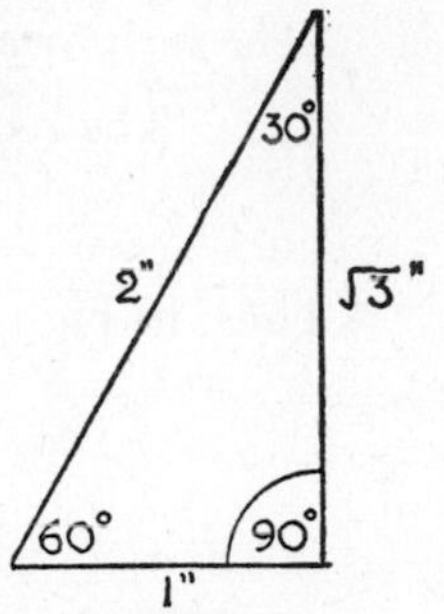

From this table we see that:

FIG. 127.

The sine of an angle equals the cosine of its complement.

Trigonometrical Ratios of 45°

Draw a rt.-∠d isosceles △ having shorter sides 1″ long as in Fig. 128. (Proceed as follows:

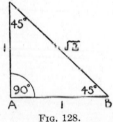

FIG. 128.

Draw AB = 1 inch. Draw AC ⊥ AB and also equal to 1 inch.)

By Pythagoras, $(CB)^2 = (CA)^2 + (AB)^2$

$$∴ (CB)^2 = 1+1 = 2$$
$$∴ CB = \sqrt{2}$$

∴ $\sin 45° = \dfrac{1}{\sqrt{2}}$ ⎫ which agrees with what we have already dis-

$\cos 45° = \dfrac{1}{\sqrt{2}}$ ⎬ covered about the sine of an angle being equal to the cosine of its complement.

$\tan 45° = 1$

It is useful at this stage to know and remember that:

$$\sqrt{3} = 1.732 \qquad \sqrt{2} = 1.414$$

Reciprocal Trigonometric Ratios

(The reciprocal of a fraction is the same fraction upside down.)

The reciprocal of sine is called cosecant.

"   "   " cosine is called secant.

"   "   " tangent is called cotangent.

Thus, in Fig. 125:

$$\csc * \theta = \frac{AC}{AB} \qquad \csc \phi = \frac{AC}{BC}$$

$$\sec \theta = \frac{AC}{BC} \qquad \sec \phi = \frac{AC}{AB}$$

$$\cot \theta = \frac{BC}{AB} \qquad \cot \phi = \frac{AB}{BC}$$

* Usually written csc.

Note that any fraction multiplied by its reciprocal = 1.

For Exercises see pp. 299–300.

CHAPTER 22

SCALE DRAWING

A very small error in a scale drawing will mean a large error in the object being drawn, so great care is necessary. Here are some hints:—

(1) Always use a very sharp pencil.

(2) In joining two points, first put your pencil point on one of the points, slide ruler up to pencil and hold that end of ruler fast. Put pencil on other point and pivot other end of ruler up to pencil.

(3) In measuring lines tilt ruler up on edge so that its thickness does not come between the line being measured and the markings on the ruler.

(4) *Scale.*—We have already met with "scale" under the heading of RATIOS (pp. 128, 129). Always choose the largest scale possible, and always state what your scale is. In drawing plans it is often useful to let 1 cm. represent feet or yards, since 1 cm. can be divided into 10 very small parts. (In drawing maps, however, keep to "inches to miles.") In writing down your scale do not say "1 in. = 1 mile." Scale is a ratio and should be expressed as such. Say "1 in. to 1 mile," or whatever it may be. We sometimes express this ratio as a fraction. This is known as the R.F. (Representative Fraction) (see p. 128).

We shall revert to this question when we come to map-drawing.

Solving Problems by Scale Drawing

Example 1. A ladder 20 ft. long leans against a wall. The bottom of the ladder is 8 ft. from the wall. Find how high the ladder reaches up the wall.

Scale: $\frac{1}{4}''$ to $1'$. (But for convenience Fig. 129 is drawn to only half this scale.)

Let x and y represent 20 ft. and 8 ft. respectively on plan.

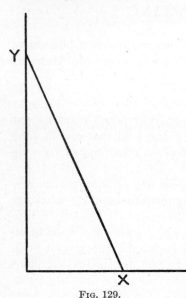

FIG. 129.

By calculation we find:

(1) $1' : \frac{1}{4}'' = 8' : x$
$$\therefore\ x = 2''$$

(2) $1' : \frac{1}{4}'' = 20' : y$
$$\therefore\ y = 5''$$

Draw lines at rt. ∠s to represent wall and Earth (use protractor).

The foot of the ladder at x will be $2''$ from "wall" in plan.

With center X and radius $5''$ draw an arc cutting "wall" at Y.

Measure height of point Y up "wall." On our plan it is $4\frac{1}{2}''$.

Now $\frac{1}{4}'' : 1' = 4\frac{1}{2}'' : z$. $\therefore\ z = 18$ ft.←

$\therefore\ 4\frac{1}{2}''$ on plan represents 18 ft. on wall.

Angle of Depression and Angle of Elevation

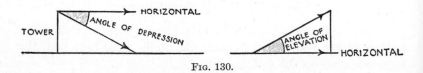

FIG. 130.

Example 2. From the top of a tower 40 ft. high the angle of depression (see Fig. 130) of a tree on the opposite side of a river is found to be 28°. Find the distance of the tree from the tower.

Scale: 1″ to 20′.

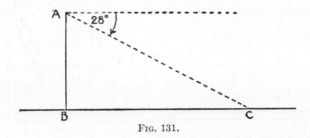

Fig. 131.

Let AB represent the tower. Drawn to scale, AB will be 2″.

At A draw horizontal line. Make angle of depression = 28° and where its arm cuts ground line will be position of tree. Call this C. Let x ft. = distance of tree from tower. On plan this distance (BC) = $3\frac{7}{8}$″.

Now from scale 1″ : 20′ = $3\frac{7}{8}$″ : x

$$\therefore \ x = \frac{20 \times 31}{8} = \frac{155}{2} = 77\frac{1}{2} \text{ ft.} \leftarrow$$

Scale Drawings—Plans

Example 3. Draw a plan of a hut 20 ft. long by 12 ft. wide.

Scale.—Largest possible. The longest measurement we have to represent is 20 ft., so we will choose 1 in. to 4 ft., which will give us a line 5 ins. long to represent 20 ft., and another line 3 ins. long to represent 12 ft.

Draw a line 5″ long. Using protractor set up a line 3″ long at right ∠s. To complete the rectangle use compasses, centers from ends of these lines. (See Fig. 132, p. 172.)

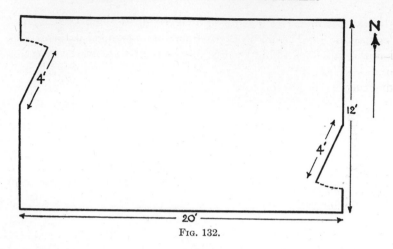

FIG. 132.

Example 4. Show on the plan in Fig. 132 two doors, each 4′ wide, one in E. end, center 3′ 6″ from S.E. corner, the other in W. end, center 3′ 6″ from N.W. corner.

As we are going to use the plan in Fig. 132 we must of course keep to the same scale: 1″ to 4′.

By ratio we see that 4′ to 1″ = $3\frac{1}{2}' : x''$ ∴ $x = \frac{7}{8}''$

∴ 3′ 6″ will be represented on plan by $\frac{7}{8}''$

So we work center of both doors $\frac{7}{8}''$ from S.E. and N.W. corners respectively. As the doors are 4′ wide we measure $\frac{1}{2}''$ (representing 2′) on either side of these central marks, and show door slightly open, as in Fig. 132, hinged either side unless told otherwise.

Example 5. An army hut is 80′×20′ and lies due E. and W. On the S. side there is a door 4′ wide whose center is 56′ from S.E. corner of hut. There are 7 windows on S. side, each 3′ wide, with centers 7′ 4″, 14′ 8″, 35′ 44′, 53′, 62′, 71′ respectively from S.W. corner. There is a similar window in the center of the W. end; and another in the E. end having its center 5′ from N.E. corner. In the E. end there is also a door 4′ wide, 1′ from S.E. corner. Partitions (whose thickness in this plan may be ignored) divide the hut into men's dining-room (W. end) 30′ long, sleeping quarters (center) 38′ long, and corporal's room (E. end) 12′ square. This last is entered by a door 3′ wide, one side of which is 1′ from E. end of hut. There are also doors (3′ wide) in the center of the partition dividing the men's quarters and in the center of the passage partition (E. end). Show all these details on a plan.

PLAN OF ARMY HUT 80′ × 20′.

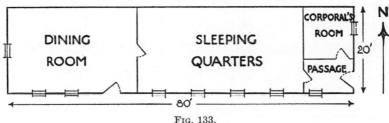

FIG. 133.

First decide on the scale you are going to use. Suppose a convenient one would be 1 cm. to 5 ft., *i.e.* 1 mm. to 6 in. Then calculate your various plan measurements from the actual measurements given. Thus, if we call length of hut on plan (*a*), width (*b*), door on S. side (*c*), and so on, we calculate:

$$\frac{5'}{1 \text{ cm.}} = \frac{80'}{a} \qquad\qquad \frac{5'}{1 \text{ cm.}} = \frac{20'}{b} \qquad\qquad \frac{5'}{1 \text{ cm.}} = \frac{4}{c}$$

$$\therefore a = 16 \text{ cm.} \qquad\qquad \therefore b = 4 \text{ cm.} \qquad\qquad \therefore c = 0.8 \text{ cm.}$$

and so on with all the other measurements in their correct order.

Now draw the plan to scale. When finished it should appear like the sketch in Fig. 133 (which is not drawn to this scale, however).

Taking Measurements from a Plan

Example 6. From *your* scale plan for *Example* 5 find:

(*a*) What is the diagonal distance across the men's sleeping quarters? (Take your reading from the plan then check by Theorem of Pythagoras to find % error in drawing.)

(b) What areas of linoleum will be required to cover (1) corporal's room, (2) passage, (3) sleeping quarters?

(a) *By measurement on plan*, diagonal is 8.59 cm. long (not quite 8.6). Now, 1 cm. : 5′ = 8.59 cm. : x ft.

$$\therefore \ x = 42.95 \text{ ft.} \leftarrow$$

By Pythagoras,
$$x^2 = (38)^2 + (20)^2$$
$$= 1444 + 400$$
$$= 1844$$
$$\therefore \ x = \sqrt{1846} = 42.94 \text{ ft.} \leftarrow$$

(For method of working see Ch. 19)

Error in drawing .01 ft.   Correct measurement = 42.96 ft.

$$\therefore \ \% \text{ error in drawing} = \frac{.01 \times 100}{42.96} = \frac{100}{4296} = .02\% \leftarrow$$

(b) (1) Area of corporal's room is obviously 144 sq. ft.

(2) Area of passage on plan
$$= 1.6 \text{ cm.} \times 2.4 \text{ cm.} = 3.84 \text{ sq. cm.}$$
∴ Area of passage in hut
1 sq. cm. : 25 sq. ft. = 3.84 sq. cm. : x sq. ft.
$$\therefore \ x = 96 \text{ sq. ft.} \leftarrow$$

(3) Area of men's sleeping quarters on plan
$$= 7.6 \text{ cm.} \times 4 \text{ cm.} = 30.4 \text{ sq. cm.}$$
∴ Area of men's sleeping quarters in hut
1 sq. cm. : 25 sq. ft. = 30.4 sq. cm. : x
$$\therefore \ x = 760 \text{ sq. ft.} \leftarrow$$

Scale Drawing—Direction

[Review Chapter IV (measurement of angles and direction, use of protractor, etc.), before proceeding farther.]

"Bearing" is a term used for the angle a line makes with

another line pointing to the North. (We shall see later that this may be True North, Magnetic North or Compass North.)

To find the bearing of a place A *from a place* B.

Draw a line from B in the direction due North.

Join BA and produce line sufficiently to make one end extend outside protractor when latter is put on BN.

Measure ∠ NBA.

This will give the bearing of A *from* B.

Bearing of A *from* B = 69°.

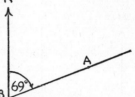

Fig. 134.

To find the bearing of B *from* A.

(Same two points)

This time we work from A.

Draw AN due North, and using protractor as shown in Ch. IV, measure reflex ∠ NAB (= 249°).

∴ The bearing of B *from* A is 249°

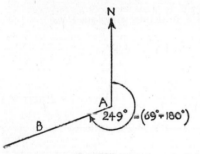

Fig. 135.

If the bearing of A from B is $x°$, the bearing of B from A is $x° \pm 180°$. In the examples above, if we first find bearing BA (A from B) we get the reverse bearing by adding 180°. If we had started with the bearing AB (B from A) we should have got the reverse bearing by subtracting 180° from 249°,

i.e. If $x < 180°$, reverse bearing is $x + 180°$.
If $x > 180°$, reverse bearing is $x - 180°$.

Example 7. A man sets out from his home (P) and cycles 5 miles to a house (H) whose bearing from P is 85°. He then cycles to a village (V) 8 miles from H, the bearing of V from H being 192°. Find (1) how far he then is from home, (2) the bearings HP, VH, PV, VP.

Scale: $\frac{1}{2}''$ to 1 mile.

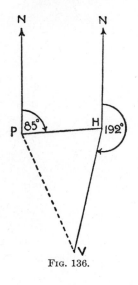

Fig. 136.

(1) Put in the bearing 85° from P.

Mark H $2\frac{1}{2}''$ from P on this bearing.

Put in the bearing 192° from H.

Mark V, 4″ from H.

Join PV and measure line PV.

$$PV = 4.1''$$

$$\frac{.5 \text{ in.}}{1 \text{ mile}} = \frac{4.1 \text{ in.}}{PV}$$

$$\therefore \ PV = 8.2 \text{ miles} \leftarrow$$

(2) Since bearing PH = 85°

$$\therefore \text{ bearing HP} = 180° + 85° = 265° \leftarrow$$

Since bearing HV = 192°

$$\therefore \text{ bearing VH} = 192° - 180° = 12° \leftarrow$$

By measurement,

$$\text{bearing PV} = 156° \leftarrow$$

$$\therefore \text{ bearing VP} = 156° + 180° = 336° \leftarrow$$

Scale Drawing—Maps

Before proceeding farther a caution must be given.

If the R.F. is given as $\frac{1}{63360}$ this means that 1 in. *length* on the map represents a *distance* of 63360 in. (or 1 mile) on the Earth. It does *not* mean that the area of the map is $\frac{1}{63360}$ of the area of the land it represents. If 1 in. on the map represents 63360 in. on land, 1 sq. in. on the map will represent $(63360)^2$ or 4,014,489,600 sq. in. on land.

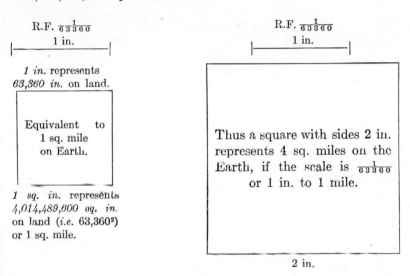

R.F. $\frac{1}{63360}$

1 in.

1 in. represents
63,360 in. on land.

Equivalent to
1 sq. mile
on Earth.

1 sq. in. represents
4,014,489,600 sq. in.
on land (*i.e.* 63,360²)
or 1 sq. mile.

R.F. $\frac{1}{63360}$

1 in.

Thus a square with sides 2 in. represents 4 sq. miles on the Earth, if the scale is $\frac{1}{63360}$ or 1 in. to 1 mile.

2 in.

Three Common Scales for Maps

The three most common British scales are:

1 in. to 1 mile; 6 in. to 1 mile; 25 in. to 1 mile.

The commonest French, German, and Continental or U.S.A. scale is:

1 cm. to Km., or 1:100,000.

Map-Making

In the long run the quickest way to learn the principles of scale-drawing, on which all map-making depends, is to get out of doors and make maps of your neighborhood for yourself. All that is needed is a table about 2 ft. square (a card-table will do), pins, paper and a little ingenuity (Fig. 137).

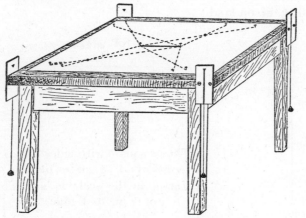

FIG. 138.

FIG. 137.—A HOME-MADE PLANE TABLE.

To get the table level, use a spirit-level each way. If none can be procured get four pieces of smooth wood, mark thin lines down each on one side (Fig. 138) fasten a string, with weight attached, to each piece on the line you have drawn, and screw the pieces of wood as shown in sketch, taking care that the lines on the pieces of wood are at right angles to the top of the table (use a protractor or set-square).

Pin a sheet of paper as large as possible to the table.

Select an open field which has a good view of the surrounding country and on it measure very carefully a "base line" (see p. 150) as long as possible provided it is level. Now draw a line XY on your paper corresponding to the base line on the Earth. (We will explain how to fix your scale later.) Get the point X right over one end of the Earth base line and your line XY directly over Earth base line and then see that the table is level (the four plumb lines will help you here). Choose some prominent object— tree, chimney, or what not—and putting your eye on the level of the paper put in a pin at X and another in a line with the prominent object (as far away from XY as the paper permits). Mark the pin "A" and make a note in your notebook that A stands for

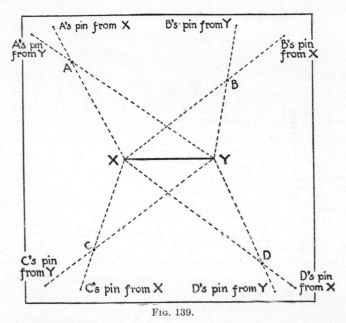

FIG. 139.

such or such an object. Now do the same with as many other prominent objects as possible, marking them B, C, D, etc. Now take your table to the other end of the Earth base line, with point Y directly over the end of it, and "pin-in" the directions of the same prominent objects as viewed from Y. Join A to X and Y, B to X and Y, etc. You will now have a paper looking like the sketch in Fig. 139.

You know enough about similar △s to realize that angles

made by prominent objects with the Earth base line are equal to the angles shown on your paper. As you know the scale or ratio between XY on your paper and the measured Earth base line, you can now easily calculate the distances on the Earth which correspond to AX, AY, BX, BY, etc. In this way maps are constructed.

Simple Calculations with the Plane Table

Example. To find the width of a river.
Scale: 1″ to 60 feet.

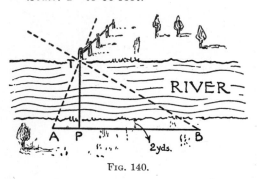

Fig. 140.

Select a straight stretch of bank and mark out base line parallel to bank and, say, 6 feet from it. Select some prominent object (T) on the farther bank and mark on plane table paper the angles BAT, ABT.

Having drawn AB to scale you can now measure a line TP which you draw on your paper at right ∠s to AB.

Suppose in our drawing TP = .6 in.
From our scale, 1 in. : 60 ft. = .6 in. : x. ∴ x = 36 ft.

Subtracting 6 feet from this length you will have the width of the river = 30 ft.←

Make your own plane table and find out for yourself the fascination of map-making.

For Exercises see pp. 300–302.

CHAPTER 23

TIME

Position of a Point on the Earth

We have seen how the position of any point on a plane surface such as a sheet of paper may be indicated by two measurements, each preceded by + or − to indicate direction.

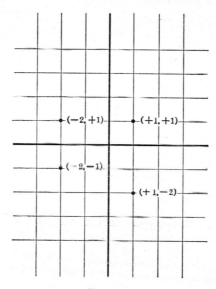

FIG. 141.

In stating the position of a point on the Earth's surface we substitute the Equator for the horizontal axis shown above, and the Meridian through Greenwich for the vertical axis. Angular measurements north or south of the Equator are marked Latitude (N. or S.); angular measurements to the right or left of the Greenwich Meridian are marked Longitude (E. or W.), as explained in Ch. 4.

It is usual to measure any arc of a Great Circle in terms of the angle it subtends or stretches at the center of the Earth. Thus the Latitude of a place may be considered as the "angular length" of its Meridian N. or S. of the Equator, while the Longitude may be considered as the "angular length" of the arc of the Equator lying between the Greenwich Meridian and the Meridian of the place in question.

Angular Measurement

The most common units are degrees (°), minutes ('), and seconds (").

$$60'' = 1'$$
$$60' = 1°$$
$$90° = 1 \text{ right angle.}$$

(A nautical mile—6080 feet—is the length of an arc of a Great Circle which subtends an angle of 1 minute at the Earth's center.)

Change of Latitude

The following examples are self-evident if studied on a map:

Initial Latitude of an aircraft	Subsequent Latitude	Change of Latitude
30° 10′ N.	35° 20′ N.	5° 10′ N.
35° 20′ N.	30° 10′ N.	5° 10′ S.
10° 26′ N.	5° 43′ S.	16° 9′ S.
5° 43′ S.	2° 05′ N.	7° 48′ N.
21° 53′ S.	3° 14′ S.	18° 39′ N.
8° 32′ S.	48° 08′ S.	39° 36′ S.

Change of Longitude

Study the following on a map:

Initial Longitude	Subsequent Longitude	Change of Longitude
10° 15′ E.	15° 04′ E.	4° 49′ E.
15° 04′ E.	10° 15′ E.	4° 49′ W.
10° 08′ E.	4° 43′ E.	5° 25′ W.
160° E.	150° W.	50° E.*
179° W.	54° E.	55′ W.*

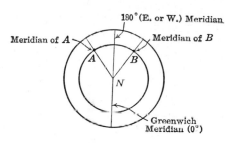

FIG. 142.

* Always give the *shorter* arc. In Fig. 142, suppose N is the North Pole. Give shorter arc AB, not longer arc AB.

Longitude and Time

The Earth rotates from W. to E. (*i.e.* in the opposite direction to the apparent movement of the Sun) once every 24 hours. This is known as a Mean Solar Day. Therefore a point on any Meridian rotates through

$$\left. \begin{array}{l} 360° \text{ every 24 hours} \\ \text{or} \quad 1° \text{ every 4 minutes} \\ \text{or} \quad 1′ \text{ every 4 seconds} \\ \text{or} \quad 1″ \text{ every } \frac{1}{15} \text{ second.} \end{array} \right\} A$$

Conversely, Mean Time can be expressed in terms of the angle through which any point on the Earth rotates in a stated time. Thus:

$$\left.\begin{array}{llll} \text{In} & \text{24 hours,} & 360° & \text{rotation} \\ \text{in} & \text{1 hour,} & 15° & \text{rotation} \\ \text{in} & \text{1 minute,} & 15' & \text{rotation} \\ \text{in} & \text{1 second,} & 15'' & \text{rotation.} \end{array}\right\}B$$

Change of Longitude and Change in Time

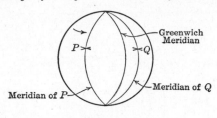

Fig. 143.

From Fig. 143 it is clear that any place E. of Greenwich will rotate into the Sun's rays before Greenwich; *i.e.* it will be "sunrise" at Q (East of Greenwich), while it is still dark at Greenwich. Therefore the Local Mean Time (L.M.T.) at Q will be *greater* than Greenwich Mean Time (G.M.T.). Conversely, L.M.T. at P (West of Greenwich) will be *less* than G.M.T.

The difference between L.M.T. and G.M.T. can therefore be calculated if the Longitude is known, or, conversely, the Longitude can be calculated if the difference between L.M.T. and G.M.T. is known.

> To convert change of Longitude into Time: Divide the degrees, minutes and seconds in turn by 15. (See Table B, above.)

Example. A place is 20° 40′ 30″ E. of Greenwich. Find L.M.T. at that place when G.M.T. is 1200 hours.

15)20°   40'   30" (1 hour
  15
  ——
  5
  60

15)340(22   *Answer:* 1 hour, 22 minutes,
  30   42 seconds later than
  ——   G.M.T. or
  40   13 hrs. 22 min. 42 sec.
  30
  ——
  10
  60

15)630(42
  60
  ——
  30
  30
  ··

There is an old ditty which, disregarding grammar and pre-supposing that "best" means "more," runs as follows:

"Longitude East, Greenwich Time least,
Longitude West, Greenwich Time best."

To convert difference in Time to change of Longitude: Multiply the seconds, minutes and hours (in that order) in turn by 15.

Example. L.M.T. at A is 16 hrs. 25 min. 20 sec. when
              L.M.T. at B is 18 hrs. 10 min. 50 sec.
              Find change of Longitude between A and B.

Difference in Time:

18	10	50
16	25	20
1	45	30

$$30 \text{ sec.} \times 15 = 450'' = \quad\quad 7' \quad 30''$$
$$45 \text{ min.} \times 15 = 675' = 11° 15'$$
$$1 \text{ hr.} \times 15 = \quad\quad\quad 15°$$
$$\overline{\quad\quad\quad\quad 26° 22' \quad 30''}$$

Since B saw the sunrise before A, B must be East of A. Therefore, the change of Longitude from A to B is 26° 22' 30" E.

Zone Time

Obviously it would lead to chaos if every place kept its own L.M.T. So the world is divided into 24 "zones" and generally speaking the time kept by countries in each zone is the L.M.T. of some place in the center of its zone.

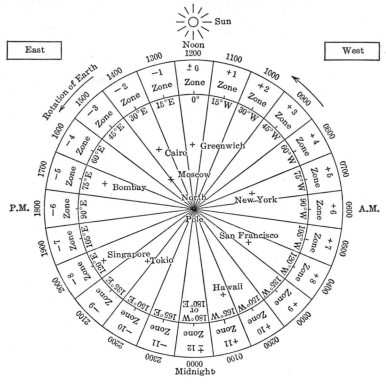

Fig. 144

(In studying the above diagram, Fig. 144, remember that you are looking at the Earth from above the North Pole, hence New York, for instance, appears to be to the right of Greenwich, instead of to its left as on an ordinary map, which supposes that you are facing the Earth from a position such as that of the Sun in the diagram. Note that if it is, say, Thursday noon in Zone 0, it can be *either* Thursday midnight or Wednesday midnight in Zone 12.)

The algebraic sum of Zone Number and Zone Time = G.M.T.

For Exercises, see p. 303.

CHAPTER 24

OTHER KINDS OF EQUATIONS

So far we have dealt only with simple equations, *i.e.* equations having only one "unknown" and that unknown a power of the 1st degree (*i.e.* x or y, not x^2, y^2, etc.).

When solving a simple equation we had to find a value for the unknown x which would satisfy the equation; *e.g.* if:

$$3x+3 = 24$$

then the only value of x which will make the left-hand side balance the right-hand side is 7.

If two equations of the 1st degree (i.e. without any x^2, etc.) each contain two unknown quantities (say x and y) there will be one value of x and one value of y which will satisfy both equations, i.e. x and y will each have a value that simultaneously (at the same time) will satisfy both equations. Such equations are called **simultaneous equations.**

Example 1. Solve: $\left. \begin{array}{l} 3x+y = 17 \\ 2x+y = 12 \end{array} \right\}$

Imagine a pair of scales.

In one pan is $3x+y$, balancing 17.

If we take away $2x+y$ from left hand pan and something equal to $2x+y$ from the right-hand pan, the balance will remain.

$$\begin{aligned} i.e. \ (3x+y)-(2x+y) &= 17-12 \\ \therefore \ x &= 5 \\ \therefore \ (\text{from 1st equation}) \ y &= 2 \end{aligned} \left. \right\} \leftarrow$$

Test. If $x = 5$, $y = 2$, then in 1st equation
$$3x+y = 15+2 = 17 = \text{right-hand side,}$$

and in 2nd equation

$$2x+y = 10+2 = 12 = \text{right-hand side}$$
$$\therefore \ x = 5, \ y = 2 \text{ satisfy the equation.}$$

Example 2. Solve: $\left.\begin{array}{l}5x+y = 26 \\ 4x-y = 10\end{array}\right\}$

Add $4x-y$ to left-hand side of 1st equation.
Add something equal to $4x-y$ to right-hand side of 1st equation.
The equation will remain balanced, *i.e.*

$$5x+y+4x-y = 26+10 \ *$$
$$\therefore \ 9x = 36$$
$$\therefore \ x = 4 \left.\vphantom{\begin{array}{l}4\\6\end{array}}\right\}$$
$$\therefore \ (\text{from 1st equation}) \ y = 6 \quad \longleftarrow$$

(Every example must be treated on its merits. Common sense will show which way to tackle these equations. Note why we *subtracted* in *Example* 1 but *added* in *Example* 2.)

   * In practice this line need not be written out. Watch the next two examples.

Example 3. Solve: $\left.\begin{array}{l}6x+2y = 10 \\ x+5y = 11\end{array}\right\}$

Here we do not subtract or add as in the previous examples until we have so altered one of the equations that subtraction or addition will cause either x or y to disappear.

In this example we may first multiply the whole of the second equation by 6 so as to make the x term in that equation equal to the x term in 1st equation, *i.e.* $6x$.

$$\begin{array}{r}6x+2y = 10 \\ \text{From 2nd equation } 6x+30y = 66\end{array}\left.\vphantom{\begin{array}{l}1\\1\end{array}}\right\}$$
$$\text{Subtract,} \quad \therefore \ -28y = -56 \quad \therefore \ y = 2$$
$$\therefore \ (\text{from 1st equation}), \ 6x+4 = 10$$
$$\therefore \ 6x = 6 \ \therefore \ x = 1$$

[Test as before]

Example 4. Solve: $5x-3y = -22$
$ 14x-7y = -56$

Here, to eliminate y we multiply top equation by coefficient of y in bottom equation, and then we multiply bottom equation by coefficient of y in top equation.

(We could, if we wished, multiply by 14 and 5 to eliminate x, but we naturally choose the easier course.)

$$\begin{cases} 5x-3y = -22 & \quad . \quad . \quad . \quad . \quad (1) \\ 14x-7y = -56 & \quad . \quad . \quad . \quad . \quad (2) \end{cases}$$

Multiply (1) by 7$\begin{cases} 35x-21y = -154 \\ 42x-21y = -168 \end{cases}$
and $ $ (2) by 3

Subtract, $\therefore\ -7x = 14 \therefore x = -2\leftarrow$

From (1) $ -10-3y = -22$

$ \therefore\ -3y = -12 \therefore y = 4\leftarrow$

[Test as before]

Graphical Solution of Simultaneous Equations

Any algebraic expression may be represented by a graph, as in Fig. 145. We read positive values of x to the right of the vertical axis, negative values of x to the left of the vertical axis; positive values of y upwards from the horizontal axis, and negative values of y downwards from the horizontal axis.

Any equation of the 1st degree (*i.e.* with no letter whose index is greater than 1) is represented graphically by a straight line, and to find the angle at which this line is to slope, we need only find two points and join them.

Take, for instance, the equations in *Example* 2:

$$\begin{cases} 5x+y = 26 & \quad . \quad . \quad . \quad . \quad (1) \\ 4x-y = 10 & \quad . \quad . \quad . \quad . \quad (2) \end{cases}$$

Write each in the form $y = $ . . . .

Every change in value of x means a corresponding change in value of y, which will be shown on the graph.

Equation (1). $y = 26-5x$.
Choose any two values for x, say $x = 3$ and $x = 5$.

Values of x	$+3$	$+5$
Values of $(26-5x)$ . . . . *i.e.* corresponding values of y . .	$+11$	$+1$

Find the point on the graph which is 3 squares to the right of vertical axis and 11 squares upwards from horizontal axis. Do the same for the values $x = 5$, $y = 1$. Join these two points and produce the straight line in both directions. This will give the graph of $y = 26-5x$ (or $5x+y = 26$). (See Fig. 145.)

Equation (2). $y = 4x-10$.
Choose any two values for x, say $x = 1$ and $x = 3$.

Values of x	1	3
Corresponding values of $4x-10$ (or y)	-6	2

Plot the points $x = 1$ (one to the right); $y = -6$ (six downwards); and $x = 3$; $y = 2$; and join these points as before. This gives the graph of $4x-y = 10$.

There is clearly only one point where the values of both x and y will satisfy **both** *equations.*

That point, we see, is where $x = 4$, $y = 6$

$\therefore$ $x = 4$, $y = 6$ satisfy both equations.

Graphical Solution of Simultaneous Equations

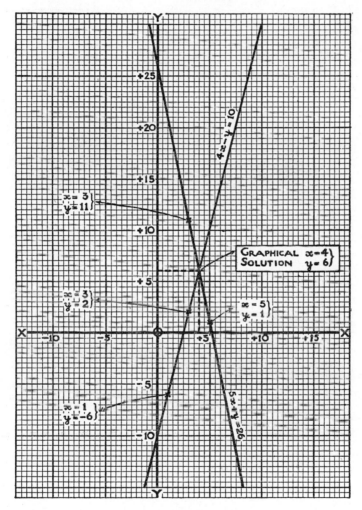

Fig. 145.

For Exercises see pp. 303–304.

Quadratic Equations

So far, we have dealt only with equations which can be satisfied by one value only of the unknown letter.

Some equations can be satisfied by more than one value of the unknown letter. *Any equation which contains a power of the second order (i.e. the square of some letter) will have two roots or values of the unknown letter, either of which satisfies the equation.*

Solution of Quadratic Equations

There are four methods:—

(1) By factors.
(2) By "Completing the Square."
(3) By the use of a formula.
(4) By drawing a graph.

Method 1.—*Solution by Factors*

Example 1.

Solve: $x^2 = 9$
$\therefore x \times x = 9$
$\therefore x = +3$ or -3 (since $-3 \times -3 = +9$).

(A short way of writing "$+3$ or -3" is ± 3)

Example 2. Solve: $x^2 = 3x$
$\therefore x^2 - 3x = 0$
Write in factors. $\therefore x(x-3) = 0$.

Now, whenever the product of any two numbers or expressions is 0, one of those numbers or expressions must itself equal 0.

$$\therefore \text{ either } x = 0$$
$$\text{or } x = 3.$$

[*N.B.*—Do not say $x = 0$ *and* 3. It cannot equal both at the same time; therefore say $x = 0$ OR 3.]

Example 3. Solve: $x^2 - 2x = 8$

Arrange equation so that right-hand side equals 0.

$$x^2 - 2x - 8 = 0$$

Factor left-hand side.

$$\therefore \ (x-4)(x+2) = 0$$
$$\therefore \text{ either } x-4 = 0$$
$$\text{or } x+2 = 0$$
$$\therefore \ x = 4 \text{ or } -2\leftarrow$$

Example 4. Solve $4x^2 + x = 3$
$$\therefore \ 4x^2 + x - 3 = 0$$
$$\therefore \ (4x-3)(x+1) = 0$$
$$\therefore \text{ either } 4x-3 = 0$$
$$\text{or } x+1 = 0$$
$$\therefore \ x = \tfrac{3}{4} \text{ or } -1\leftarrow$$

Method 2.—*"Completing the Square"*

We know that $x^2 + 6x + 9 = (x+3)^2$.

$\therefore$ to turn $x^2 + 6x$ into a perfect square we must add 9, i.e. *the square of half the coefficient of* x. (Half of 6 = 3; $3^2 = 9$.)

Similarly, $x^2+8x+16 = (x+4)^2$.

$\therefore$ to turn x^2+8x into a perfect square we add 16, i.e. *the square of half the coefficient of x*.

Similarly, $x^2-10x+25 = (x-5)^2$.

$\therefore$ to turn x^2-10x into a perfect square we add 25, i.e. *the square of half the coefficient of x*.

Example. Solve: $x^2+6x-5 = 0$.

We find we cannot factor.

$\therefore$ we put independent term (term without letter) on right-hand side.

$$\therefore x^2+6x = 5.$$

Now complete the square of left-hand side *by adding the square of half the coefficient of x.* To preserve the balance of the equation we must add the same amount to right-hand side.

$$\therefore x^2+6x+(3)^2 = 5+(3^2)$$

Factor left-hand side.

$$\therefore (x+3)^2 = 5+9 = 14$$
$$\therefore x+3 = \pm\sqrt{14}$$
$$\therefore x+3 = \pm3.74$$
$$\therefore \text{either } x = -3+3.74$$
$$= 0.74\leftarrow$$
$$\text{or } x = -3-3.74$$
$$= -6.74\leftarrow$$

Never use Method 2 when factors can be found.

Method 3.—*Using a Formula*

The tiresome labor of Method 2 may be avoided, even when factors cannot be found, if the *answer* to the following solution of the "general quadratic" is committed to memory:

$$ax^2+bx+c = 0$$

Using Method 2, we get

$$x^2 + \frac{b}{a}x = -\frac{c}{a}$$

$$\therefore\ x^2 + \frac{b}{a}x + \left(\frac{b}{2a}\right)^2 = -\frac{c}{a} + \frac{b^2}{4a^2}$$

$$\therefore\ \left(x + \frac{b}{2a}\right)^2 = \frac{b^2-4ac}{4a^2}$$

$$\therefore\ x = -\frac{b}{2a} \pm \sqrt{\frac{b^2-4ac}{4a^2}}$$

$$x = \frac{-b \pm \sqrt{b^2 - 4ac}}{2a}$$

N.B. (1) Any quadratic can be arranged in the form

$$ax^2+bx+c = 0$$

by putting all the terms on one side of the equation.

(2) a stands for the coefficient of x^2

b stands for the coefficient of x

c stands for the independent term (term with no "x" or "x^2").

Example. Solve: $6x^2+4x = 3$.

First, put equation in the form $ax^2+bx+c = 0$. We get $6x^2+4x-3 = 0$. (Here $a = 6$, $b = 4$, $c = -3$)

$\therefore$ where $6x^2+4x-3 = 0$

Since $\qquad x = \dfrac{-b\pm\sqrt{b^2-4ac}}{2a}$

$$\therefore\ x = \dfrac{-4\pm\sqrt{16+72}}{12}$$

$$= \dfrac{-4\pm\sqrt{88}}{12}$$

$$= \dfrac{-4\pm9.38}{12}$$

$\therefore$ either $x = \dfrac{5.38}{12} = 0.45$ (correct to 2 decimal places)$\leftarrow$

or $x = \dfrac{-13.38}{12} = -1.12$ (to 2 decimal places)$\leftarrow$

Example. Solve: $5x^2-7x = 6$

$$\therefore\ 5x^2-7x-6 = 0$$

$\therefore\ x = \dfrac{-b\pm\sqrt{b^2-4ac}}{2a}$ where $a = 5,\, b = -7,\, c = -6$

$$\therefore\ x = \dfrac{+7\pm\sqrt{49+120}}{10} = \dfrac{+7\pm\sqrt{169}}{10}$$

$$\therefore\ x = \dfrac{+7\pm13}{10} = \dfrac{20}{10} \text{ or } -\dfrac{6}{10}$$

$\therefore\ x = 2$ or $-\tfrac{3}{5}\leftarrow$

Method 4.—*Graphical Solution*

Any algebraic expression (or "function") may be expressed as a graph.

To draw the Graph of the Expression "x^2-5x+6"

As the value of x changes, the value of the expression corresponding changes. Make a table of these values, taking x, say, from -1 to 6.*

Values of x . .	-1	0	1	2	3	4	5	6	$2\frac{1}{2}$ †
Values of x^2 .	1	0	1	4	9	16	25	36	$\dfrac{25}{4}$
Values of $-5x$.	5	0	-5	-10	-15	-20	-25	-30	$-\dfrac{25}{2}$
Values of x^2-5x+6	12	6	2	0	0	2	6	12	$-\dfrac{1}{4}$

* A quick method of finding the value of a function such as x^2-5x+6 for various values of x, is to proceed as follows:

(1) Write down the coefficients and the independent term.
(2) Multiply the first coefficient by the value to be given to x and add this product to the second coefficient.
(3) Multiply this sum by the x value and add this product to the independent term. This result is the value of the function for that particular value of x.

E.g. Find the value of x^2-5x+6 if $x = -1$.

$$
\begin{array}{cccc}
1 & -5 & +6 & (x = -1) \\
 & -1 & +6 & \\
 & -6 & \boxed{+12} &
\end{array}
$$

After a little practice you can still further cut down the time and labor involved, by writing the top line on a separate slip of paper (at the bottom edge) and sliding the paper down your page. You need then only write down the two bottom lines for each value you give to x. This method is very helpful when dealing with more complicated functions.

E.g. Find the value of $3x^4-5x^3+7x^2-6x+3$ if $x = 5$.

$$
\begin{array}{ccccc}
3 & -5 & +7 & -6 & +3 \\
 & +15 & +50 & +285 & +1395 \quad (x = 5) \\
 & +10 & +57 & +279 & \boxed{+1398}
\end{array}
$$

† We note that the values of x^2-5x+6 "balance round" a point whose x value lies between 2 and 3. Therefore to help us draw an accurate curve we find the value of x^2-5x+6 when $x = 2\frac{1}{2}$.

We now plot values of x horizontally and of the expression vertically, and join these points by a smooth curve.

Now, from the graph (Fig. 146), we see that the value of the expression x^2-5x+6 is 0 when $x = 2$ or 3 (see points A and B).

Also, the value of the expression x^2-5x+6 is 1 when $x = 1.4$ or 3.6 approximately (see points C and D).

Also, the value of the expression x^2-5x+6 is 2 when $x = 1$ or 4 (see points E and F).

and so on.

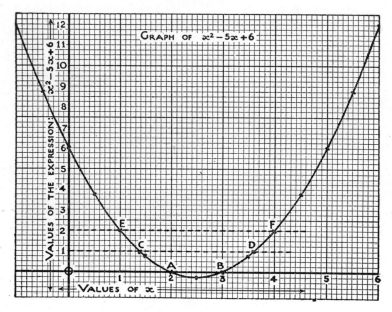

Fig. 146.

This means then that:

if $x^2-5x+6 = 0$ then $x = 2$ or 3

if $x^2-5x+6 = 1$ then $x = 1.4$ or 3.6 approx.

if $x^2-5x+6 = 2$ then $x = 1$ or 4

and so on.

Thus, several quadratic equations may often be solved from one graph. Suppose we have to solve $x^2 - 5x + 1 = 0$. We see that the particular equation may be written $x^2 - 5x + 6 = 5$ (by adding 5 to each side). From the graph already drawn of the function $x^2 - 5x + 6$ we see that the values of x which make this function equal to 5 are 4.8 and 0.2 (approx.).

$$\therefore \text{ if } x^2 - 5x + 1 = 0, \quad x = 4.8 \text{ or } 0.2 \text{ (approx.)}$$

For Exercises see pp. 303-304.

CHAPTER 25

TWELVE IMPORTANT FACTS ABOUT A CIRCLE

(For definitions, see p. 55.)

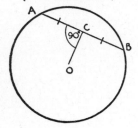

(1) *The line from the center of a ⊙ to the mid-point of any chord is perpendicular to that chord.*

i.e. Given AC = CB

it follows that

OC ⊥ AC.

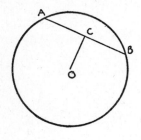

(2) (Converse of (1)).

[*N.B.*—In a "converse" you are given the opposite of same theorem.]

i.e. Given OC ⊥ AB

it follows that

AC = CB.

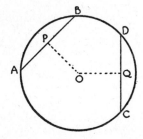

(3) *Equal chords of a ⊙ are equidistant from the center.*

i.e. Given AB = CD

it follows that

OP = OQ.

Fig. 147.

(4) (Converse of (3))

Given OP = OQ

it follows that

AB = CD.

[*N.B.*—A "converse" is not *always* true. *e.g.* "I love you" does not necessarily mean "you love me."]

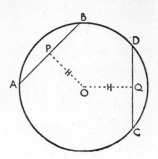

(5) *The angle at the center subtended ("stretched") by any chord is double any angle at the circumference subtended by the same chord.*

∠ AOB = 2 ∠ ACB or any other ∠

in major segment.

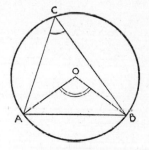

(6) Same as last but dealing with ∠s in minor segment.

i.e. Reflex ∠ AOB
= 2 ∠ ADB
or any other ∠ in minor segment.

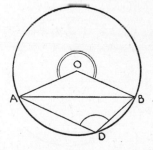

Fig. 148.

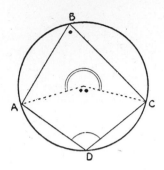

(7) *The opposite angles of a cyclic quadrilateral (i.e.* a quadrilateral whose corners are on a ⊙), *are together equal to 2 rt. ∠s.*

$$i.e. \quad \angle B + \angle D = 180°$$
$$also \quad \angle A + \angle C = 180°$$

(Apply last 2 Theorems.)

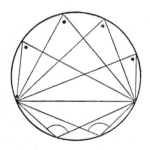

(8) *All angles in the same segment are equal (i.e. all angles at the circumference subtended by the same chord).*

(Two sets of equal ∠s: all the acute ∠s in major segment, and all the obtuse ∠s in minor segment.)

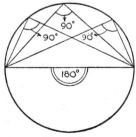

Fig. 149.

(9) *Any angle in a semicircle is a rt. angle.*

[Now turn back to construction of ⊥s (Ch. 15) and see the reason for the construction.]

(10) *A tangent is ⊥ to the radius at its point of contact with the ⊙.*

(A tangent to a circle is a line that *touches* a ⊙ at one point only.)

i.e.   TN ⊥ OA.

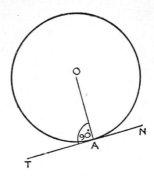

(11) *The two tangents to a ⊙ from any point outside it are equal.*

i.e.   TA = TN.

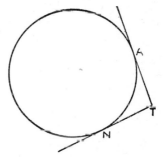

(12) *The angle made by a tangent and a chord drawn from the point of contact equals any angle in the opposite segment.*

i.e.   ∠ NAP = ∠ ACP

(or any other ∠ in that segment)

and   ∠ TAC = ∠ APC

(or any other ∠ in that segment).

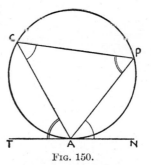

Fig. 150.

CHAPTER 26

VELOCITY AND ACCELERATION

Velocity means the speed at which a body is moving in a certain direction.

Acceleration means the increase in speed every second (or given unit of time). Thus, if a motorist accelerates from 44 feet per second to 46 feet per second in one second, his acceleration is 2 ft. per sec. per sec. (written 2 ft./sec.^{2}).

Here are some useful formulas connected with speed and acceleration:

If　u = initial velocity, in ft./sec.
　　v = final velocity, in ft./sec.
　　a = acceleration, in ft./sec.^{2}
　　t = time taken, in seconds
　　s = distance covered, in feet;

then

$$v = u + at$$
$$s = ut + \tfrac{1}{2}at^2$$
$$v = u^2 + 2as$$

How to use these formulas:—

Example. A body is observed to be moving at a velocity of 15 ft. per sec. and with an acceleration of 5 ft. per sec. per sec. What will be its speed (1) when it has covered 40 ft., (2) after 9 secs.?

(1) Here we have to deal with
　　u (initial velocity) = 15 ft./sec.
　　a (acceleration)　 = 5 ft./sec.^{2}
　　s (distance)　　　 = 40 ft.
　　and from them find v (final velocity).

We therefore choose Formula (3).

$$v^2 = u^2 + 2as$$
$$\therefore \; v^2 = 15^2 + 2 \times 5 \times 40$$
$$= 225 + 400$$
$$= 625$$
$$\therefore \; v = 25 \text{ ft./sec.} \leftarrow$$

(2) Here we have to deal with u, a and t, and from them find v. We therefore choose Formula (1).

$$v = u + at$$
$$\therefore \; v = 15 + (5 \times 9)$$
$$= 15 + 45$$
$$= 60 \text{ ft./sec.} \leftarrow$$

> *Note.*—When a body starts from rest, $u = 0$.
> When a body comes to rest, $v = 0$.

For Exercises see pp. 304–305.

CHAPTER 27

GRAVITY

Galileo (1564–1642) upset the mistaken belief of centuries by proving that if a "heavy" and a "light" body were dropped simultaneously from any height they would reach the ground simultaneously (unless of course air resistance held up one of them, *e.g.* a piece of paper or a feather).

Galileo dropped two unequal weights at the same moment from the top of the Leaning Tower at Pisa, which is 179 ft. high and 14 ft. out of the perpendicular. They both reached the ground at the same moment.

Later Newton (1642–1727), one of the greatest mathematicians the world has ever known, showed that if a feather and a coin were dropped simultaneously in a vacuum, the feather, unhindered by air resistance, fell at the same speed as the coin.

An apple leaves a bough and moves towards the Earth because, as Newton discovered, the Earth attracts it.

The nearer anything on or above the Earth's surface is to the center of the Earth, the greater is the force of this attraction exerted by Gravity. This can be shown by weighing any object *in a spring balance* (*a*) at the Equator, (*b*) near the North or South Pole. The weight at (*a*) will be slightly less than the weight at (*b*) because since the Earth is slightly flattened at its Poles, its surface there is slightly nearer the center of attraction than is its surface at the Equator.

A packet of tea placed on a *spring balance* at sea-level and recording 1 lb. weight there, would record slightly less than 1 lb. weight if placed on the same spring balance at the top of a high mountain.

A man weighing 168 lb. (*spring balance weight*) on the ground would weigh only 167.45 lb. if weighed by spring balance in an aircraft 5 miles up.

We are now in a position to understand the note at the bottom of p. 28 about mass and weight.

In both the examples we have just given, both the tea and the man, respectively, would, of course, retain the same amount of "matter" in them wherever weighed. *The amount of "stuff" or "matter" in a thing is called its "mass," the attraction of Gravity is called its "weight."*

We see now that there is, strictly speaking, a difference between mass and weight, but the difference is so slight that in practice we ignore it.

The *mass* is found by comparing the balancing power of the article with some standard mass, *e.g.* a piece of metal labeled "1 lb." or what not. The comparison must be made on a *pair of scales* in order that the standard piece of metal may be subjected to the same gravitational attraction as the object whose mass is to be found.

Thus a packet of tea which records 1 lb. "weight" on scales at sea-level will record the same "weight" on the top of a mountain or at the North Pole. Strictly speaking, we ought to substitute "mass" for "weight" in the last sentence, for it is the mass which remains constant, the weight (*i.e.* gravitational attraction) varies.

Velocity and Acceleration (or Retardation) due to Gravity

A body falls vertically to the Earth with a velocity which accelerates at 32 ft. per sec. per sec. (more exactly, at the Equator this acceleration due to Gravity is 32.091 ft. sec.², at Lat. $51\frac{1}{2}°$ N. it is 32.191 and at the North Pole 32.252. This is why in the example about a pendulum on p. 73 we stated the Latitude).

When indicating this gravitational acceleration we write "*g.*" If the body under observation is rising in the air the gravitational retardation is "$-g.$"

All three velocity formulas apply to objects falling vertically downwards to Earth or rising vertically upwards from the Earth.

If the body is thrown or otherwise projected downwards it will have an initial velocity *u.* If falling from rest (*e.g.* an apple) there will be no initial velocity. If rising from the Earth there must of course be an initial velocity greater than gravitational attraction (otherwise you say you can't lift the thing), and when a body has reached its greatest height there is no final velocity v.

To summarize:—

(a) Bodies projected vertically *downwards*.

$$v = u+gt$$
$$s = ut+\tfrac{1}{2}gt^2$$
$$v^2 = u^2+2gs$$

(b) Falling bodies (not projected).

$$v = gt$$
$$s = \tfrac{1}{2}gt^2 \left.\right\} \text{since in each}$$
$$v^2 = 2gs \left.\right\} \text{case } u = 0$$

(c) Bodies projected vertically *upwards*.

$$v = u-gt$$
$$s = ut-\tfrac{1}{2}gt^2$$
$$v^2 = u^2-2gs$$

From formula (b), calling "g" 32 ft. per sec. per sec., we get $s = 16t^2$, i.e. *the number of feet a body falls from rest is 16 times the square of the number of seconds it takes to fall.*

For Exercises see pp. 305–306.

CHAPTER 28

RELATIVE VELOCITY AND THE PARALLELOGRAM AND TRIANGLE OF VELOCITIES

Every velocity has *magnitude* and *direction,* both of which can be represented by a straight line drawn at the correct angle and to a scale, the angle indicating direction and the length representing magnitude.

So far, we have been considering bodies moving with but one velocity. We will now deal with bodies which may be considered to possess two or more velocities at the same time.

For instance, a man walking down the corridor of a moving train has the velocity of the train and also the velocity at which he is walking. If the train is moving at 50 m.p.h. and he walks at 3 m.p.h. relative to the train and in the same direction as the train, his resultant speed *relative to the Earth* is 53 m.p.h. If he walks in the opposite direction his resultant speed relative to the train will still be 3 m.p.h., but relative to the Earth it will be only 47 m.p.h.

Component Velocities { 3 →   50 →

Resultant Velocity of } man (relative to Earth) 53 →

FIG. 151.—Man walking down corridor in same direction as train.

Component Velocities { 50   3 ←

Resultant Velocity of } man (relative to Earth) 47 →

FIG. 152.—Man walking down corridor in opposite direction to that of train.

Relative velocities, when the components are parallel to each other, as in this example, are very easily dealt with, as we see.

Now consider a more complicated case: [Fig. 153]

A Canadian lumberman climbs across a raft from L_1 to L_2. His speed in climbing across is 3 ft. per sec., the speed of the raft drifting downstream is 4 ft. per sec. What is the man's speed and direction relative to the Earth?

We will draw two lines representing the two velocities (of the man relative to the raft and of the raft relative to the Earth) showing both their magnitude and their direction. The "resultant," in both magnitude and direction, will give us the man's velocity relative to the Earth in both magnitude and direction.

Scale: $\frac{1}{2}''$ to 1 ft. per sec.

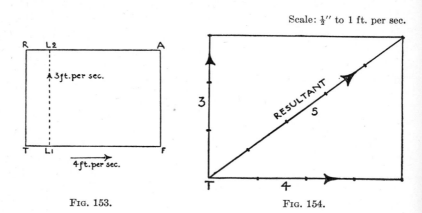

FIG. 153.   FIG. 154.

Since the man climbs across the raft at right angles to the direction in which the raft is moving, we draw the two components at right angles [Fig. 154]. *Complete the parallelogram*, and its diagonal from T will represent the velocity of the man relative to the Earth. We see that he goes at a relative velocity of 5 ft. per sec. at an angle (to the direction of the river's current) whose tangent is $\frac{3}{4}$. By looking this up in a table of "natural tangents" we find the angle is 36° 50′ approximately.

Note. The parallelogram in Fig. 154 does not represent the raft. Its sides represent *the two velocities*.

A Quicker Method than the "Parallelogram of Velocities"

Draw AB to scale to represent velocity of raft (Fig. 155). Put arrow-head on AB to represent direction of that velocity.

From B draw BC to represent the man's climbing-across velocity in magnitude and direction. Put arrow-head on BC.

Join CA and *put arrow-head on AC in opposite sense to last two arrow-heads* (*i.e.* if they were clockwise, put AC contra-clockwise, or *vice versa* as in Fig. 155). Then AC represents the resultant velocity in magnitude and direction.

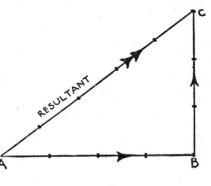

Fig. 155.

This is called the triangle of velocities.

We proceed in the same way, no matter in what direction the lumberman climbs across the raft. Thus Fig. 156 shows the triangle of velocities where the lumberman climbs across at an angle of $\phi°$. We see, therefore, that he goes at a relative velocity of x ft. per sec. at an angle (to the river's current) of $\theta°$. (By measurement x is found to be 6.5 ft. per sec. and angle θ 18° 15′.)

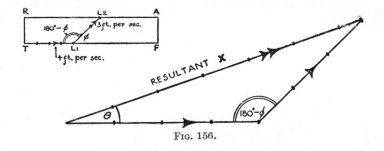

Fig. 156.

The Triangle of Velocities as Used in Air Navigation

First of all we must deal with some terms as used by air navigators.

True North.—The direction of the N. Pole from any point on the Earth's surface.

Magnetic North.—The direction in which the needle of a compass points if it is influenced *only* by the Earth's Magnetic Field.

Compass North.—The direction in which any particular compass needle points when under the influence of magnetic fields additional to the Earth's Magnetic Field.

Variation.—The angle between True North and Magnetic North (measured E. or W. of True North. See ∠TOM Fig. 157).

Deviation.—The angle between Magnetic North and the direction in which the needle of some particular compass points when it is influenced by some magnetic attraction additional to that of the Earth's Magnetic Field (measured E. or W. of Magnetic North. See ∠COM Fig. 157).

Bearing.—(1) *Great Circle Bearing* (or *"Azimuth"* or *"True Bearing"*). See ∠TOX Fig. 157.
(2) *Magnetic Bearing.* See ∠MOX Fig. 157.
(3) *Compass Bearing.* See ∠COX Fig. 157.
(4) *Relative Bearing.* The angle between the True Course of an aircraft and the direction (found by Direction Finding) of a wireless station. See Fig. 158.

All bearings are measured from 0° to 360° in a clockwise direction.

Course (or "Heading").—The direction in which an aircraft is headed. (See Fig. 159.)

Track (or "Course Made Good").—The direction of an aircraft relative to the Earth (if no cross-wind, Course and Track must be identical, not otherwise). (See Fig. 159.)

Air Speed.—The speed an aircraft would have in still air. (The speed with which the air enters the "pitot" head, the open-end of a tube in the Air Speed Indicator.)

Ground Speed.—The speed of an aircraft relative to the Earth, *i.e.* taking the influence of wind into account.

Drift.—The angle between Course and Track. Measured to Port or Starboard of Course. (See Fig. 160.)

Direction of Wind.—Direction *from which* wind blows.

Vector.—A line drawn to scale in proper direction to represent Velocity (or Force).

Port.—The left-hand side, facing forward.

Starboard.—The right-hand side, facing forward.

Knot.—A speed of 1 nautical mile per hour.

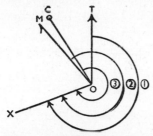

T = True North
M = Magnetic North
C = Direction in which particular compass
    needle points.

FIG. 157.—Bearing of X from O
[Observer at O]

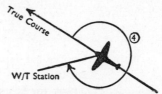

FIG. 158.—Relative Bearing.

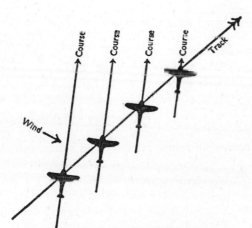

FIG. 159.—It is obvious from this sketch of
four consecutive positions of an aircraft that
wind must always blow FROM Course TO Track.

Always link together:

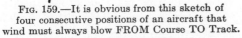

Angle of Drift
(Here, Starboard)
FIG. 160.

The Triangle of Velocities as Used in Air Navigation

Application of the triangle of velocities to connect together Course and Air Speed; Track and Ground Speed; Wind Direction and Speed:

Example 1. Given: Course and Air Speed
                      Track and Ground Speed:
                  To find Wind Direction and Speed.

Suppose Course (or Heading)	062° True
Air Speed	95 Kts
Track (or Course made good)	075° T
Ground Speed	80 Kts.

(1) Draw a line through any point A to represent True North (this line is sometimes called the "True Meridian" of A). (Fig. 161.)

(2) From A draw AB at an angle of 62° clockwise from True North, making AB represent 95 Kts (to some convenient scale, as large as possible). *Mark* AB *with single arrow* (Course).

(3) From A draw AC at an angle of 75° to True North to represent 80 Kts (same scale as AB). *Mark* AC *with double arrow* (Track).

(4) Join BC. Since this will be the wind vector, *mark with single arrow pointing in same sense as Course Vector* AB.

(5) Draw the True Meridian of C (*i.e.* a line parallel to AN) and measure ∠NCB (since wind is always named by the direction *from which* it comes).

(6) Measure BC and, using same scale as previously, calculate speed of wind.

Beginners, when studying the triangle of velocities, are sometimes puzzled by what appears to be a contradiction of the obvious fact that wind must always blow from Course to Track. The arrows inserted in the triangle of velocities may sometimes appear to contradict this fact. The explanation is that the triangle of velocities is really a "short cut" to obtain the diagonal (or "resultant") of a parallelogram of velocities. If time were unnecessarily spent in drawing the latter the wind vector could always be

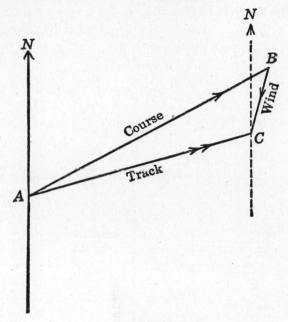

FIG. 161.

BC 24.4 mm., and CB lies at an angle of 14° with True Meridian at C.
Wind Velocity 014°, 24 Knots. This is written 014/24 K.

shown pointing from Course to Track, by choosing one or other
of the two triangles into which the parallelogram would be divided.

But to avoid waste of time we only draw half the parallelogram
(*i.e.* the triangle), consequently the following rule must be applied
for putting in the direction arrows on the vectors:

Wind and Course Vectors: Single arrows following one another
round in the same sense.

Track Vector: Double arrow pointing in the opposite sense to the other two vectors.

All this must be borne in mind in the next example.

Example 2. Given: Track 205° T

Wind Velocity $\boxed{315/25m}$ (*i.e.* coming from the direction 315° T at 25 m.p.h.):

A/S 110 m.p.h.

To find True Course to steer, and Ground Speed.

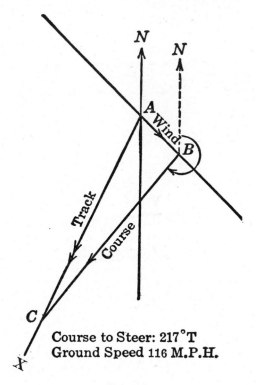

Course to Steer: 217°T
Ground Speed 116 M.P.H.

Fig. 162.

(1) Set off AX from A to represent Track 205° T.

(2) Set off AB from A to represent wind direction and speed. (*N.B.* B must be placed to the right of A in order to get wind arrow in opposite sense to Track arrow.)

(3) With center B mark off BC = 110 (to scale) and cutting AX in C. Mark with single arrow in same sense as AB.

(4) Measure the angle between BC and True Meridian at B. This gives the Course to steer.

(5) Measure AC. This gives the Ground Speed.

Example 3. Given: Air Speed   90 Kts
               Course   208° T
               Wind   095/20 K

To find Track and Ground Speed

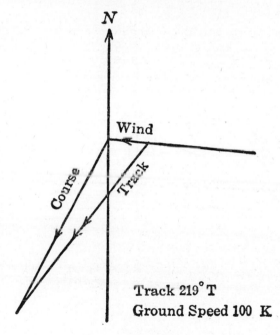

Track 219° T
Ground Speed 100 K

Fig. 163.

For Exercises see pp. 306–308.

CHAPTER 29

CENTER OF GRAVITY

If a rod of uniform thickness is supported by two spring balances at its ends (Fig. 164) so that each balance gives the same reading, and if a weight is hung on the rod anywhere except at its center, the spring balance nearer to the weight will record a heavier "thrust" than will the other; *but wherever the weight is hung on the rod the sum of the additional thrusts on both balances will always equal the weight itself.*

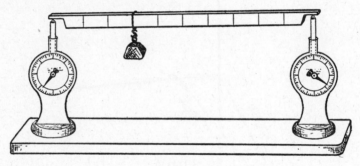

Fig. 164.

The same will be true no matter how many weights are hung along the rod—*their total weight will always equal the sum of the additional thrusts recorded by the spring balances.*

Every object is made up of innumerable tiny little bits, each of which has its own weight (by which we now know we mean the "pull" of the force of gravity vertically downwards).

The sum of all these tiny gravitational forces may be regarded as being concentrated into one bigger gravitational force which we call the weight of the object and which we may regard as operating from one point in the object known as the *Center of Gravity*.

The Center of Gravity of a rod like the one shown in Fig. 164 can be found by marking the spot on it where a weight causes *the same extra thrust on both balances—in other words, it is the point where the rod balances.*

The Center of Gravity may not be the geometrical center of the rod unless the rod is symmetrical and of the same density throughout. Balance a fountain-pen on a pencil. The point at which it balances will be nearer the "thick end" of the pen and will be its Center of Gravity. Sometimes the Center of Gravity is outside the object, *e.g.* in a cardboard or metal letter **L**.

The Center of Gravity of a triangular piece of cardboard may be found as follows:—

Rub colored chalk on a plumb-line. Hang the plumb-line on a hook. Fasten pieces of thread to two corners of the cardboard and tie each successively to the hook, allowing the chalk

Fɪɢ. 165.

on the plumb-line to mark the cardboard each time. Pencil in the faint chalk marks (Fig. 165). The Center of Gravity must lie on both, therefore the point where they intersect will be the Center of Gravity of the triangular piece of cardboard.

If a thread is fastened to the third corner of the triangle, the plumb-line mark will go through the same point of intersection (Fig. 166).

Fig. 166.

These "plumb-line" lines on a triangle are called *Medians*.

The following important facts about medians should be noted:—

(1) The median from any corner of a △ bisects the opposite side.

(2) The medians meet at a point called the Center of Gravity. In Geometry this is called the Centroid.

(3) This point is $\frac{1}{3}$ up each median (starting at the end bisecting the side of the △).

To find geometrically the Center of Gravity of thin pieces of card-board, etc., in the shape of (a) *Triangle*, (b) *Parallelogram*, (c) *Circle*.

(a) *Triangle*.—Draw any two medians. Where they intersect is Center of Gravity.

(b) *Parallelogram*.—Center of Gravity is point of intersection of the diagonals.

(c) *Circle*.—Center of Gravity is the geometrical center of the circle. (If center unknown, draw any two chords not parallel and bisect them perpendicularly. The point of intersection of the bisectors will be the center of the ⊙ and its Center of Gravity.)

If a rod hangs balanced at its middle point C, and if equal weights are hung at equal distances from C, the rod will remain balanced.

If two unequal weights are hung on it in such a way that each weight multiplied by its distance from C *gives the same product, the rod will still remain balanced.* (This is the reason why a little boy can balance a bigger boy on a see-saw, provided he gets farther away from the Center of Gravity of the see-saw than is the heavier boy.)

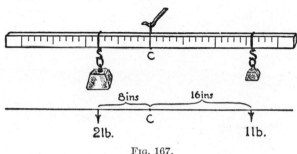

Fig. 167.

Thus, in Fig. 167, since $2 \times 8 = 16 \times 1$, we know a rod would balance at C with a weight of 2 lb. hung 8 in. from C and a weight of 1 lb. hung 16 in. from C.

Moment of a Force with Respect to a Point

The product of a weight and its distance from the point of balance is called the *Moment* of the force represented by that weight.

If the sum of the moments of all the forces on one side of the Center of Gravity of a rod is equal to the sum of the moments of all forces on the other side of the Center of Gravity, the rod is balanced at its Center of Gravity.

To find the Center of Gravity (i.e. *the point of balance*) *of a rod bearing several weights.*

Suppose three weights m lb., n lb., and p lb. are hanging on a rod, their distances from one end of the rod being a in., b in., and c in. respectively.

Let the rod balance (*i.e.* have its Center of Gravity) x in. from A.

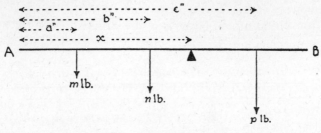

FIG. 168.

Now the distance of weight m from C.G. $= x-a$ in.
　the distance of weight n from C.G. $= x-b$ in.
　the distance of weight p from C.G. $= c-x$ in.

∴ The moment of weight m is $m(x-a)$
　The moment of weight n is $n(x-b)$
　The moment of weight p is $p(c-x)$

Since the rod is to balance,

$$m(x-a)+n(x-b) = p(c-x)$$
$$\therefore \ mx-ma+nx-nb = pc-px$$
$$\therefore \ mx+nx+px = ma+nb+pc$$
$$\therefore \ x(m+n+p) = ma+nb+pc$$

$$\therefore \ x = \frac{ma+nb+pc}{m+n+p} = \text{distance of C.G. from A}$$

That is, *to find the Center of Gravity of a rod bearing any number of weights, multiply each weight by its distance from one end of rod; add these products; divide the sum by the sum of the weights.*

Example 1. A uniform 3 ft. rod weighing 12 lb. has four weights of 2, 4, 6, and 8 lb. hung on it at intervals of 1 foot. Find where it will balance (*i.e.* find the Center of Gravity when these weights are attached).

Before the weights are attached, the Center of Gravity is at the center of the rod, where the weight of the rod (12 lb.) operates (Fig. 169).

When the weights are added, the Center of Gravity is clearly shifted, since the weights are unequal and are at equal distances along the rod. The weight of the rod will still exert its thrust at the center of the rod, though this point will no longer be the Center of Gravity.

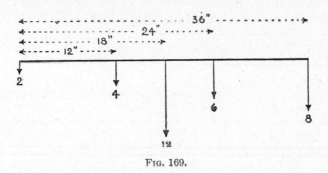

Fig. 169.

∴ Distance of Center of Gravity from left-hand end of rod

$$= \frac{(2\times0)+(4\times12)+(12\times18)+(6\times24)+(8\times36)}{2+4+12+6+8}$$

$$= \frac{0+48+216+144+288}{32} = \frac{696}{32}$$

$$= 21\tfrac{3}{4}'' \text{ from 2 lb. weight}\leftarrow$$

Example 2. Find how far the 8 lb. weight must be moved in (last example, Fig. 169) so that the rod may balance (*i.e.* have its Center of Gravity) at its own center.

Given Center of Gravity is 18″ from left-hand end of rod.

$$\therefore\ 18 = \frac{(2\times0)+(4\times12)+(12\times18)+(6\times24)+(8\times p)}{2+4+12+6+8}$$

$$\therefore\ 18 = \frac{408+8p}{32}$$

$$\therefore\ 18\times32 = 408+8p$$

$$\therefore\ 8p = 576-408$$

$$\therefore\ p = \frac{168}{8} = 21''\ \text{from 2 lb. weight}$$

i.e. the 8 lb. weight must be moved 15″ nearer to 2 lb. weight←

For Exercises see pp. 308–309.

CHAPTER 30

LOGARITHMS

By the use of logarithms we have a ready method of turning multiplication and division of large numbers into addition and subtraction, and of finding square root, cube root, etc. by simple division.

We know that $10 = 10^1$ and $100 = 10^2$ and so any number between 10 and 100, *i.e.* between 10^1 and 10^2, must equal 10 to the power 1 point "something."

Similarly, since $1000 = 10^3$ then *e.g.* $467 = 10^{2.\ \text{"something,"}}$
and since $10,000 = 10^4$ then *e.g.* $2399 = 10^{3.\ \text{"something,"}}$
and so on.

We say that 1 is the logarithm of   10
2 is the logarithm of   100
3 is the logarithm of   1000
4 is the logarithm of 10000, etc.

It is therefore clear that 1. "something" is the logarithm of   92
2. "something" is the logarithm of   467
3. "something" is the logarithm of 2399,
etc.

All this is more shortly written down thus:
$1 = \log 10$ 1. ...(*i.e.* 1 point something) $- \log 92$
$2 = \log 100$ 2. ...(*i.e.* 2 point something) $= \log 467$
$3 = \log 1000$ 3. ...(*i.e.* 3 point something) $= \log 2399$
and so on.

Every logarithm consists of two parts—the whole-number part called the "characteristic," and the decimal part called the "mantissa."

Example. The logarithm of 467 is 2.66932.

characteristic mantissa

We see that the whole-number part of each of these logs can easily be written down, as it is always one less than the number of digits in the number concerned.

Look at Ch. 7 and you will see that $x^0 = 1$

$\therefore 10^0 = 1$ and so the logarithm of 1 = 0.

We can now find the whole-number part (*i.e.* the characteristic) of the log of any number from 1 upwards, by simply counting one less than the number of digits in the number concerned.

Example. The characteristic of log 3649 is 3, of log 567 is 2, of log 7 is 0, of log 41279 is 4.

Characteristics of Decimals

We saw (Ch. 8) that

$10^{-1} = .1$	$\therefore \log .1 = -1$ (written $\bar{1}$)
Similarly $10^{-2} = .01$	$\therefore \log .01 = \bar{2}$
$10^{-3} = .001$	$\therefore \log .001 = \bar{3}$
$10^{-4} = .0001$	$\therefore \log .0001 = \bar{4}$
$10^{-5} = .00001$	$\therefore \log .00001 = \bar{5}.$

We see therefore that in the case of a decimal, the characteristic is always negative and is 1 more than the number of zeros immediately following the decimal point.

Note that, as shown above, the minus sign of the characteristic is written above the latter, since the mantissa is always positive.

Note the difference between

$\bar{2}.30546 \quad (= -2 + .30546)$

and $-2.30546 \quad (= -2.30546$, the decimal also being negative)

A minus written over a number is sometimes called "bar" ($\bar{3}$ is sometimes read "bar three").

Remember that this minus characteristic only applies to a decimal which has no whole number before it.

Thus,

$$\log .236 = \bar{1} + \text{some decimal}$$
$$\log .002913 = \bar{3} + \text{some decimal}$$

but

$$\log 81.236 = 1 + \text{some decimal}$$
$$\log 1.002913 = 0 + \text{some decimal}$$

To Find the Mantissa of a Logarithm

The decimal part of the log of every number has been worked out and is to be found in log tables, a specimen page of which is shown on page 228.

Study this table and note

(a) Decimal points are omitted for clearness.

(b) To save space, the first two decimal places are printed only in the column headed 0 and are not repeated in subsequent columns. If an asterisk (*) occurs, it means we must take these first two decimal figures from *below*. If no asterisk occurs we take them from *alongside or above*.

To find the log of a number consisting of less than 5 significant figures.

e.g. Find log 2398.

Characteristic $\boxed{3}$

Mantissa (a) Look at 239 (first three digits) under column "N."

(b) Run your eye along that line until you reach the figures under column 8 (the last digit of our number). This gives $\boxed{985}$, the last three digits of the required mantissa.

200–250

N.	0	1	2	3	4	5	6	7	8	9
200	30 103	125	146	168	190	211	233	253	276	298
01	320	341	363	384	406	428	449	471	492	514
02	535	557	578	600	621	643	664	685	707	728
03	750	771	792	814	835	856	878	899	920	942
04	963	984	*006	*027	*048	*069	*091	*112	*133	*154
05	31 175	197	218	239	260	281	302	323	345	366
06	387	408	429	450	471	492	513	534	555	576
07	597	618	639	660	681	702	723	744	765	785
08	806	827	848	869	890	911	931	952	973	994
09	32 015	035	056	077	098	118	139	160	181	201
210	222	243	263	284	305	325	346	366	387	408
11	428	449	469	490	510	531	552	572	593	613
12	634	654	675	695	715	736	756	777	797	818
13	838	858	879	899	919	940	960	980	*001	*021
14	33 041	062	082	102	122	143	163	183	203	224
15	244	264	284	304	325	345	365	385	405	425
16	445	465	486	506	526	546	566	586	606	626
17	646	666	686	706	726	746	766	786	806	826
18	846	866	885	905	925	945	965	985	*005	*025
19	34 044	064	084	104	124	143	163	183	203	223
220	242	262	282	301	321	341	361	380	400	420
21	439	459	479	498	518	537	557	577	596	616
22	635	655	674	694	713	733	.753	772	792	811
23	830	850	869	889	908	928	947	967	986	*005
24	35 025	044	064	083	102	122	141	160	180	199
25	218	238	257	276	295	315	334	353	372	392
26	411	430	449	468	488	507	526	545	564	583
27	603	622	641	660	679	698	717	736	755	774
28	793	813	832	851	870	889	908	927	946	965
29	984	*003	*021	*040	*059	*078	*097	*116	*135	*154
230	36 173	192	211	229	248	267	286	305	324	342
31	361	380	399	418	436	455	474	493	511	530
32	549	568	586	605	624	642	661	680	698	717
33	736	754	773	791	810	829	847	866	884	903
34	922	940	959	977	996	*014	*033	*051	*070	*088
35	37 107	125	144	162	181	199	218	236	254	273
36	291	310	328	346	365	383	401	420	438	457
37	475	493	511	530	548	566	585	603	621	639
38	658	676	694	712	731	749	767	785	803	822
39	840	858	876	894	912	931	949	967	985	*003
240	38 021	039	057	075	093	112	130	148	166	184
41	202	220	238	256	274	292	310	328	346	364
42	382	399	417	435	453	471	489	507	525	543
43	561	578	596	614	632	650	668	686	703	721
44	739	757	775	792	810	828	846	863	881	899
45	917	934	952	970	987	*005	*023	*041	*058	*076
46	39 094	111	129	146	164	182	199	217	235	252
47	270	287	305	322	340	358	375	393	410	428
48	445	463	480	498	515	533	550	568	585	602
49	620	637	655	672	690	707	724	742	759	777
250	794	811	829	846	863	881	898	915	933	950
N.	0	1	2	3	4	5	6	7	8	9

Prop. Pts.

	22	21
1	2.2	2.1
2	4.4	4.2
3	6.6	6.3
4	8.8	8.4
5	11.0	10.5
6	13.2	12.6
7	15.4	14.7
8	17.6	16.8
9	19.8	18.9

	20
1	2.0
2	4.0
3	6.0
4	8.0
5	10.0
6	12.0
7	14.0
8	16.0
9	18.0

	19
1	1.9
2	3.8
3	5.7
4	7.6
5	9.5
6	11.4
7	13.3
8	15.2
9	17.1

	18
1	1.8
2	3.6
3	5.4
4	7.2
5	9.0
6	10.8
7	12.6
8	14.4
9	16.2

	17
1	1.7
2	3.4
3	5.1
4	6.8
5	8.5
6	10.2
7	11.9
8	13.6
9	15.3

(c) Since in this case there is no asterisk, the first two digits of the mantissa will be found either alongside or above, under column 0 (here they are above and are $\boxed{37}$).

$$\therefore \ \log 2398 = 3.37985\leftarrow$$

It is now very easy to write down the logs of any numbers having 2398 as their digits, since the only differences between their logs will lie in their characteristics.

$$e.g. \quad \log 239.8 = 2.37985$$
$$\log 23.98 = 1.37985$$
$$\log 2.398 = 0.37985$$
$$\log .2398 = \overline{1}.37985$$
$$\log .02398 = \overline{2}.37985$$
and so on.

Similarly
$$\log 2000 = 3.30103$$
$$\log 200 = 2.30103$$
$$\log 20 = 1.30103$$
$$\log 2 = 0.30103$$
$$\log 20000 = 4.30103$$
and so on.

To find the log of a number consisting of more than four significant figures.

This cannot be found directly from our tables, so we must *interpolate i.e.* calculate the value of our log from its position between two known logs.

Example: Find log 2.2978.

2.29**78** lies between 2.29**70** and 2.29**80**. The logs of 2.2970 and 2.2980 will be respectively the same as the logs of 2.297 and 2.298.

Now the last digit of 2.2978 is $\frac{8}{10}$ of the way from 0 to 10.

$\therefore$ the final decimal places of the log of 2.29**78** will be approximately $\frac{8}{10}$ of the way between the final decimal places of the logs of 2.29**70** and 2.29**80**.

Now   log 2.29**70** = 0.36116
                log 2.29**80** = 0.36135
                difference = 0.00019
Now $\frac{8}{10}$ of .00019 = .000152
                         = .00015 approx.
∴ log 2.29**78** is .00015 greater than log 2.29**70**
Now   log 2.29**70** = 0.36116
                add   0.00015
       ∴ log 2.29**78** = 0.36131←

Time may be saved when interpolating if use is made of the *Proportional Parts* printed on the margin of the tables.

Thus, in the last example, having noted the fraction $\frac{8}{10}$ and the difference .00019, we may turn to the marginal column headed Prop. Pts. (which ignores the three zeros of the mantissas) and find the little column headed 19. Under this will be found the various tenths of 19 worked out for us. We see that $\frac{8}{10}$ of 19 is given as 15.2, the result we obtained above by interpolation.

To find the number which corresponds to a given logarithm.
Here we reverse the previous process.

Example: If log x = 2.34171, find x.

   (*a*) The characteristic 2 tells us that our answer will consist of a whole number of three digits. The characteristic has now done its work and may be ignored.

   (*b*) We now find in the table the mantissa next smaller than .34171, namely .34163. We note the difference between them, namely .00008.

   (*c*) The digits under the N column and at the top of our .34163 column are $\boxed{2196}$.

   (*d*) The difference between .34163 and the next higher mantissa in the table is .00020. Looking at the Prop.

Pts. margin under "20" we see that **8** is $\frac{4}{10}$ of 20 ∴ our last digit is $\boxed{4}$

$$\therefore x = 219.64\leftarrow$$

Labor-saving uses of logarithms

(1) Since $10^m \times 10^n = 10^{m+n}$ (see Chapter 7); to multiply any numbers, write them in log form and *add.*

(2) Since $10^m \div 10^n = 10^{m-n}$; to divide any two numbers, write them in log form and subtract the log of the divisor from the log of the dividend.

(3) Since $(10^m)^n = 10^{mn}$; to raise any number to a higher power, write the number in log form and multiply by that power.

(4) Since $\sqrt[n]{10^n} = 10^{\frac{n}{m}}$, to find any root (square root, cube root, etc.) of a number write the number in log form and divide by the required root.

Example 1.   .0654×41.92×2695

$$\log .0654 = \overline{2}.81558$$
$$\log 41.92 = 1.62242$$
$$\log 2695 = 3.43056$$

By addition 3.86856
∴ Product is 7388.5←

Example 2. Divide 0.026 by 158.3.

[We shall have to bear in mind that $\overline{D}.11497$ means $-2+.41497$. We shall also have to remember the rule for subtraction ("change the sign of bottom line and then proceed as in addition." See Chapter 8.)]

$$\log 0.026 = \overline{2}.41497$$
$$\log 158.3 = 2.19948$$

By subtraction $\overline{4}.21549$
∴ Quotient is .0001642←

Example 3. Find the square of 314.2.

$$\log 314.2 = 2.49721$$
$$\therefore \ \log (314.2)^2 = 4.99442 \text{ (multiplying by 2)}$$
$$\therefore \ (314.2)^2 = 98721 \leftarrow$$

(This answer is only approximate as we worked with 5-figure log tables.)

Example 4. Find the square root of 314.2.

$$\log 314.2 = 2.49721$$
$$\therefore \ \log \sqrt{314.2} = 1.24861 \text{ (dividing by 2)}$$
$$\therefore \ \sqrt{314.2} = 17.726 \text{ approx.} \leftarrow$$

Example 5. Find the cube root of 314.2.

$$\log 314.2 = 2.49721$$
$$\therefore \ \log \sqrt[3]{314.2} = 0.83240 \text{ (dividing by 3)}$$
$$\therefore \ \sqrt[3]{314.2} = 6.7981 \text{ approx.} \leftarrow$$

We sometimes have to divide a negative characteristic followed by a positive mantissa by numbers such as 2, 3, . . .

For example, divide $\bar{1}.3264$ by 2.

To avoid the complication of "carrying" a minus quantity to a plus decimal you are advised to use the following manipulation:

(1) Increase the negative whole number to the smallest negative whole number divisible by your divisor.

(2) Balance matters by making a similar *positive* addition to your positive mantissa.

e.g. (a)
$$\bar{1}.3264 \div 2$$
$$= (\bar{2} + 1.3264) \div 2$$
$$= \bar{1}.6632 \leftarrow$$

(b)
$$\bar{1}.3364 \div 3$$
$$= (\bar{3} + 2.3364) \div 3$$
$$= \bar{1}.7788 \leftarrow$$

(c)
$$\bar{2}.3364 \div 3$$
$$= (\bar{3} + 1.3364) \div 3$$
$$= \bar{1}.4455 \leftarrow$$

Example 6. If the volume of a sphere is 49.56 cc., find its radius in cm.

The volume of a sphere $= \frac{4}{3}\pi r^3 (\pi = 3.1416)$

$$\therefore r^3 = \frac{\text{Vol. of sphere}}{\frac{4}{3}\pi} = \frac{3 \times 49.56}{4 \times 3.1416}$$

$$\therefore r = \sqrt[3]{\frac{3 \times 49.56}{4 \times 3.1416}} = \sqrt[3]{\frac{148.68}{12.566}}$$

$$\therefore \log r = \frac{1}{3}(\log 148.68 - \log 12.566)$$

$$\log 148.68 = 2.17225$$

$$\log 12.566 = 1.09920$$

$$\therefore \log \text{quotient} = \overline{1.07305}$$

$$\therefore \log \sqrt[3]{\text{quotient}} = 0.35768$$

$$r = 2.2787 \text{ cm.} \leftarrow$$

This chapter is much less difficult than it sounds. As the Dodo said in *Alice in Wonderland* "the best way to explain it is to do it."

For Exercises see p. 309.

CHAPTER 31

TRIGONOMETRICAL RATIOS: THE SOLUTION OF TRIANGLES

The Meaning of "Projection"

Suppose a ruler is held parallel to a plane or flat surface, and suppose there is a light a great distance away (so that its rays are parallel as they strike the ruler) *and directly over the ruler*.

The shadow cast by the ruler on the plane will be the same length as the ruler itself. If the ruler is now turned through an angle of 90° until it is at right angles to the plane, its shadow will get less and less until it equals only the thickness of the ruler.

Now substitute a geometrical *line* for the ruler (and remember that a line has no thickness theoretically) and substitute the mathematical term "projection" for "shadow," and we get the following results:—

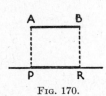

Fig. 170.   Fig. 171.   Fig. 172.

Projection PR = AB.   Projection PR < AB.   Projection = 0.

If the line is touching the plane, we get:—

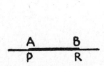

Trigonometrical Ratios of Angles greater than 90°

Having grasped the meaning of sin, cos, tan, etc., for acute angles (see Ch. 21) we must now discover the meaning of the six trigonometrical ratios of angles greater than acute angles.

To do this we must consider a line OR revolving round a point. This point is the "origin," or point of intersection of the "axes," with which we are familiar.

If OR revolves in an anti-clockwise direction, the angle it passes through is considered positive (+). If the direction is clockwise, the angle is negative (−).

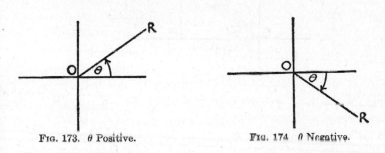

Fig. 173. θ Positive.   Fig. 174. θ Negative.

We shall now have to consider the *Projection* of OR on the horizontal axis as OR revolves in an anti-clockwise direction as in Fig. 173. When OR lies along the horizontal axis its projection equals OR in length. As OR revolves, the length of the projection gradually diminishes until, when OR is at right angles to its original position, the length of its projection is 0. As OR continues to revolve, the reverse process takes place until, when OR is again on the horizontal axis its projection is again equal in length to OR, though in all these positions in the "second quadrant" (*i.e.* when θ is between 90° and 180°) the projection is negative in sign, since it points to the left of the vertical axis.

Now consider the changes in length of the perpendicular from R *to the horizontal axis as* OR *revolves from 0° to 180°.*

When $\theta = 0°$ the perpendicular $= 0$.
When $\theta = 90°$ "   " $= $ OR.
When $\theta = 180°$ "   " $= 0$.

The perpendicular in all the positions from 0° to 180° will be positive, since it points upwards from the horizontal axis.

We can now substitute better mathematical terms for "Opposite," "Adjacent," "Hypotenuse" in defining the trigonometrical ratios.

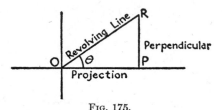

Fig. 175.

[The "Revolving Line" is also known as the "distance."
The "Perpendicular" is also known as the "ordinate."
The "Projection" is also known as the "abscissa."
(The terms "ordinate" and "abscissa" are of course the respective distances of the point R from the horizontal and the vertical axes. The "distance" is the distance of the point R from the origin O.)]

$$\sin \theta = \frac{\text{Perpendicular}}{\text{Revolving line}} \qquad \operatorname{cosec} \theta = \frac{\text{Revolving line}}{\text{Perpendicular}}$$

$$\cos \theta = \frac{\text{Projection}}{\text{Revolving line}} \qquad \sec \theta = \frac{\text{Revolving line}}{\text{Projection}}$$

$$\tan \theta = \frac{\text{Perpendicular}}{\text{Projection}} \qquad \cot \theta = \frac{\text{Projection}}{\text{Perpendicular}}$$

By using these definitions we can find the trigonometrical ratios of angles greater than 90°, provided we bear in mind that lines pointing to the left of the vertical axis or downwards from the horizontal axis are negative.

(The revolving line is always positive.)
Let OR revolve through an obtuse angle θ.

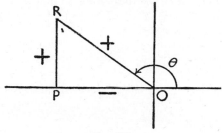

FIG. 176.

We see that $\sin \theta = \dfrac{PR}{OR}$

but $\cos \theta = -\dfrac{OP}{OR}$ since OP is negative

and $\tan \theta = -\dfrac{PR}{OP}$ since OP is negative.

Similarly we can find these ratios for angles of any magnitude, by revolving OR farther round O through the other quadrants. We shall find that:

All ratios in the 1st Quadrant are $+$
Only the sine and reciprocal in the 2nd Quadrant are $+$
Only the tangent and reciprocal in the 3rd Quadrant are $+$
Only the cosine and reciprocal in the 4th Quadrant are $+$

$$
\begin{array}{c|c}
\left.\begin{array}{l}\sin \\ \csc\end{array}\right\} + & \text{all} + \\
\hline
\left.\begin{array}{l}\tan \\ \cot\end{array}\right\} + & \left.\begin{array}{l}\cos \\ \sec\end{array}\right\} +
\end{array}
$$

[Memorize by the word "Allsintancos."]

To find the trigonometrical ratios of 0°, 90°.

(1) If $\theta = 0°$, OP = OR, PR = 0, therefore:—

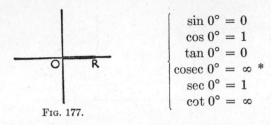

FIG. 177.

$$
\begin{cases}
\sin 0° = 0 \\
\cos 0° = 1 \\
\tan 0° = 0 \\
\operatorname{cosec} 0° = \infty \;* \\
\sec 0° = 1 \\
\cot 0° = \infty
\end{cases}
$$

(2) If $\theta = 90°$, OP = 0, PR = OR, therefore:—

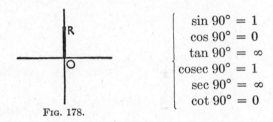

FIG. 178.

$$
\begin{cases}
\sin 90° = 1 \\
\cos 90° = 0 \\
\tan 90° = \infty \\
\operatorname{cosec} 90° = 1 \\
\sec 90° = \infty \\
\cot 90° = 0
\end{cases}
$$

Note carefully that—
    As the size of an angle increases from 0° to 90° its sine increases from 0 to 1 but its cosine decreases from 1 to 0. Verify this from the tables of "Natural sines" and "Natural cosines."

In using "Proportional Parts" columns in the "Natural" or Log. tables, remember that the bigger the angle the bigger the sine; the bigger the angle the *smaller* the cosine.

* ∞ (shorthand for "infinity"). The shorter the perpendicular (ordinate) the larger will be the value of the fraction $\dfrac{\text{length of revolving line}}{\text{length of perpendicular}}$. As the value of this denominator approaches very near to zero the value of the fraction approaches "infinity."

To prove that—

$\sin (180° - \theta) = \sin \theta$
$\cos (180° - \theta) = -\cos \theta$
$\tan (180° - \theta) = -\tan \theta$

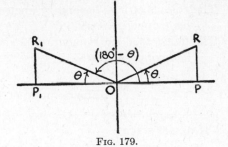

FIG. 179.

Let OR revolve first through an angle θ, then let it start again and revolve through $180° - \theta$. By proving $\triangle$ ORP $\equiv$ $\triangle$ OR$_1$P$_1$ (SAA) we get

$$OR_1 = OR \text{ in length and both are } +$$
$$P_1R_1 = PR \text{ " " " " " } +$$
$$OP_1 = OP \text{ " " but OP}_1 \text{ is } -$$

$$\therefore \sin (180° - \theta) \left[= \frac{P_1R_1}{OR_1} = \frac{PR}{OR} \right] = \sin \theta$$

$$\cos (180° - \theta) \left[= \frac{-OP_1}{OR_1} = -\frac{OP}{OR} \right] = -\cos \theta$$

$$\tan (180° - \theta) \left[= \frac{P_1R_1}{-OP_1} = -\frac{PR}{OP} \right] = -\tan \theta$$

These results are most important as they enable us to find the trigo-nometrical ratios of obtuse angles from the "Natural" tables for acute angles. *E.g.*

Find cos 140°.

140° = (180° − 40°) and cos (180° − 40°) = cos 40° with the sign changed.

Now cos 40° = .76604 $\therefore$ cos (180° − 40°) = −.76604

i.e. cos 140° = −.76604←

We see then that:

The sines of supplementary angles are equal in magnitude and have the same sign.

The cosines of supplementary angles are equal in magnitude but have opposite signs.

The tangents of supplementary angles are equal in magnitude but have opposite signs.

The Solution of Triangles

If we are given:

      (*a*) the 3 sides,

or (*b*) 2 sides and the angle between them,

or (*c*) 1 side and any 2 angles,

or (*d*) 2 sides and the angle opposite one of them,

we can "solve" the triangle, *i.e.* find all the other sides and/or angles.

To do this we make use of one or more of the following formulas:—

$$(1)\quad A+B+C = 180°$$

$$(2)\quad \cos A = \frac{b^2+c^2-a^2}{2bc} \text{ etc.}$$

$$(3)\quad \frac{a}{\sin A} = \frac{b}{\sin B} \text{ etc.}$$

We shall proceed to prove formulas (2) and (3) as they are of great importance.

To prove that—

$$\cos A = \frac{b^2+c^2-a^2}{2bc}$$

$$\cos B = \frac{c^2+a^2-b^2}{2ca}$$

$$\cos C = \frac{a^2+b^2-c^2}{2ab}$$

Case 1. **When C is acute**

BC = BD+DC

Now $\dfrac{BD}{AB}$ = cos B $\therefore$ BD = AB cos B

and $\dfrac{DC}{AC}$ = cos C $\therefore$ DC = AC cos C

$\therefore\ a = c \cos B + b \cos C$

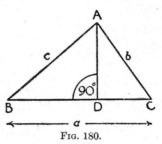

FIG. 180.

Case 2. **When C is obtuse**

BC = BD− DC

Now $\dfrac{BD}{AB}$ = cos B $\therefore$ BD = AB cos B

and $\dfrac{DC}{AC}$ = cos (180°−C) = −cos C

$\therefore$ DC = AC(−cos C) = −AC cos C

$\therefore$ BD−DC = AB cos B+AC cos C

$\therefore\ a = c \cos B + b \cos C$

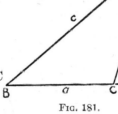

FIG. 181.

We see, then, that for acute or obtuse angles,

$$a = b \cos C + c \cos B \ \ldots \ldots \ (1)$$

Similarly, $b = a \cos C + c \cos A \ \ldots \ldots \ (2)$

and $c = a \cos B + b \cos A \ \ldots \ldots \ (3)$

Multiplying throughout in (1) by a, in (2) by b, in (3) by c:

$$a^2 = ab \cos C + ac \cos B \ \ldots \ldots \ (1)$$

$$b^2 = ab \cos C + bc \cos A \ \ldots \ldots \ (2)$$

$$c^2 = ac \cos B + bc \cos A \ \ldots \ldots \ (3)$$

Adding together (1) and (2) and subtracting (3):

$$a^2 + b^2 - c^2 = 2ab \cos C$$

$$\therefore \cos C = \frac{a^2 + b^2 - c^2}{2ab}$$

$$\text{Similarly, } \cos B = \frac{c^2 + a^2 - b^2}{2ca}$$

$$\text{and } \cos A = \frac{b^2 + c^2 - a^2}{2bc}$$

To memorize these formulas, place a, b, c on a circle, as in Fig. 182.

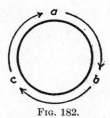

Fig. 182.

Bearing in mind that the last term of the numerator is always *minus* and that the denominator always has the numerical coefficient 2, we can write down these three formulas by simply "going round the circle" (using "a, b, c" for sides or angles). Thus:—

"$\cos A = b^2 + c^2 - a^2$ over **2bc**"
"$\cos B = c^2 + a^2 - b^2$ over **2ca**"
"$\cos C = a^2 + b^2 - c^2$ over **2ab**"

NOTE.—As these formulas lead to complicated working, it is wiser to use **Haversine formulas** if *Inmun's Haversine Tables* are available (as they are for navigators).

$$\text{Versine A} = 1-\cos A.$$

$$\text{Haversine A}(= \text{"Half Versine" A}) = \frac{1-\cos A}{2}$$

The previous formulas then become:

$$\text{Hav A} = \frac{(s-b)(s-c)}{bc} \left.\begin{array}{l} \\ \\ \\ \\ \end{array}\right\}$$

$$\text{Hav B} = \frac{(s-c)(s-a)}{ca} \quad \text{where } s = \tfrac{1}{2}(a+b+c).$$

$$\text{Hav C} = \frac{(s-a)(s-b)}{ab}$$

To prove that—

$$\boxed{\frac{a}{\sin A} = \frac{b}{\sin B} = \frac{c}{\sin C}.}$$

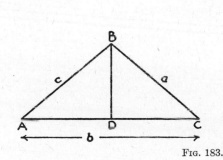
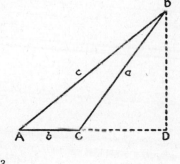

FIG. 183.

$\dfrac{BD}{AB} = \sin A \;\; \therefore BD = AB \sin A$

$\dfrac{BD}{BC} = \sin C \;\; \therefore BD = BC \sin C$

$\therefore AB \sin A = BC \sin C$

$\dfrac{BD}{AB} = \sin A \;\; \therefore BD = AB \sin A$

$\dfrac{BD}{BC} = \sin (180°-C) = \sin C$

$\therefore BD = BC \sin C$

$\therefore AB \sin A = BC \sin C$

$\therefore$ in either case   AB sin A = BC sin C

i.e. c sin A = a sin C

$$\therefore \frac{a}{\sin A} = \frac{c}{\sin C}$$

Similarly, it can be proved that either of these ratios equals $\frac{b}{\sin B}$.

Therefore
$$\boxed{\frac{a}{\sin A} = \frac{b}{\sin B} = \frac{c}{\sin C}}$$

[In logarithmic form these formulas will become:

log a = log b+log sin A−log sin B

log b = log a+log sin B−log sin A

log c = log a+log sin C−log sin A

To memorize:—

"*ab*AB"

"*ba*BA"

"*ca*CA"

(remembering last term always minus),

but it is safer to work from $\dfrac{a}{\sin A} = \dfrac{b}{\sin B}$ etc. and turn into log form.]

Solution of Triangles

For the Solution of Triangles you are advised to follow the rules given below:

Data:	Solve △ by using:	
SSS	$\cos A = \dfrac{b^2+c^2-a^2}{2bc}$ etc. [or Hav $A = \dfrac{(s-b)(s-c)}{bc}$ etc.]	
SAS	(1) $\cos A = \dfrac{b^2+c^2-a^2}{2bc}$ (2) $\dfrac{a}{\sin A} = \dfrac{b}{\sin B}$ etc. (3) $A+B+C = 180°$	
SAA	(1) $A+B+C = 180°$ (2) $\dfrac{a}{\sin A} = \dfrac{b}{\sin B}$ etc.	
SSA	$\dfrac{a}{\sin A} = \dfrac{b}{\sin B}$ etc.	*N.B.*—If the given angle is opposite the *smaller* of the two given sides you must find *two* solutions. (See Fig. 184.)

Note on the "ambiguous case," given two sides and the angle opposite one of them.

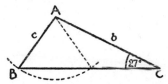 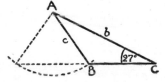

Fig. 184.

Suppose $c = 1''$
$b = 1.8''$
$C = 27°$

Since the given angle C is opposite the smaller given side we get the *two* triangles in Fig. 184, either of which satisfies the given conditions.

In working this case, therefore, you must calculate B (acute) and B (obtuse), remembering that sin B = sin (180°−B).

Application of Logarithms to Solution of Triangles

sin 10° = .17365 (from table of Natural Sines)

∴ log sin 10° = log .17365 = $\bar{1}$.23967. There is, however, no need to work this out, for it has been done for us and the logs of all trigonometrical ratios of all angles are available under Log sin, Log cosine, etc., tables.

These logs are precisely like the logs of ordinary numbers and can be used in conjunction with such logs.

Since many of the trigonometrical ratios are less than 1 (*i.e.* decimals), their logarithms have negative characteristics. To avoid the inconvenience of printing these "bar" signs over all the characteristics, some tables increase each log by 10.

e.g. Log sin 10° = 10+log sin 10° = 10+$\bar{1}$.23967
= 9.23967

If such tables are used, this 10 must be taken away from the given characteristic to get the true log.

Example. Solve △ ABC, given that a = 681 feet, c = 243 feet, B = 50°42'. Draw a figure roughly to scale:

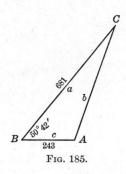

Fig. 185.

Obviously we cannot use the simpler sine formula, so we must fall back on the cosine formula.

Now $\cos B = \dfrac{c^2 + a^2 - b^2}{2ca}$

$\therefore\; b^2 = c^2 + a^2 - 2ca \cos B$

Letter or Number		Log	Number	
c	243	2.38561		
c^2		4.77122	59049	
a	681	2.83315		
a^2		5.66630	463770 *	
			522819	$= c^2 + a^2$
	2	0.30103		
c	243	2.38561 †		
a	681	2.83315 †		
$\cos B$	50° 42′	$\overline{1}$.80166		
$2ca \cos B$		5.32145	209624	
$c^2 + a^2 - 2ca \cos B$		5.49581	313195 ‡	$= b^2$
$\therefore\; b =$		2.74791	559.63 ←	

Now $\dfrac{a}{\sin A} = \dfrac{b}{\sin B}$

$\therefore\; \dfrac{681}{\sin A} = \dfrac{559.63}{\sin 50° 42′}$

$\therefore\; \log \sin A = \log 681 + \log \sin 50° 42′ - \log 559.63$

$= 2.83315 + \overline{1}.88865 - 2.74791$

$= \overline{1}.97389$

$\therefore\; A = 70° 20′$, or $109° 40′$ [since $\sin A = \sin (180 - A)$]

$\therefore\; A = 109° 40′,\; C = 19° 38′,\; b = 559.63$ feet.←

For Exercises see pp. 309–310.

* Approx. only since only 5-figure log tables were used.
† Already found, above.
‡ Subtraction first, then insert log.

CHAPTER 32

CALCULATING RELATIVE GROWTH: THE IDEA BEHIND THE DIFFERENTIAL CALCULUS *

Consider △ ABC, rt. ∠'d at C. (Fig. 186).

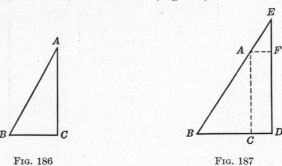

FIG. 186   FIG. 187

Now increase BC by a length CD and complete a △ similar to △ ABC (Fig. 187). We see that CA will be increased by the length FE.

It is clear that △ EAF is similar to △ ABC.

$$\therefore \frac{EF}{AF} \left(= \frac{EF}{CD} \right) = \frac{AC}{BC} \quad \cdot \quad \cdot \quad \cdot \quad (1)$$

Now let us call BC "x" and AC "y" and let us suppose the increase CD and the increase FA to be indefinitely small, *i.e.* tiny fractions of BC and CA respectively.

The "shorthand" for "a tiny fraction of" is the letter d.

* This Chapter is included for the general reader who wishes to get a very brief introduction to the idea of the Calculus.

Thus dx means "a tiny fraction of x"

dy means "a tiny fraction of y,"

and so on. (Do not imagine this means "d times x, d times y"; it does not.)

Using this new form of shorthand, Fig. 187 now becomes

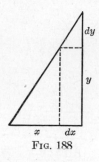

(*N.B.* We have had to exaggerate dx and dy enormously, in order to be able to see them. They are meant to be indefinitely small lengths.)

Fig. 188

From equation (1) above,

$$\frac{EF}{CD} = \frac{AC}{BC}$$

i.e. $\dfrac{dy}{dx} = \dfrac{y}{x}.$

Now suppose we know that $\angle$ B $= 60°$. Then

$$\frac{y}{x} = \tan 60° = \frac{\sqrt{3}}{1}$$

$\therefore$ in that case $\dfrac{dy}{dx} = \dfrac{\sqrt{3}}{1}$

i.e. the rate of growth of y compared with the rate of growth of x is $\sqrt{3}:1$.

The ratio $\dfrac{dy}{dx}$ is known as "the differential coefficient of y with respect to x" and is read "Dee y by dee x."

Now let us consider the growth of the area of a square as the length of its side increases.

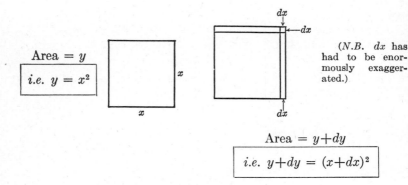

Area $= y$

i.e. $y = x^2$

x

x

dx

dx

(*N.B.* dx has had to be enormously exaggerated.)

Area $= y+dy$

i.e. $y+dy = (x+dx)^2$

Fig. 189.

It is clear from the above figures that *if x is increased by an indefinitely small amount* (not by a relatively large amount, as shown in the figure on the right) the tiny square at the right-hand top corner becomes negligible in area.

So, if dx is indefinitely small, it follows that

$$y+dy = (x+dx)^2 = x^2+2x(dx),$$

i.e. the original area x^2 plus the two thin rectangles.

$$\therefore \ y+dy = x^2+2x(dx)$$
$$\text{But} \ \ y = x^2$$

$\therefore$ by subtraction $dy = 2x(dx)$

$$\therefore \frac{dy}{dx} = 2x.$$

We have found then that if $y = x^2$, $\frac{dy}{dx} = 2x$.

N.B. It must always be remembered that dx and dy are indefinitely small, so that the tiny square is negligible.

*Now let us consider the growth in volume of a cube as the **length** of its side increases.*

Let original length   of side $= x$
"   "   volume of cube $= y$
"   new   length   of side $= x + dx$
"   "   volume of cube $= y + dy$.

Now by multiplication, $(x+dx)^3 = x^3 + 3x^2(dx) + 3x(dx)^2 + (dx)^3$. Since, however, dx is indefinitely small, $(dx)^2$ and $(dx)^3$ must be negligible (*e.g.* suppose $dx = \frac{1}{10,000}$, then $(dx)^2 = \frac{1}{100,000,000}$ and $(dx)^3 = \frac{1}{1,000,000,000,000}$).

$$\therefore (x+dx)^3 = x^3 + 3x^2(dx),$$
$$i.e. \quad y + dy = x^3 + 3x^2(dx).$$
$$\text{But} \quad y = x^3$$
$$\therefore dy = 3x^2(dx)$$

$$\therefore \frac{dy}{dx} = 3x^2.$$

We have seen then that

$$\text{if } y = x^2, \qquad \frac{dy}{dx} = 2x$$

$$\text{if } y = x^3, \qquad \frac{dy}{dx} = 3x^2$$

$$\text{Similarly, if } y = x^4, \qquad \frac{dy}{dx} = 4x^3$$

$$y = x^5, \qquad \frac{dy}{dx} = 5x^4$$

$$y = x, \qquad \frac{dy}{dx} (= 1x^0) = 1 \quad (\text{Since } x^0 = 1)$$

$$y = x^{\frac{1}{2}}, \qquad \frac{dy}{dx} = \frac{1}{2}x^{-\frac{1}{2}} = \frac{1}{2x^{\frac{1}{2}}} = \frac{1}{2\sqrt{x}}$$

$$y = x^{\frac{1}{3}}, \qquad \frac{dy}{dx} = \frac{1}{3}x^{-\frac{2}{3}} = \frac{1}{3x^{\frac{2}{3}}} = \frac{1}{3\sqrt[3]{x^2}}$$

and so forth.

Now suppose we start off with a square whose area is (x^2+5), i.e. $y = x^2+5$.

As before, $y+dy = (x+dx)^2+5$
$$= x^2+2x(dx)+(dx)^2+5.$$

Ignoring $(dx)^2$ we get

$$y+dy = x^2+2x(dx)+5$$

$$\text{But} \quad y = x^2+5$$
$$\therefore \ dy = 2x(dx)$$

$$\therefore \ \frac{dy}{dx} = 2x$$

which we see is precisely the same as the result of differentiating $y = x^2$, i.e. *we ignore any added or subtracted constant numbers (or letters) when we differentiate.*

Now consider the case where we have a numerical coefficient.

$$\boxed{\text{Suppose } y = 5x^3.}$$

As before,
$$y+dy = 5(x+dx)^3$$
$$= 5\{x^3+3x^2(dx)+3x(dx)^2+(dx)^3\}$$
$$\therefore \ y+dy = 5\{x^3+3x^2(dx)\}$$
$$\therefore \ y+dy = 5x^3+15x^2(dx)$$
$$\text{But} \quad y = 5x^3$$
$$\therefore \ dy = 15x^2(dx)$$

$$\therefore \ \frac{dy}{dx} = 15x^2$$

$$\boxed{\begin{array}{c} i.e. \text{ if } \quad y = 5x^3, \dfrac{dy}{dx} = 15x^2 \\[2mm] \text{Similarly, if} \quad y = 9x^5, \dfrac{dy}{dx} = 15x^4, \\[2mm] \text{and so forth.} \end{array}}$$

Sum or Difference

Suppose $y = (x^4+2)+(x^3-7)$,

$$\boxed{\frac{dy}{dx} = 4x^3+3x^2}$$

Similarly, if $y = (3x^9-18)-(5x^4+6)$,

$$\boxed{\frac{dy}{dx} = 27x^8-20x^3}$$

Products

$$\boxed{\text{Suppose } y = (5x^2+2)(2x^3+3)}$$

Multiplying out, $y = 10x^5+4x^3+15x^2+6$

$$\therefore \frac{dy}{dx} = 50x^4+12x^2+30x \leftarrow$$

This result can usually be obtained more easily by adding the product of $(5x^2+2)$ and $\dfrac{d(2x^3+3)}{dx}$ to the product of $(2x^3+3)$ and $\dfrac{d(5x^2+2)}{dx}$, thus:

$$\frac{dy}{dx} = (5x^2+2) \cdot \frac{d(2x^3+3)}{dx} + (2x^3+3) \cdot \frac{d(5x^2+2)}{dx}$$

$$= (5x^2+2) \times 6x^2 + (2x^3+3) \times 10x$$
$$= 30x^4+12x^2+20x^4+30x$$
$$= 50x^4+12x^2+30x \leftarrow$$

Quotients

$$\boxed{\text{Suppose } y = \frac{a}{b}}$$

where a and b stand for functions of x.

$$\text{Then } y+dy = \frac{a+da}{b+db}$$

Let us work the division sum

$$\frac{a+da}{b+db}$$

$$b+db\overline{)a + da} \qquad \left(\frac{a}{b} + \frac{da}{b} - \frac{a(db)}{b^2} - \dots\right.$$

$$a \qquad + \frac{a(db)}{b}$$

$$\overline{\quad da - \frac{a(db)}{b}\quad}$$

$$da \qquad\qquad + \frac{(da)(db)}{b}$$

$$\overline{\quad - \frac{a(db)}{b} - \frac{(da)(db)}{b}\quad}$$

$$- \frac{a(db)}{b} \qquad\qquad - \frac{a(db)^2}{b^2}$$

$$\overline{\quad - \frac{(da)(db)}{b} + \frac{a(db)^2}{b^2}\quad}$$

We may ignore the rest of the quotient and the remainder, since every term in both of them will now contain either $(db)^2$ or $(da)(db)$ or some still higher power of da and/or db.

$$\therefore\ y+dy = \frac{a}{b} + \frac{da}{b} - \frac{a(db)}{b^2}$$

$$\therefore\ y+dy = \frac{a}{b} + \frac{b(da)-a(db)}{b^2}$$

$$\text{But}\quad y = \frac{a}{b}$$

$$\therefore\ dy = \frac{b(da)-a(db)}{b^2}$$

and, since a and b are functions of x,

$$\therefore\ \frac{dy}{dx} = \frac{b\dfrac{da}{dx} - a\dfrac{db}{dx}}{b^2}$$

For example:

$$\text{If} \quad y = \frac{8x^4+3}{x^3+4}$$

$$\text{Then} \quad \frac{dy}{dx} = \frac{(x^3+4)(32x^3)-(8x^4+3)(3x^2)}{(x^3+4)^2}$$

i.e.,

$$\frac{\text{the denominator} \times \dfrac{d \text{ numerator}}{dx} - \text{numerator} \times \dfrac{d \text{ denominator}}{dx}}{(\text{denominator})^2}$$

Continuing our differentiation and simplifying the right-hand side we get

$$\frac{dy}{dx} = \frac{32x^6+128x^3-24x^6-9x^2}{(x^3+4)^2}$$

$$= \frac{8x^6+128x^3-9x^2}{(x^3+4)^2}$$

We have come a long way from the pebble ("calculus") used by the Romans to assist their "calculations"!

So far we have dealt only with *first derivatives*. If it is possible to differentiate twice over, we obtain what is known as a *second derivative*.

$$\text{e.g. if} \quad y = c+bx^2+ex^5$$

$$\frac{dy}{dx} = 2bx+5ex^4$$

and differentiating again, we get

$$\frac{d\left(\dfrac{dy}{dx}\right)}{dx} = 2b+20ex^3$$

This is known as the "second derivative" and is written

$$\frac{d^2y}{dx^2} = 2b + 20ex^3$$

(Read "dee 2 y over dee x squared.")

We can sometimes get third, fourth . . . derivatives.

Problems involving Time

Innumerable problems involving Time can quickly be solved by the Calculus.

We have seen that Speed $= \dfrac{\text{distance}}{\text{time}}$ but this formula only gives us the average speed over a certain distance (or over a certain period of time). It does not tell us the speed at any given moment.

The speed of a locomotive over a certain journey is never uniform. It must increase gradually from zero and (as a rule, it is hoped) decrease gradually to zero.

Consider then the speed during a tiny fraction of time which we will call "dt." Suppose the corresponding distance covered during that tiny period of time were dy.

Then the speed during that tiny period was $\dfrac{dy}{dt}$

Acceleration

Acceleration means an increase (or decrease) in *speed* during a certain period of time. Therefore the acceleration during a tiny fraction of time will be

$$\frac{d\ (\text{speed})}{dt} = \frac{d\left(\dfrac{dy}{dt}\right)}{dt}$$

which is usually written $\dfrac{d^2y}{dt^2}$ (read "dee 2 y over dee t squared") and is called the second derivative of y, the first derivative being $\dfrac{dy}{dt}$ (the speed).

Example 1. (First derivative.)

If a body falls from rest, the number of feet it will fall in t seconds is given, as we have seen, by the formula

$$s = 16t^2$$

$$\text{Velocity} = \frac{ds}{dt} = 32t.$$

∴ at the end of, say, the 4th second, its velocity will be (32×4) ft. per sec. = 128 ft. per sec.←

Example 2. (Second derivative.)

If a body moves so that the distance covered (s feet) equals $18 + 3t + 8.4t^2$, t being the number of seconds, then

(a) its velocity at the end of t seconds will be

$$\frac{ds}{dt} = 3 + 16.8t \leftarrow$$

and   (b) its acceleration will be

$$\frac{d^2s}{dt^2} = 16.8 \text{ ft./sec}^2 \leftarrow$$

In formula (a) we may substitute any number for t. Formula (b) tells us that the acceleration in this case is uniform and does not vary, no matter what value t may have.

For Exercises see pp. 310–311.

[*Note:* For a fuller discussion of these and many other matters connected with the Calculus, the beginner is referred to *Calculus Made Easy*, by Professor Sylvanus P. Thompson (Macmillan).]

The reader should now be in a position to tackle with ease more advanced works such as Hill and Linker's *Introduction to College Mathematics* or Griffin's *Introduction to Mathematical Analysis*.

CHAPTER 33

RADIANS AND MILS*

There are other ways of measuring angles besides the sexagesimal system (degrees, minutes, seconds).

A **radian** is the angle subtended at the center of a circle by part of the circumference equal in length to the radius.

In this figure, if $\angle BOA = 1$ radian,

it follows that

$$S = r\theta \text{ radians}$$

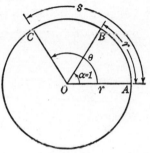

FIG. 190

Since

$$\frac{\text{arc } AC}{\text{arc } AB} = \frac{\theta}{\alpha}$$

Also, from the figure, it follows that

$$\frac{1 \text{ radian}}{360°} = \frac{r}{\text{circumference}}$$

i.e.

$$1 \text{ radian} = \frac{180°}{\pi}$$

and

$$1° = \frac{\pi}{180} \text{ radians}$$

A **mil** was originally $\frac{1}{1000}$ of a radian. This is approximately an angle of $\frac{1}{6400}$ of a complete revolution, and is a convenient unit for rapid calculation, hence is used by the Mobile Artillery and Infantry of the United States Army.

* See the report of the Sub-Committee on Education for Service of the War Preparedness Committee of the American Mathematical Society and the Mathematical Association of America—"The Mil as an Angular Unit and Its Importance to the Army"—by R. S. Burington: *Am. Math. Monthly,* Vol. 48, No. 3, Mar. 1941, pp. 188–189, quoted in Crathorne and Moore's Appendix to "Brief Trigonometry," p. 119, from which work the examples and exercises in this chapter are reproduced, by permission.

For *small* angles measured in mils (where an arc is almost the same length as the chord joining its ends), the length of the chord is approximately equal to $\frac{1}{1000}$ of the distance of the chord from the center, *i.e.*,

$$\text{chord} = \frac{\text{radius} \times \text{angle in mils}}{1000}$$

chord and radius being measured in the same units.

Hence, to a very close approximation,

> 1 mil subtends a chord of 1 yard   at 1000 yards,
>   "   "   "   "   " 1 foot   " 1000 feet,
> 1   "   "   "   "   " 2 yards " 2000 yards
> and so on.

Conversion table:—

$90° = 1600$ mils	1 mil $= 0.05625° = 3.375'$
$1° = 17.778$ mils	1 radian $= 1018.6$ mils
$1' = 0.2963$ mils	1 mil $= 0.0009817$ radians.

Example 1. "An observer finds that the angular distance between two objects, P_1 and P_2, 4000 yards away, is 22 mils. Find the distance P_1P_2."

$$\text{Since chord} = \frac{\text{radius} \times \text{angle in mils}}{1000}$$

$$\therefore P_1P_2 = \frac{4000 \times 22}{1000} = 88 \text{ yards} \leftarrow$$

Example 2. "A tank, known to be 25 feet long is seen to subtend an angle of 2.5 mils at an observation post. How far away is it?"

$$\text{Here, } 25 = \frac{r(2.5)}{1000}$$

$$\therefore r = \frac{25 \times 1000}{2.5} = 10,000 \text{ ft.} \leftarrow$$

For Exercises see p. 311.

EXERCISES

CHAPTER 2

Decimals

(A) (1) Write as decimals: 7 tenths; 8 hundredths; 7 thousandths; 13 hundredths; 79 thousandths; 73 hundredths.

    (2) Write as vulgar fractions: .7, .09, .003, 3.3, 3.03, 3.333, 7.41, 7.041.

    (3) Arrange the following in the ascending order of size: 0.92, 0.29, 0.099, 1.02, 0.28.

    (4) Change into decimals: $\frac{1}{5}$, $\frac{3}{20}$, $\frac{19}{25}$, $\frac{17}{50}$, $\frac{19}{40}$, $\frac{103}{250}$, $\frac{13}{500}$, $\frac{3}{8}$, $\frac{7}{8}$.

    (5) Write down the results in the following multiplication and division exercises:

0.35×10	0.038×100	$29 \div 10$	$\dfrac{0.3}{100}$	$\dfrac{0.43}{1000}$
0.305×10	3.08×100	$0.7 \div 10$		

0.007×10	30.34×1000	$3.47 \div 10$	$\dfrac{0.004}{100}$	$\dfrac{2.7}{10000}$
		$.29 \div 100$		

    (6) Find the value of each of the following:—

6.23×20; 9.57×40; 0.475×60; $.3217 \times 30$;
$2.19 \div 30$; $35.7 \div 70$; $.0112 \div 40$; $1.71 \div 900$; $.0102 \div 6000$.

Add together:

(B)   (1) 9.423, 21.956, .788, 4.912.

    (2) .00412, 2.34, 9.6004, 147.01016.

    (3) 2.65, 9.3008, .457, .0708, 3.9, 502.703.

Find the value of:

    (4) 14.5 + 0.97 + 7.24 + 3.457 + 0.005 + 17.5.

    (5) 0.778 + 523.7 + 2.9273 + 0.00705 + 85.26 + 9.784.

    (6) 0.012 + 12.0012 + 1.2 + 1200.1 + 1.201212.

(7) A road runs through five districts, the lengths of the road in each district being: 3.124 mi., 1.29 mi., 7.265 mi., 3.196 mi., .478 mi. What is the total length of the road?

(8) The rainfall in the four weeks of one month was 0.39 in., 1.08 in., 0.7 in., 0.92 in. Find the total rainfall for the month.

(9) The lengths of the sides of a triangle are 49.3 in., 57.5 in., 67 in. Find the perimeter in inches.

(10) Add each line horizontally; add each column vertically; then add up the horizontal results and compare with the sum of the vertical results.

7.231	17.4597	0.4213	72.986
47.497	.6844	16.01	.009
4.0007	746.29	3.078	1.2987
362.8	3.459	562.96	36.09

(C) (1) Subtract the second number from the first:

9.68	6.42	0.234	5.6	2.
7.45	1.97	0.192	2.49	0.671

(2) Take 27.2519 from 119.4689.

(3) From 1.029 take .6473.

(4) $10.721 - 9.027$.   (5) $13.065 - 12.849$.   (6) $0.1 - 0.0002$.

(7) Subtract the difference between 3.105 and 1.598 from their sum.

(8) Take three hundredths from three hundred.

(9) $10 - 0.06 - 0.03 + 0.01$.

(10) The external diameter of a pipe is 4.93 in., and the internal diameter is 4.83 in. How thick is the pipe metal? ("Diameter," see p. 55).

Find the values of:

(D) (1) 3.14×5.7.   (2) 197×7.32.   (3) 4.59×0.15.

(4) 0.317×0.49.   (5) 5.023×37.4.

(6) $3.017 \times .0041$.   (7) 0.0709×1300.

(8) 0.0617×0.46.

Give the following products correct to two decimal places:

(9) 13.58×4.12.   (10)   0.356×11.4.   (11) 1.732×3.14.

Find the products of the following correct to three significant figures:

(12) .56×1.081.   (13) 5.93×.00173.
          (14) .0078×.0405.   (15) 3.27×.00159.
(16) Find the total height to the nearest inch of a pile of 47 books if each is 1.63 in. thick.
(17) A steamer travels at 18.4 miles per hour. How far will it go in 23.7 hours? (Answer to the nearest mile.)
(18) An aircraft travels at 237.5 miles an hour. How far does it go in 2.56 hours?

(E) Express as decimals:

(1) .91÷7.   (2) 0.045÷6.   (3) 0.056÷7.   (4) 0.4÷8.
          (5) 0.0027÷6.   (6) 2.222÷11.   (7) 0.06363÷7.

In the following examples, divide by factors:

(8) 2.04÷15.   (9) .091÷28.   (10) 4.048÷44.
          (11) .0024÷.32.   (12) 1.365÷2.1.
          (13) 1.0008÷4.5.   (14) 10.01÷140.

(F) Evaluate:

(1) 152.703÷36.1.   (2) 2.54334÷437.
          (3) 384.006÷0.123.   (4) 379.44÷0.024.
          (5) .03782÷.62.   (6) .002871÷.495.
          (7) .93075÷.0876.

Work out the following correct to three decimal places:

(8) 71.425÷0.512.   (9) 52.987÷21.7.
          (10) .00729÷0.2735.   (11) 0.091÷0.729.
          (12) 824.6÷73.6.

Work out the following correct to four significant figures:

(13) .05073÷3.1416.   (14) 824.6÷73.6.   (15) $2\frac{4}{11}$.
          (16) $6\frac{3}{7}$.

CHAPTER 3

Angles

Give (with short reasons) the size of the angles marked with letters.

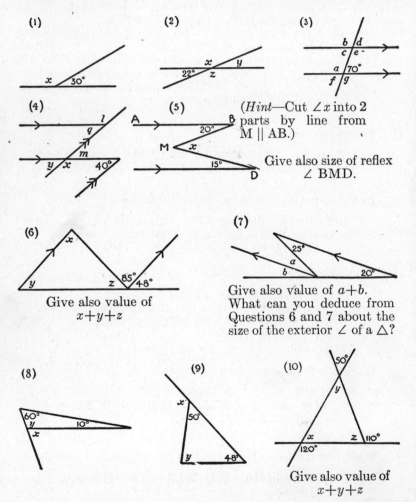

(1)

(2)

(3)

(4)

(5)

(*Hint*—Cut ∠x into 2 parts by line from M ‖ AB.)

Give also size of reflex ∠ BMD.

(6)

Give also value of $x+y+z$

(7)

Give also value of $a+b$. What can you deduce from Questions 6 and 7 about the size of the exterior ∠ of a △?

(8)

(9)

(10)

Give also value of $x+y+z$

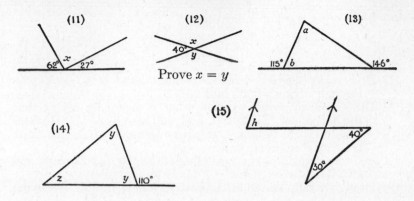

(11)

(12)

Prove $x = y$

(13)

(14)

(15)

CHAPTER 4

Measurement of Direction

Using a protractor, measure all the angles in the following figures:

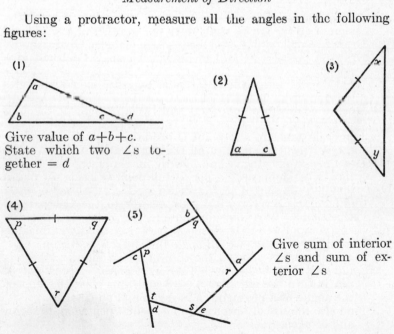

(1)

Give value of $a+b+c$.
State which two ∠s to-gether $= d$

(2)

(3)

(4)

(5)

Give sum of interior ∠s and sum of ex-terior ∠s

(6) State other ways of indicating:

(a)	S. 20° E.	(c)	N. 80° W.	(e)	N. 1° W.
(b)	255°.	(d)	N.W.	(f)	S. by W.

(7) How many degrees does the minute-hand of a clock pass through between 0825 and 0837?

(8) Draw a rough sketch to show what is meant by saying that the latitude of X is 20° N. and that of Y is 65° N. If their longitudes are the same, calculate the approximate distance between them in sea-miles.

State also which of the two places is nearer the Equator and give its distance from the Equator in sea-miles.

(9) Draw a rough sketch to indicate what is meant by saying that a place P is "longitude 65° W."

CHAPTER 5

Plane and Solid Figures

(1) A brick has how many faces? Edges? Corners? What is the sum of all the angles that touch one another at any corner?

(2) Draw an equilateral △ and measure each angle. Give answers. Draw an isosceles △ and measure each angle. Do not give answers.

What do you notice about the sides opposite the equal angles in an isosceles triangle?

(3) Draw a convex pentagon and find by measurement the sum of its angles.

Join each corner to any point O inside the figure and find by measurement the sum of all the angles at O.

(4) Draw a convex octagon and find by measurement the sum of its angles. Join each corner to any point O inside the figure and find the sum of all the angles at O.

Compare this answer with your answer to the last part of Question 3. What fact do you infer?

(5) Using your answer to Question 3, pt. 1, say what you imagine would be the size of each angle in a *regular* pentagon.

(6) If a polygon has n sides, the sum of all its interior angles is $(2n-4)$ right angles or $90(2n-4)$ degrees. Instead of n, put in turn the numbers 5, 6, 8 and thus state the sum of the angles of a pentagon, a hexagon and an octagon.

Find also the size of *each* angle in a regular pentagon, hexagon and octagon.

CHAPTER 6

The Metric System

A. (1) Express in meters:

5 Km. 3 Hm. 2 Dm. 4 m.; 7 Km. 3 Dm. 7 m.; 4 Dm.
2 m. 3 cm.; 378 cm. 49 cm. 5049 cm. 579 mm.

(2) Express in Km.:

427 m.; 3 m. 4 dm.; 40,225 m.; 2 Dm. 3 m. 4 dm.

(3) Express in cm.:

.023 m.; .001 Km.; 5 Dm. 2 m. 4 mm.

(4) Reduce 20,635 mm. to m., dm., etc.

(5) Reduce 31,752 m. to Km., Hm., etc.

(6) Express .0275 Km. as m. and as cm.

B. Express as sq. millimeters:

(1) 7 sq. m., 16 sq. dm., 50 sq. cm.

(2) 3 sq. m., 4 sq. dm., 17 sq. cm., 9 sq. mm.

Express as sq. meters:

(3) 5 sq. Hm., 17 sq. Dm., 23 sq. m.

(4) 17 sq. Hm., 3 sq. Dm. 2 sq. m.

Express in sq. m. and decimals of 1 sq. m.:

(5) 5392 sq. dm. (6) 3,569,008 sq. mm. (7) 38 sq. dm.,
9 sq. cm., 40 sq. mm.

C. (1) Reduce 5 cu.m. 235 cu.dm. to c.c.

(2) Reduce 24 cu.m. 57 cu.dm. 9 c.c. to c.c.

(3) Reduce 17 cu.m. 36 c.c. to c.c.

(4) Reduce 5 g. 4 cg. 5 mg. to g.

(5) Reduce 23 g. 8 mg. to g.

(6) Reduce 9 g. 5 cg. to mg.

(7) Reduce 8 Kg. 3 Hg. 5 Dg. to g.

(8) Express 46,597 g. as Kg.

(9) Express 549.8 Dg. as Kg.

(10) Express 23,456 dg. as Kg.

D. (1) Add 3 Kg. 7 Hg. 6 Dg. 5 g.; 4 Kg. 3 Dg. 7 g.; 14 Kg. 2 Hg.
8 g.; 5 Dg. 9 g.

(2) Add 4.375 m., 56.7 dm., 1256 cm., 97 mm.
Answer in meters.

(3) Add 127 cm., 4569 cm., 98 cm., 47.9 cm., 3.4 cm.
Give the result in m., dm., etc.

(4) Add 7 Km. 3 Hm. 7 m.+9 Km. 4 Hm. 3 Dm. 4 m. 5 dm.
+1 Km. 5 Dm. 3 dm. 7 cm.+5 Km. 7 Hm. 3 m. 4 dm.
3 cm.
Answer in Km., Hm., etc.

(5) Express in Hectoliters:
483 Hl.+19.47 Hl.+346 l.+19 Dl.+5 Hl.+3 Dl. 8 l.

(6) Three squares have sides 2.9 m., 1.4 m., and 3.5 m.,
respectively. What is the sum of their areas (i) in
sq.m., (ii) in sq.dm.?

(7) A liter of gasoline weighs 0.71 Kg. Find in Kg. the total
weight if 2 liters of gasoline are put into a tin which
weighs 290 grams when empty.

(8) A weighs 64.5 Kg.; B weighs .729 Kg. more than A;
C weighs 1.102 Kg. more than B; and D weighs 6.28 Kg.
more than A. What is the total weight of A, B, C
and D?

E. (1) Subtract 2 Kg. 180 g. from 7 Kg. 375 g. Give answer in Kg.

(2) Subtract 94 g. from 9 Hg. Give answer in Kg.

(3) Subtract 23 mm. from 3 dm. Give answer in mm.

(4) Subtract 394 sq. cm. from 1 sq. m. Give answer in sq. m.

(5) A bottle contains a liter of wine. How many c.c. remain
when 450 c.c. have been poured out?

(6) From a sheet of cardboard 3 dm. square, a square portion
of side 1.5 dm. is cut off. Find in sq. dm. the area of
what remains.

(7) The external diameter of a hollow metal pipe is 7.9 cm.
and the internal diameter is 6.7. Find the thickness of
the metal.

(8) Find the value of 2.35 cm.×600. Give answer in m.

(9) Find the value of 5.267 m.×2.05. Give answer in m.

(10) Find the value of 12.5 g.×64. Give answer in Kg.

(11) Find the value of 3 m. 7 cm. 4 mm.×450. Give answer in
Km.

(12) A pile of 220 sheets of paper is 6.6 cm. high. Find the
thickness of 1 sheet in mm.

(13) A consignment of 6500 tins of salmon has a total weight of
1916 Kg. Find the weight, in grams, of 1 tin.

(14) Divide 129 Dm. of cloth among 27 girls. How much does
each receive in meters (answer to the nearest whole
number) and in yards? (1 m. = 39.37 in.)

(15) The area of a certain country is 322,000 sq. Km. and the
inhabitants number 23 million. How many sq. Dm. does
this give to a person?

F. (1) How many liters can a tank hold if it measures internally 35 cm. by 28 cm. by 16 cm.?

(2) The volume of a rectangular box is 1.34 cu. meters and the area of the base is .785 sq. meters. Find the height of the box correct to two decimal places. Answer in in.

(3) If 1 in. = 2.54 cm., express 4.78 in. in cm. correct to two decimal places.

(4) How many lengths of wire each 7.56 cm. can be cut off from a length of 2 m.? What length will be left over?

(5) A man walks 6 Km. in 50 minutes. Find his speed in Km. per hour.

(6) A racing car travels 850 meters in 10 seconds. Express this speed in Kilometers per hour.

(7) A flask weighs 63.49 grams when empty and 147.238 grams when full of water. Find its weight when it is half full of water.

(8) 3000 packages each containing 20 cigarettes have the total weight of 99.56 Kilograms. One empty package by itself weighs 8.84 grams. Find the weight of one cigarette to the nearest .001 gram.

(9) After a length of 17.2 cm. has been cut off as often as possible from a string $10\frac{1}{2}$ meters long, what length remains?

CHAPTER 7

Algebra

(1) Multiply:

(i) $4a \times 3a$. (ii) $a^4 \times a^3$. (iii) $4a^4 \times 3a^3$. (iv) $ab \times a$.
(v) $a^2b \times 6ab^2$. (vi) $5ab^2 \times 6a^2b$. (vii) $3a^2b^2c \times 5a^4b$.
(viii) $8abx \times b^2x^2y$. (ix) $4x^2yz^3 \times 5a^2yx$.
(x) $7m^4n^4pq \times 3p^2m^2q^4y$.

(2) Find the areas of the squares whose sides are the following lengths (all answers in sq. cm.):

(i) x cm. (ii) $5p$ cm. (iii) $10z$ cm. (iv) $12y$ cm.

(3) Find the length of a side of each of the squares with the following areas:

(i) x^2 sq. cm. (ii) $25y^2$ sq. cm. (iii) $144a^2$ sq. cm.
(iv) $49p^2$ sq. cm.

(4) Give the square, and the square root of each of the following:

(i) $4a^2$; (ii) $9b^4$; (iii) $16a^{16}$; (iv) a^4x^{12}; (v) $25p^2q^4r^{10}$;

(vi) $\dfrac{16x^9}{9y^2}$

(5) Split up each of the following numbers into their prime factors and find their square roots:

    (i) 625.   (ii) 1296.   (iii) 900.   (iv) 2304.   (v) 2916.   (vi) 9216.

(6) Write down the square roots of each of the following terms:

$$a^8, \quad x^{16}, \quad x, \quad x^4 y^9, \quad 100 x^{100} b^{50}, \quad \frac{121 m^2 n^2 p^6}{z^{16}}.$$

(7) Work the following division sums:

    (i) $x^9 \div x^5$ (ii) $x^9 \div x^3$ (iii) $\dfrac{a^8}{a^2}$

    (iv) $\dfrac{a^2 b^3 c^4}{abc}$ (v) $\dfrac{a^2 b}{b}$ (vi) $\dfrac{ab^2}{b}$

    (vii) $\dfrac{a^2 b^2}{b}$ (viii) $\dfrac{a^2 b^5}{ac}$ (ix) $\dfrac{p^2 q r^3}{p^2 q}$

    (x) $\dfrac{6 a^2 b}{3a}$ (xi) $\dfrac{24 x^5 y^3}{16 x^4 y z^2}$ (xii) $\dfrac{36 m^2 q^2 r}{48 m^2 q^2 r}$

CHAPTER 8

"Direction" in Algebra

A. Simplify the following expressions and test every answer after that of Question 2 by putting small numbers (1, 2, 3 . . .) for the letters. See Example in Chap. 8.

    (1) $5 + 9 - 4 - 8$.
    (2) $13 - 9 + 2 - 4 - 8$.
    (3) $3a + 5b - 2a$.
    (4) $7a - 5b - 3a - 3b$.
    (5) $5x - 3y + 12z - 4x + 3y - 2z + y - 10z$.
    (6) $3a^2 - 5b^2 + 2a^2 + 3b^2$.
    (7) $3(2a) + 5(3b) - 4(3c)$.
    (8) $4x - 5(x + y) - 3(y - x)$.
    (9) $3a - \{2b - (a + b)\}$.
    (10) $2[3a + \{6b - (2a - b)\}]$.
    (11) $3[2x - \{3y - 3(2x + y)\}]$.
    (12) $3[(-x) - 2(-y)] - [(+x) - (-2y)]$.

B. (1) From $3x$ take $5x$.
   (2) Take $4z$ from $-2z$. (*N.B.*—Always put "from" quantity first.)
   (3) Take $(2x+3y)$ from $(3x-y)$.
   (4) Take $(3x-y)$ from $(2x+3y)$.
   (5) From $2x-3y$ take $x-5y$ (use brackets as in Nos. 3 and 4).
   (6) Subtract $a^2-3b^2+c^2$ from $3a^2+4b^2+c^2$.
   (7) What must be added to 3 to make 7?
   (8) What must be added to a to make b? (How did you do No. 7?)
   (9) What must be added to -8 to make -3?
   (10) What must be added to x^2-1 to make 1?
   (11) What must be added to $3a-b$ to make $2c-b$?

C. (1) Show that $x^3 \times x^4 = x^7$.
   (2) Write in shorter form:

   $x^2 \times x^4$; $x \times x^3$; $x^4 \times x^5 \times x$; $x^{\frac{1}{2}} \times x^{\frac{1}{2}}$; $a^3 \times a^{n-2}$.

   (3) Show that $x^6 \div x^2 = x^4$.

   (4) Simplify $x^7 \div x^4$; $x^5 \div x$; $x^8 \div x^4$; $\dfrac{6x^2y \times 4xy}{3y}$; $\dfrac{x^4 \times x^9 \times x}{x^2 \times x^3}$; $\dfrac{x^5}{x^5}$.

   (5) Write down the values of:

   $(p^2)^2$; $(q^3)^2$; $(x^3)^4$; $(x^4)^3$; $(k^4)^4$.

   (6) What is the value of each of the following?

   $\sqrt{25}$; $\sqrt{x^2}$; $\sqrt{x^{10}}$; $\sqrt{25a^2}$; $\sqrt{36a^4b^2}$; $\sqrt{p^2q^6}$; $\sqrt{144a^{12}}$; if $x^1 = \sqrt{x^2}$, what is the square root of x?

CHAPTER 9

Construction of Triangles: Congruency

A. (1) Draw $\triangle$ ABC having $a = 3''$, $b = 2.7''$, $c = 2.1''$.
   [Note that side a is opposite $\angle$ A; side b opposite $\angle$ B and side c opposite $\angle$ C.] Measure angles B and C.
   (2) Draw $\triangle$ ABC having $a = 7.0$ cm., $b = 5.6$ cm., $c = 4.2$ cm. Measure angle A. What kind of triangle is this?
   (3) Draw $\triangle$ PQR having QR $= 6$ cm., PQ $= 4$ cm., $\angle$ Q $= 135°$. Measure PR. How would you describe this triangle?
   (4) Draw $\triangle$ ABC with $a = 3''$, $\angle$ B $= 75°$, $\angle$ C $= 45°$. Measure b and c.

(5) Draw a right-angled △ whose hypotenuse = 8.5 cm. and one of whose sides = 4 cm. Draw the 4 cm. side first. Measure the other side.

(6) Draw a right-angled △ PQR with the hypotenuse QR = 2.1″ and side PQ = 1.5″.
Can you do this by drawing QR first in a horizontal direction? Measure PR and the angles Q and R. Do you notice anything of interest about the results?

(7) Draw quadrilateral ABCD having AB = 5 cm., BC = 6 cm., CD = 7 cm., ∠ B = 120°, ∠ C = 80°.

B.   Find the size of each angle marked with a letter, giving reasons.

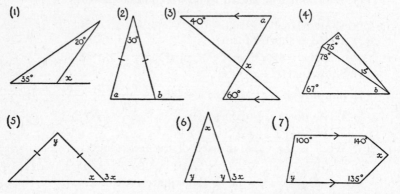

C.   State whether the following pairs of △'s are congruent. If so, state case ("shorthand" form). (See p. 60.)

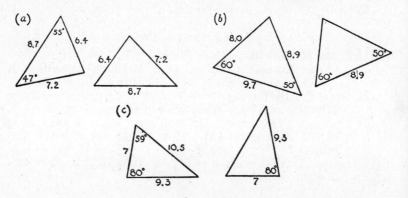

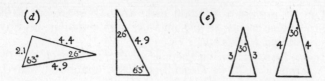

CHAPTER 10

Statistical Graphs

(1) Draw a graph showing the number of fatal road accidents in Scotland in the years 1929–1938.

Year:	1929	1930	1931	1932	1933	1934	1935	1936	1937	1938
Number of Fatal Accidents	688	757	644	687	680	699	626	625	654	631

Horizontal scale $\frac{1}{2}'' = 1$ year; Vertical scale $1'' = 100$ accidents.

(2) *Mean Temperature ° F.*

	Jan.	Feb.	Mar.	Apr.	May.	Jun.	July	Aug.	Sep.	Oct.	Nov.	Dec.
Paris	36.7	39.4	43.3	49.2	56.2	61.6	64.7	63.8	58.4	50.0	42.5	38.1
Cape Town	69.9	70.3	68.1	63.2	58.9	55.7	54.7	55.6	57.9	61.2	64.6	67.9

Represent each month horizontally by $\frac{1}{2}''$.
Represent 10° vertically by $1''$.
Can you explain the difference in the general shapes of the graphs?

(3) *Imports of Apples at a Certain Port—1934–1938*

	1934	1935	1936	1937	1938	
Thousands of cwt.	620	688	544	559	681	Quantities
Thousands of $	627	713	551	558	681	Values

Draw two graphs on the same diagram: let $1''$ represent 100,000 cwt., and $1''$ represent \$100,000.

(4) *Imports of Oranges at a Certain Port—1934–1938*

	1934	1935	1936	1937	1938
Thousands of cwt.	868	972	735	1024	913
Thousands of $	593	682	569	651	652

Let 1″ represent 100,000 cwt. and 1″ represent $100,000. Study the graphs of (3) and (4) and comment on any outstanding features.

(5) Index figures showing the cost of living for each month from January, 1939 to December, 1940, compared with 100 at August, 1914 (in Britain).

	Jan.	Feb.	Mar.	Apr.	May	Jun.	July	Aug.	Sep.	Oct.	Nov.	Dec.
1939	155	155	153	153	153	156	156	155	155	165	169	173
1940	174	177	179	178	180	181	187	185	187	189	192	195

Scales: Horizontal .4″ = 1 month; Vertical 1″ = 10 per cent. What explanation can you give for the sudden steepness at one point?

(6) Expectation of life of an Australian at different ages.

Age in Years . . .	10	20	30	40	50	60	70
Expectation in Years .	58.0	48.3	39.9	31.1	22.8	15.6	9.6

Find (i) how much longer an Australian may expect to live when he is 26 and 42 years old; (ii) at what age he may expect to live 33, 18 years longer.

(7) The following figures give the percentage of insured British workers unemployed in the occupations of shipbuilding and housebuilding in January of each year from 1926 to 1939.
Draw two graphs on the same diagram using the scales: Horizontal .4″ = 1 year; Vertical 1″ = 10 per cent.
In what year would you say unemployment was most acute? Can you with the same confidence say when unemployment was least? Give reasons.

	1926	1927	1928	1929	1930	1931	1932	1933	1934	1935	1936	1937	1938	1939
Shipbuilding	37.3	37.1	20.6	27.6	23.4	46.6	60.1	63.3	54.7	46.1	36.6	26.4	21.3	23.0
Housebuilding	14.8	15.1	17.4	19.9	18.5	27.0	32.8	37.7	26.2	25.1	28.1	17.9	19.5	23.9

Speed Graphs

(8) Draw on the same diagram graphs showing A walking at 4 m.p.h., B running at 10 m.p.h., C push-biking at 15 m.p.h., D motoring at 30 m.p.h., and E motor-cycling at 45 m.p.h. Assume that they all start at the same time.
Scales: Horizontal 1″ = 1 hour; Vertical 1″ = 20 miles.

(9) From the graphs obtained in Question 8, read off:
  (i) How far A and E have each gone in $2\frac{1}{2}$ hours.
  (ii) How far D is ahead of C in 1 hour 20 min.
(10) A motor-car A starts at 1200 hours and goes at a uniform rate of 20 miles an hour. At 1330 hours another car B sets off from the same starting point and keeps up a uniform speed of 30 miles an hour. When and where will B overtake A?
  At what time will B be (i) 10 miles behind A; (ii) 10 miles ahead of A?
  Use the scales: Horizontal $1'' = 1$ hour; Vertical $1'' = 25$ miles.
(11) Draw the graphs of the following speeds. Find which is the fastest and slowest and express each in miles per hour.

  (X) 34 miles in 40 min.; (Y) 36 miles in 48 min.; (Z) 21 miles in $22\frac{1}{2}$ min.

  Let $1'' = 10$ min.; $1'' = 10$ miles.
(12) Two towns P and Q are connected by a road $26\frac{1}{4}$ miles long. A starts to walk from P to Q at the rate of 4 m.p.h. at the same time as B sets out from Q to P at $3\frac{1}{3}$ m.p.h.
  When and where will they meet? Choose suitable units.
(13) Two cyclists ride to meet each other from two places 75 miles apart. A starts at 0900 hours at 10 miles an hour and B starts at 1030 hours at 14 miles an hour.
  Find graphically when and where they meet and at what times they are 12 miles apart.
(14) Two trains start from P and go to Q. The first starts at 1000 hours and travels at 30 miles per hour while the second starts at 1100 hours and goes at 45 miles an hour. If they arrive at Q simultaneously what is the distance PQ?
  Scales: Horizontal $1.2'' = 1$ hour; Vertical $1'' = 50$ miles.

Proportion Graphs

In the following exercises join the points by a continuous smooth line.

(15) The weight in lb. required to stretch a spiral spring and the resultant length of the spring in inches are given thus:

Weight	0	1	2	3	4	5	6	8
Length of Spring	3	3.25	3.55	3.85	4.1	4.4	4.7	5.25

Draw the graph.   What weight will stretch the spring (i) .75 in., (ii) 2 in.? What is the length for a weight of 7 lb.?

(16) The temperatures in ° F. at different altitudes in feet are given in the following table:

Altitude	0	5,000	10,000	15,000	20,000	25,000	30,000
Temperature	59	41	23.4	5.5	−12.3	−30	−48

Draw the graph taking 1″ horizontal = 5000 ft.; 1″ vertical = 20° F. (Note the negative values.) Find the temperature at (i) 9000 ft.; (ii) 27,000 ft.

(17) The following table gives the circumference C, of a circle of given radius r in any unit of length:

r	0	1	2	3	4	8	10
C	0	6.28	12.56	18.84	25.12	50.24	62.8

Draw the graph; choose suitable scales. Read off the circumference of a circle whose radius is (i) 5 in., (ii) 7 ft., and the radius of a circle whose circumference is (iii) 30 in., (iv) 33 yards.

(18) The following table shows the thickness (diameter) of the iron in a link chain that will safely carry a given number of tons.

Thickness in inches	$\frac{3}{8}$	$\frac{4}{8}$	$\frac{5}{8}$	$\frac{6}{8}$	$\frac{7}{8}$	1
Safe load in tons	.9	1.6	2.5	3.6	4.9	6.4

Draw the graph.   Scales: Horizontal 1″ = $\frac{1}{8}$″; Vertical 1″ = 2 tons.
Find from your graph the thickness (to the nearest $\frac{1}{8}$″) of the chain that will bear 4 tons *safely*.

(19) The following figures show the times (t) necessary to complete a certain journey at varying speeds (v).

t	24	20	15	12	10	8	4	3	2
v	5	6	8	10	12	15	30	40	60

Let 1″ horizontal = 5 hours, 1″ vertical = 10 m.p.h.
How long would the journey take at 25 m.p.h.?
What speed would be necessary to do the journey in 16 hours?

(20) The following table gives the relation between the length (l)
of a pendulum in feet and the time (t) in seconds taken
to make a certain number of swings.

l	0.2	0.4	0.6	0.8	1.0	1.2	1.4	1.6	1.8	2.0
t	2.5	3.6	4.4	5.1	5.7	6.2	6.7	7.2	7.6	8.0

Plot these points, measuring l horizontally (1 in. = 0.4 ft.)
and t vertically (1 in. = 2 seconds); and join the points
by a smooth curve.
Find as accurately as you can from your diagram:
  (a) The length of the pendulum that takes 6½ seconds to
    make the number of swings;
  (b) The number of seconds taken by a pendulum 1.7 ft.
    long to make the number of swings.

(21) A boy can throw a stone a distance in feet equal to—
      25   45   81   108   122   122   108   81   45   25
When the elevation is—
      5°   10°   20°   30°   40°   50°   60°   70°   80°   85°
Draw a smooth curve to illustrate this. What is the greatest
distance he can throw the stone? What angle of elevation
is necessary?

CHAPTER 11

Algebraic Binomials

A. Find the product of the following:

(1) $(3x+2)(2x+5)$ (4) $(6x-3)(4x+5)$ (7) $(5x+3y)(3x+4y)$
(2) $(4x+1)(3x+1)$ (5) $(8x+4)(9x-2)$ (8) $(x-3y)(x-4y)$
(3) $(2x-3)(4x+5)$ (6) $(2x+y)(3x+2y)$ (9) $(3x+2y)(2x-3y)$
                        (10) $(4x-5y)(2x-y)$

B. Write down the following products:

(1) $(x+4)(x+5) =$
(2) $(x+3)(x+7) =$
(3) $(3x+1)(x+5) =$
(4) $(2x+4)(3x+7) =$
(5) $(3x-4)(3x+7) =$
(6) $(2x-3)(6x+1) =$
(7) $(3x-4)(2x-3) =$
(8) $(2x-4)(2x+4) =$
(9) $(x-7)(2x-6) =$
(10) $(3x-2)(3x-2) =$

(11) $(2x+6)^2 =$
(12) $(4x-4y)^2 =$
(13) $(4x^2+6)^2 =$
(14) $(5x^2-1)^2 =$
(15) $(2x^2-3y^2)^2 =$
(16) $(3a^2-5b^2)^2 =$
(17) $[(2x+3)+3y]^2 =$
(18) $[(2x)+(3x+y)]^2 =$
(19) $(2x-3y-4z)^2 =$
(20) $(x+y+4)(x+y-4) =$

(21) $(a+b+5)(a+b-5) =$
(22) Simplify: $(x+3)(x+4)+(3x+2)(x+5)$
(23) Simplify: $(2x-5)(x+4)+(3x-1)(x+2)$
(24) Simplify: $(3a-2)(a-5)-(2a-1)(a-4)$

C. Factor:

(1) $3a+6b$
(2) $4a-8b$
(3) $ab-bc$
(4) $5a+10b+15c$
(5) x^3+x^2-x
(6) $10x^3y-15xy^4$
(7) $14a^3+21a^2b+7ab^2$
(8) $pqr+qrs$
(9) $3x^3y^2-6x^2y^2+9x^2y^4$
(10) $2x(p+q)-3x(p+q)$
(11) $a^2x+a^2(a-x)$
(12) $a(p-q)+b(p-q)$
(13) $(a+b)^2+b(a+b)$ (14) $(a+b)^2+(a+b)(a-b)$

D. Factor:

(1) $5x^2+5x+4x+4$
(2) $x^2+xy+2x+2y$
(3) $3x^2-3x+2x-2$
(4) $x^2+xy+xz+yz$
(5) $xy-y^2-xz+yz$
(6) a^3-a^2+a-1
(7) $5a^2-5ax-3x+3a$
(8) a^3-a^2-a+1
(9) $ax-2ay+2by-bx$
(10) $p^2-pq+p-q$
(11) $x^5-x^4+x^3-x^2+x-1$
(12) $ax+ay+az-bx-by-bz$
(13) $(a+b)(a-b)+3(a+b)$

E. Factor:

(1) $x^2+7x+12$
(2) $x^2+9x+20$
(3) $x^2+12x+36$
(4) x^2+2x+1
(5) x^2-3x+2
(6) $x^2-15x+56$
(7) $x^2+23x+132$
(8) $x^2y^2+7xy+6$
(9) $21-10ab+a^2b^2$

F. Factor:

(1) $x^2+3x-18$
(2) x^2-6x+5
(3) x^2-x-56
(4) $x^2-10x+25$
(5) x^2-2x-3
(6) $x^2-14x+48$
(7) $x^2-9x-36$
(8) x^2-x-20
(9) $x^2+2x-24$
(10) x^2+x-72
(11) $x^2+4x-21$
(12) $x^2+10x+9$

G. Factor:

(1) x^2-4

(2) y^2-49

(3) $9-a^2$

(4) a^2c^2-36

(5) $9x^4-16$

(6) $25x^2-y^2$

(7) $25p^4-16$

(8) $81-4a^2c^2$

(9) $x^2y^2-81a^4$

(10) $9x^6-25$

(11) $64a^2-9b^{10}$

(12) $49a^2-36b^2c^8$

(13) $(x+y)^2-1$

(14) $(a+b)^2-c^2$

(15) $(a-b)^2-c^2$

(16) $(x+5y)^2-9z^2$

(17) $1-(a+3b)^2$

(18) $a^2-(b-c)^2$

(19) $(a+b)^2-(c+d)^2$

(20) $(3x+2y)^2-(2z+1)^2$

(21) $(a+3b)^2-(1+x)^2$

(22) $(x+y)^2-(a-b)^2$

(23) $(2a-b)^2-(3x+4y)^2$

(24) $(x-3y)^2-(2a-3c)^2$

(25) $x^2+2xy+y^2-1$

(26) $1-a^2-2ab-b^2$

(27) $a^2-2ab+b^2-c^2$

(28) $9y^2-a^2-b^2+2ab$

CHAPTER 12

Fractions other than Decimal Fractions

(1) Convert into mixed numbers:
$\frac{12}{7}$, $\frac{13}{5}$, $\frac{43}{8}$, $\frac{57}{10}$, $\frac{143}{14}$, $\frac{93}{13}$, $\frac{97}{12}$, $\frac{283}{17}$.

(2) Convert into improper fractions:
$6\frac{2}{7}$, $6\frac{2}{9}$, $6\frac{6}{11}$, $5\frac{3}{10}$, $4\frac{5}{6}$, $2\frac{10}{19}$, $9\frac{8}{9}$, $4\frac{3}{10}$.

(3) Simplify: $\frac{3}{7}\times\frac{4}{15}$; $\frac{7}{16}\times\frac{4}{21}$; $\frac{38}{85}\times\frac{51}{49}$; $\frac{95}{108}\times4\frac{5}{19}$; $\frac{24}{35}\times\frac{25}{72}$; $12\frac{1}{12}\times\frac{6}{29}$.

(4) Simplify: $\frac{45}{49}\div\frac{5}{7}$; $\frac{2}{9}\div\frac{8}{15}$; $\frac{1}{3}\div\frac{1}{4}$; $3\frac{1}{4}\div4\frac{1}{3}$; $4\frac{1}{7}\div5\frac{4}{5}$; $\frac{135}{169}\div2\frac{1}{13}$; $\frac{3}{4}\div\frac{3}{4}$.

(5) Simplify: $8\div\frac{4}{7}$; $1\div\frac{7}{8}$; $7\frac{3}{4}\times\frac{8}{11}\div6\frac{1}{5}$; $5\frac{6}{17}\div\frac{1}{2}$ of $4\frac{1}{3}$; $\frac{2}{3}\times\frac{9}{4}\times\frac{4}{5}\div\frac{2}{5}$.

(6) Simplify: $\frac{x}{a}\times2$; $\frac{x}{a}\times\frac{1}{2}$; $\frac{x}{a}\times a$; $\frac{x}{a}\times\frac{1}{a}$; $\frac{x}{a}\times2a$; $\frac{x}{a}\times a^2$;

$\frac{2x}{a^2}\times\frac{2a}{x}$; $\frac{6ax}{5a^2x}\times\frac{10x^2}{9a^2}$; $\frac{pq}{p^2}\times\frac{p}{q}$; $\frac{4pq}{15p^2}\times\frac{9pq}{2p}$; $\frac{5x}{12a^2}\times\frac{6a}{15x}$;

$\frac{12x^4y^2z^2}{5x^2y^3z^4}\times\frac{10xyz}{9y}$

(7) $\frac{x}{a}\div2$; $\frac{x}{a}\div\frac{1}{2}$; $\frac{x}{a}\div a$; $\frac{pq}{p^2}\div\frac{p^2}{q^2}$; $\frac{5a^2}{7b^2}\div\frac{25a}{49b}$; $\frac{81abc^2}{54x^2y^2z}\div\frac{9a^2bc}{6xyz}$

(8) Find by prime factors the H.C.F. of: 120, 252; 245, 385; 546, 882; 63, 105; 780, 702; 165, 550; 625, 875; 2815, 3941; 510, 714, 1122.

(9) Write down the H.C.F. of: $4a^2b$, $5bc^2$; $15xy$, $20xz$; $14p^2q$, $25pq^2$; $18a^3b^2$, $24a^2b^3$; $21a^2cd$, $14ac^2$; $55x^3y^2$, $143xy^3$; $5x^3y$, $3xy^2$.

(10) Find by prime factors the L.C.M. of: (1) 6, 9, 12.
(2) 6, 10, 15. (3) 15, 24, 27, 30. (4) 63, 12, 84, 28, 70.
(5) 1760, 990.

(11) Write down the L.C.M. of: (1) $3a$, $4a$. (2) $3a^2$, $6a^3$.
(3) $5a^2b$, $4ab^2$. (4) x^2, x^3, x^5. (5) a, b, c. (6) $6a, 8b, 10c$.
(7) a^2b, b^2c, c^2a.

(12) (1) In each of the following pairs of fractions, which is the
greater? $\frac{8}{11}$ or $\frac{7}{9}$; $\frac{5}{9}$ or $\frac{7}{15}$; $\frac{9}{14}$ or $\frac{11}{16}$; $\frac{9}{13}$ or $\frac{19}{29}$.
(2) Arrange each of the following groups of fractions in
"ascending" order: $\frac{1}{4}, \frac{1}{3}, \frac{1}{5}$; $\frac{3}{4}, \frac{2}{3}, \frac{4}{5}$; $\frac{5}{12}, \frac{2}{9}, \frac{1}{2}, \frac{3}{10}$.

(13) Addition of fractions: $\frac{2}{3}+\frac{3}{4}+\frac{4}{5}$; $\frac{2}{11}+\frac{3}{4}+\frac{1}{5}$; $2\frac{7}{15}+2\frac{2}{7}+\frac{3}{35}$;
$1\frac{5}{9}+2\frac{7}{8}+\frac{5}{12}$.

(14) Subtraction of fractions: $\frac{7}{8}-\frac{3}{8}$; $\frac{3}{4}-\frac{2}{3}$; $\frac{4}{9}-\frac{3}{7}$; $3\frac{2}{7}-2\frac{1}{6}$; $5\frac{1}{4}-4\frac{7}{12}$.

(15) Simplify: $\frac{19}{24}+\frac{19}{30}-\frac{19}{72}$; $\frac{7}{10}-\frac{11}{15}+\frac{17}{60}$; $5\frac{1}{2}-7\frac{1}{6}+3\frac{1}{4}$,
$2\frac{1}{7}+4\frac{5}{8}-3\frac{9}{14}+1\frac{1}{4}$.

(16) Simplify: (1) $\dfrac{2}{a} + \dfrac{3}{a} + \dfrac{4}{a}$ (2) $\dfrac{a}{2} + \dfrac{a}{3} + \dfrac{a}{4}$ (3) $\dfrac{1}{a} + \dfrac{1}{b}$

(4) $\dfrac{3}{a} + \dfrac{4}{b} + \dfrac{5}{ab}$ (5) $\dfrac{1}{2a} + \dfrac{1}{3b}$ (6) $\dfrac{2}{3a} + \dfrac{3}{4a}$

(7) $\dfrac{p}{a} + \dfrac{q}{b} + \dfrac{r}{c}$ (8) $\dfrac{1}{u} + \dfrac{1}{v}$ (9) $\dfrac{1}{ab} + \dfrac{1}{bc} + \dfrac{1}{ca}$

(10) $\dfrac{3}{a} + \dfrac{4}{a^2}$ (11) $\dfrac{1}{a} - \dfrac{1}{b}$ (12) $\frac{1}{2}x - \frac{1}{3}x$

(13) $x + \dfrac{x}{y}$ (14) $\dfrac{x}{2} + \dfrac{x}{3} - \dfrac{x}{5}$ (15) $a - \dfrac{1}{a}$

(16) $\dfrac{2x}{5} - \dfrac{3x}{10}$ (17) $\dfrac{2x}{y} + \dfrac{3y}{x} + 1$ (18) $\dfrac{a}{xy} + \dfrac{b}{yz} - \dfrac{c}{xz}$

(17) Simplify: (1) $\frac{3}{4}+\frac{1}{3}-\frac{1}{2}$.   (2) $8\frac{3}{7}\div177$.   (3) $\frac{5}{6}+2\frac{1}{3}-1\frac{7}{12}$.
(4) $\left(\frac{2}{3}+\frac{3}{4}\right)\times\frac{4}{5}$.   (5) $\frac{2}{3}+\frac{3}{4}\div\frac{4}{5}$.   (6) $\left(\frac{2}{3}+\frac{3}{4}\right)\div\frac{4}{5}$.
(7) $4\frac{1}{2}\div\left(\frac{3}{4}-\frac{5}{7}\right)$.   (8) $4\frac{1}{6}\div\frac{3}{5}$ of $3\frac{1}{3}$.   (9) $4\frac{1}{6}\div\frac{3}{5}\times3\frac{1}{3}$.
(10) $\left(\frac{3}{8}+\frac{1}{5}\right)\div\left(\frac{1}{3}+\frac{4}{11}\right)$.   (11) $12\frac{2}{3}-4\frac{3}{4}$ of $2\frac{1}{3}+5\frac{1}{12}$.

(18) Convert into decimals:

(1) $\frac{1}{2}, \frac{1}{3}, \frac{1}{4}, \frac{1}{5}, \frac{1}{6}, \frac{1}{7}, \frac{1}{8}, \frac{1}{9}, \frac{1}{10}$ (correct to three places).
(2) $\frac{1}{20}, \frac{1}{16}, \frac{1}{25}, \frac{1}{40}, \frac{1}{50}, \frac{37}{100}, \frac{19}{1000}$ (exactly).
(3) $\frac{2}{3}, \frac{4}{5}, \frac{5}{6}, \frac{4}{7}, \frac{5}{8}, \frac{4}{9}, \frac{5}{11}, 2\frac{4}{13}, 7\frac{7}{30}, 4\frac{4}{9}, 8\frac{8}{9}$ (to three places).

(19) Convert into common fractions in their lowest terms:
.75, .6, .875, .7, .95, 6.35, 17.04, 9.625, 8.05, 3.24.

CHAPTER 13

Simple Equations

Solve:

(1) $x+7 = 12-4x$
(2) $9-3x = 3x+19-2x$
(3) $6x+9+3x = 2x-12$
(4) $4x-16-7x = 9-2x+3$
(5) $3x-13-12x+5 = 19-5x-7$
(6) $9x-16+15x = 9+5x-25+8x$
(7) $6-4x+7x = 5-3x+9-6x$
(8) $\frac{2}{3}x = -8$

(9) $\frac{x}{4} - \frac{x}{5} = 1$

(10) $\frac{3}{5}x - \frac{7}{10} = \frac{1}{2}$
(11) $\frac{1}{4}x - \frac{2}{3} = \frac{5}{6}x + \frac{1}{2}$
(12) $4(x+2) = 3(x+5)$
(13) $5(x-3)+7(4-2x) = -14$

(14) $5-(x-5)+3 = 2(x-7)$

(15) $\dfrac{x-5}{3} - \dfrac{x+4}{5} = \dfrac{9-x}{2}$

(16) $0.04x = .28$
(17) $0.02+4x = 0.136$
(18) $.3(x-.1)+.02(x-4) = .05$
(19) $0.02(x+2)+.2(x-3) = .21$
(20) $.4(.1x+.2) = .03-.3(.2x-.5)$

CHAPTER 14

A.   *Construction of Formulas*

(1) Use n in a formula giving any odd number.
(2) If the circumference of a circle is $\frac{4\,4}{7}$ times the radius, find the formula for the circumference, in terms of d, the diameter.
(3) If x is the number of degrees in the base angle of an isosceles triangle, give a formula for the vertical angle.
(4) If v is the number of degrees in the vertical angle of an isosceles triangle, give a formula for a base angle.
(5) If a postman delivers letters on the side of a street where the numbers are even, give a formula to tell how many houses he must pass before he comes to number "n." Assume that he starts from the beginning of the street.
(6) The postage charged on letters for the U. S. (except local delivery) is 3¢ an ounce or fraction thereof. Give a formula for the charge in dollars for x letters, each less than 1 oz., and y letters, each between 1 oz. and 2 oz.

(7) If the amount of floor space in a school classroom insisted on by the Board of Education is 300 sq. ft.+5 sq. ft. for every pupil, express this as a formula letting p = the number of pupils.

(8) The area of the four walls of a room is given by multiplying twice the sum of the length (l) and breadth (b) by the height (h). Make the necessary formula.

(9) Find a formula for changing any rate of feet per second into miles per hour.
    (a) x ft. per sec. =   m.p.h.   (b) x m.p.h. =   ft. per sec.

(10) Make a formula for expressing the length H of the hypotenuse of a right-angled triangle knowing that it is the square root of the sum of the squares of the other two sides, a and b.

(11) A length of wire in the shape of a square, each of whose sides is l, is bent into the shape of a circle. Express the diameter (d) in terms of l. Assume that the circumference of a circle is π times the diameter.

(12) From the result obtained in (11) find the formula for the *area* of the circle formed by the wire. Assume that the area of any circle equals π times the square of the radius.

(13) Two trains start simultaneously from the same point going in opposite directions, one at p miles per hour, the other at q miles per hour. Make a formula showing D the distance between them after going n hours.

(14) a boys have an average of x marks, b boys have an average of y marks. What is the average of all the boys?

(15) Find the gain (g) in selling for $\$p$ an article which cost q¢.

(16) If one man takes r days to do a piece of work while another takes p days to do the same, find a formula that will give the time (t) in days that both would take if working together.

(17) A room l feet long and b feet wide has a carpet leaving a margin d feet wide all round. Find formula for giving the area of the margin in square feet.

$$A =$$

(18) A plot l feet by b feet has a path d feet all round it. Find the formula for giving the area of the path in square feet.

$$A =$$

Change of Subject of Formulas

B. In each of the following exercises make the quantity indicated by the letter in the right-hand column the subject of the formula, *e.g.:*

Formula	New Subject		
$A = lb$	l		$\therefore\ l = \dfrac{A}{b}$

Formula	New Subject	Formula	New Subject
(1) $X = a+b$	$a =$	(13) $t = 2\pi\sqrt{\dfrac{l}{g}}$	$l =$
(2) $X = a-b$	$a =$		
	$b =$		
(3) $X = ab$	$a =$	(14) $s = 2\pi rl$	$l =$
(4) $X = \dfrac{a}{b}$	$a =$		$r =$
	$b =$	(15) $s = vt - \frac{1}{2}gl^2$	$v =$
(5) $X = a^2$	$a =$	(16) $D = \sqrt{\dfrac{50h}{33}}$	$h =$
(6) $X = \sqrt{a}$	$a =$		
(7) $c = 2\pi r$	$r =$	(17) $C = \dfrac{5(F-32)}{9}$	$F =$
(8) $s = vl$	$v =$		

Before doing any more examples check your answers to see if you understand the simple processes involved.

Formula	New Subject	Formula	New Subject
		(18) $\dfrac{1}{u} + \dfrac{1}{v} = \dfrac{1}{f}$	$f =$
			$u =$
		(19) $P = \dfrac{2x}{5+y}$	$y =$
(9) $A = 2(l+b)h$	$h =$	(20) $V = \frac{1}{3}Ah$	$h =$
(10) $T = \frac{1}{2}(a+b)h$	$h =$	(21) $S = \dfrac{5x}{1+y}$	$y =$
(11) $A = \frac{1}{2}bh$	$b =$		
	$h =$	(22) $T = \dfrac{B^2(L-0.6B)}{188}$	$L =$
(12) $A = \pi r^2$	$r =$		

Use of Formulas

C. In the following exercises, when you are asked to find the numerical value of a letter, make that letter the subject of the formula.

(1) $A = \frac{1}{2}bh$; find A when $b = 4,\ h = 1.8$;
    find b when $A = 3,\ h = 5$.
(2) $C = 2\pi r$; find r when $C = 88$ in., $\pi = 3\frac{1}{7}$.

(3) Area of circle $= \pi r^2$; find r when area $= 7.065$ sq. ft. and $\pi = 3.14$. [To find the square root of a number, see Chapter 19.]

(4) $V = \frac{1}{3}\pi r^2 h$ (volume of cone);

find V when $r = 10$ cm.   find h when $V = 6.16$ cu. in.

$h = 5$ cm. $r = 1.4$

$\pi = 3.14$. $\pi = 3\frac{1}{7}$.

(5) $D = \sqrt{\dfrac{50h}{33}}$; find h when $D = 10$.

(6) $A = \pi(R+r)(R-r)$; find A when $R = 1.8$ cm., $r = 1.7$ cm., $\pi = \dfrac{22}{7}$ (Area of ring).

(7) $T = \dfrac{\frac{1}{2}(L-\frac{3}{5}B)B^2}{94}$ T = tonnage of a sailing vessel; L = length in feet; B = breadth in feet.

Find T if $L = 240$, $B = 32$.

(8) $\triangle = \sqrt{s(s-a)(s-b)(s-c)}$ is the formula for obtaining the area ($\triangle$) of a triangle, whose sides are a, b and c, s being $\frac{1}{2}(a+b+c)$.

Find $\triangle$ when $a = 13$, $b = 12$, $c = 5$.

(9) What is the height (H) of a lighthouse if its light can be seen at a distance (D) of 12 miles? H is the height in feet. D is the distance in miles.

$$D = \sqrt{\tfrac{3}{2}H}$$

(10) If $L = \dfrac{Mk^2 f}{g}$, find K if $L = 450$, $M = 8$, $f = 2$, $g = 32$.

(11) If $V = \dfrac{h}{3}(A+B+\sqrt{AB})$, find V when $A = 50$, $B = 18$, $h = 20$.

(12) Find the value of $2\sqrt{DR-(\frac{1}{2}D)^2}$, if $D = 11$, $R = 591$.

Problems Leading to Simple Equations

D.

(1) Find a number such that if you add 10 to a quarter of it the result is the same as if you added 8 to a third of it.

(2) There are 27 coins in a bag, some of them dimes, the rest quarters. If the total value of the coins is $3.15, how many of each kind are there?

(3) By selling a car for $1040 a man gains three times as much as he would lose if he sold it for $720. What did it cost him?

(4) A field is three times as long as it is broad. The distance round it is 320 yards. What are its length and breadth?

(5) The angles of a triangle ABC are such that A = 3C and B = 2C. Find the size of each angle in degrees.

(6) Divide a line of 10½ in. into two parts so that one part may be three quarters of the other.

(7) At a meeting where 238 people voted, the majority for a motion as opposed to an amendment was 22. How many people voted for the motion?

(8) I would pay the same income tax whether I paid 12¢ on the $ on all my income above $1000 or 32¢ on the $ on all my income above $1500. What is my income?

(9) At a shooting range a man is paid 2¢ if he hits the target and pays 1¢ if he misses it. He has to pay 3¢. How many times did he hit the target out of 51 shots? When would he neither win nor lose any money?

(10) A boy going to school 3 miles away has to start walking at 0815 hours to be just in time. If he goes by bus which travels five times as fast as he walks he need not start till 0851 hours. At what rate does the boy walk?

(11) Find the fraction which becomes ½ when 1 is added to the denominator and becomes ⅔ when 2 is added to the numerator.

(12) A force of 1240 men is made up of three divisions; the second is a quarter more than the first, while the third is 90 more than half the second. How many men are there in each division?

CHAPTER 15

Geometrical Constructions

(1) Draw a line and bisect it geometrically.
Draw an angle and bisect it geometrically.
Draw an angle equal to a given angle.

(2) Draw AB. Bisect it at X by a line PQ (geometrical construction again).
Join AP, PB, BQ, QA.
Prove △ APQ ≡ △ PBQ.
Prove △ APX ≡ △ PBX.
What more can you now say about PQ?
What have you proved about PQ besides this?

(3) Draw an acute $\angle$ ABC. Bisect it geometrically by a line **BL**. (Let the arc cut BA at P and BC at Q.) Join PL, QL. Prove $\triangle$ BPL $\equiv$ $\triangle$ LQB. Thus prove the correctness of your construction.

(4) Draw a line $\perp$ another line (*a*) from a point on the line, (*b*) from a point outside it.

(5) What can you say about lines parallel to one side of a $\triangle$ which cut another side into a number of equal parts?

(6) Show there is a mathematical explanation for the quick method of drawing parallel lines with set square (or protractor) and ruler.

CHAPTER 16

A *Parallelograms and Triangles*

(1)

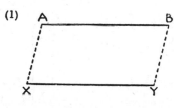

If AB = XY and AB ‖ XY, prove (1) AX = BY, (2) AX ‖ BY. (*Hints.*—Mark on your figure all lines given equal or parallel. Draw a diagonal. Mark equal ∠s. Find two triangles containing the lines you want to prove equal and parallel. Prove the △s congruent. Then imagine one twisted round and fitted on the other.)

(2)

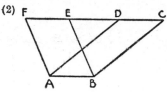

Given: (1) AB ‖ CF, (2) ABEF, ABCD are ▱s. Find two congruent △s. (Prove them congruent.)

(3)

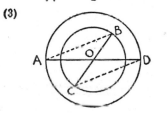

Two ⊙s have same center O. AOD, COB are lines crossing the ⊙s and passing through O (*i.e.* they are diameters). Prove △ AOB ≡ △ COD. Find an angle equal to ∠ CDO. If AC, BD were joined, what could you say about quadrilateral ABDC?

(4)

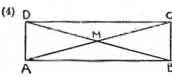

ABCD is an oblong. ∠ AMD = 30°. Find ∠ CBD, ∠ MCD, ∠ CDM, ∠ CAB, giving reasons for each step in your work.

(5)

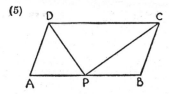

Given: {ABCD is a ▱, DP bisects ∠ ADC, CP bisects ∠ DCB}
Prove DC = 2CB.

(6) Prove that the diagonals of a rhombus cut at rt. ∠s. (Use congruent △s.)

B. *Areas of Rectangles and Triangles*

Find the areas of each of the following figures. (Measurements are in feet, so answers will be in square feet.)

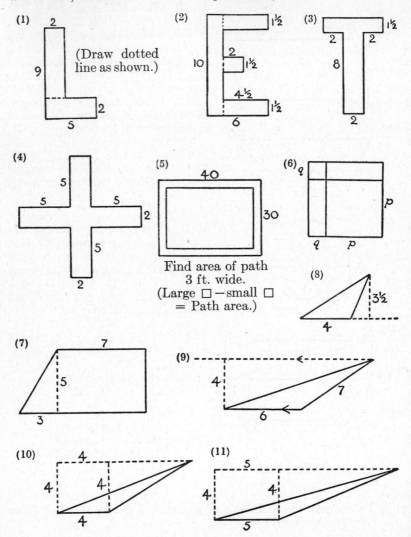

C. Name △s which are equal in area in the following figures:

(1)
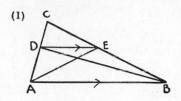

(2)
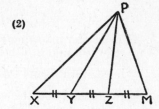

(3)
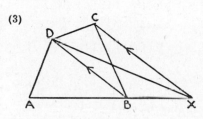

Also find a △ equal in area to quadrilateral ABCD.

D. Calculate the areas of the following figures. Measurements are given in yards.

(1)
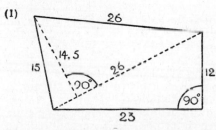

(4)
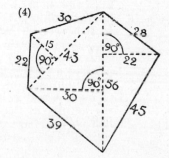

Find area of this field.

(2)
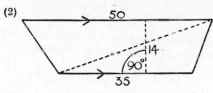

(3)
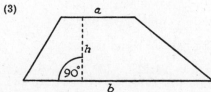

(5)
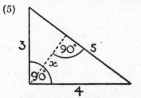

Calculate length of x.

CHAPTER 17

Ratios

A. Express the following ratios as simply as possible (*i.e.* reduce to lowest unit in either, make a fraction and cancel if possible) in the form $\frac{x}{y}$ and state what fraction the first quantity is of the second and the second of the first.

(1) 9 inches : 12 inches.
(2) 5 ft. 3 in. : 3 ft. 6 in.
(3) $1\frac{1}{4}$ hours : 45 minutes.
(4) $2\frac{1}{2}$ cwt : 3 cwt.
(5) 5 pt. : 5 qt.
(6) 40 m. : 1 Km.
(7) 1 m. : 85 cm.
(8) $3\frac{1}{2} : 5\frac{3}{5}$.
(9) $1.2 : 1.6$.

B. (1) A school contains 420 boys and 315 girls. Find the ratio of (i) the number of girls to the number of boys; (ii) the number of boys to the number of pupils.

(2) The sides of two squares are $2''$ and $3''$. Find the ratio of (i) their perimeters; (ii) their areas.

(3) In 1937, Henke flew from Berlin to New York twice, the first time in 24 hours (approx.), the second time in 18 hours (approx.). What is the ratio of the first time taken to the second? What is the ratio of the speed of the first journey to the speed of the second journey?

(4) A man rows on still water at the rate of $3\frac{3}{4}$ m.p.h. If he rows on a stream flowing at $1\frac{1}{4}$ m.p.h., find the ratio of his rate up stream with that of his rate down stream.

(5) Two men, A and B, cycle a distance of 63 miles. A does the journey at the rate of 10 miles an hour; B starting half an hour later arrives 33 minutes sooner. Find the ratio of their speeds.

C. Express in the form $x:1$ the following ratios:

(1) $\frac{8}{4}$ (2) $\frac{17.1}{5.7}$ (3) $\frac{.4}{1.2}$ (4) $\frac{\$7.50}{\$5}$ (5) $\frac{3 \text{ hr. 15 min.}}{1 \text{ hr. 30 min.}}$ (6) $\frac{1\frac{3}{4}}{4\frac{1}{5}}$

(7) $\frac{2 \text{ Kg.}}{250 \text{ g.}}$ (8) $\frac{\frac{1}{2} \text{ mile}}{100 \text{ yd.}}$ (9) $\frac{60 \text{ miles per hour}}{66 \text{ ft. per sec.}}$

D. Find x in each of the following pairs of equal ratios:

(1) $96:24 = x:1$.   (2) $x:6 = 14:21$.   (3) $35:21 = 10:x$.
(4) $4:7 = x:11$.   (5) $x:\$4.20 = 15 \text{ cwt.} : 10 \text{ cwt.}$

(6) $3.60:$5.20 = x:3.   (7) x:8 francs = 3 tons:16 cwt.

(8) 5 yd.:8 yd. = $7\frac{1}{2}$ in.:x.

E. (1) The scale of a map is 1 in. to 50 yards. Find its R.F.

(2) The scale of a map is 10 cm. to 1 Km. Find its R.F.

(3) If the scale of a map is 1:20,000 find the length in feet of a road which on the map measures $\frac{3}{4}''$.

(4) The scale on a French map is 1:100,000. What is the length of a river which measures 4 cm.?

(5) Change a scale of 3 in. to the mile into a R.F. What length on the map would represent a real distance of 770 yards?

(6) Change the following R.F.'s to inches to a mile, and also to miles to an inch:

(a) $\dfrac{1}{63360}$ (b) $\dfrac{1}{500,000}$ (c) $\dfrac{1}{\text{Million}}$

(d) $\dfrac{1}{126,720}$ (e) $\dfrac{1}{2,500,000}$ (f) $\dfrac{1}{190,080}$

(7) State the connection between (a), (d), and (f), and between (c), (b), and (e) in Question 6.

(8) The R.F. on a map is $\dfrac{1}{500,000}$. Find the number of inches on the map between two places 50 miles apart (to nearest $\frac{1}{10}$ of an inch).

(9) The R.F. on a map is $\dfrac{1}{\text{Million}}$. Find the distance between two places which are 3.8 inches apart on the map (to nearest $\frac{1}{100}$ of a mile.)

F. *Direct Variation:*

(1) If a train takes 3 hours 40 minutes to cover 154 miles, how long will it take to travel 105 miles?

(2) If 9.1 meters of material are worth $65, find the value of 3.5 meters.

(3) A church tower 145 ft. high casts a shadow 105 ft. long. What length of shadow is cast at the same hour of day by a pole 9 ft. 8 in. high?

(4) If iron costs $1.50 per cwt, how many tons could be bought for $1040?

(5) A purveyor agrees to cater for 22 guests for $8.25. If 4 more than that number are present, what would he charge?

G. *Inverse Variation:*

    (1) If 9 fires burn a ton of coal in 16 days, for how many days should a ton supply 8 fires?

    (2) A motorist travels a certain distance for 5 hours at 28 miles an hour. How long would he have taken if he had gone at 35 miles per hour?

    (3) A garrison has food that will last 72 men 39 days. How long would the same food last 78 men?

    (4) Instead of giving 11 men each $3.40 it is decided to share the total among 20 men. What will each receive?

    (5) A man walking at 4 m.p.h. finishes a journey in $1\frac{1}{4}$ hours. At what rate would he need to cycle to do the same journey in 20 minutes?

    (6) If a garrison of 41 men has enough food to last them 18 days and is reinforced by 4 men, how long will the food now last?

    (7) A gang of workmen can do a job in 12 days of 7 hours each. How many hours a day would the same gang need to work to do the same job in 9 days?

    (8) A person by reading $2\frac{1}{2}$ hours a day can read through a book in 7 days; how many days will it take him to read it if he reads $3\frac{1}{2}$ hours daily?

    (9) How many lb. of tea at 95¢ should be given in exchange for 228 lb. of coffee at 50¢?

    (10) I buy 750 copies of a book at 26¢ each. If the books had been each a cent cheaper, how many more copies could I have bought with the same money?

H. *Compound Proportion:*

    (1) If 32 men can do a piece of work in 27 days of 8 hours each, how many days of 6 hours each will 48 men take to do a similar piece of work?

    (2) How much will it cost to send 20 tons 14 miles if it costs $1.20 to send 2 tons 3 miles?

    (3) If 24 men can do a piece of work in 12 days of 7 hours each, how many men will do the same work in 14 days of 8 hours each?

    (4) If 640 men on full rations consume 210 cwt. of meat in 49 days, how many men on half rations will consume 120 cwt. in 28 days?

    (5) A man undertakes to complete a job in 17 days and puts 15 men on it. After 7 days he finds that only one-third of the work has been done. How many more men will be needed to do the job in time?

J. *Taxes, Speeds, etc.*

(1) The taxes on a house rented at $1020 per annum amount to $204. What should be the tax on a house whose annual rent is $820?

(2) If taxes at 40¢ on the $ produce $11,000, find what taxes at 45¢ on the $ should produce.

(3) How long would a train of length 396 ft. traveling at 45 m.p.h., take to pass: (i) a signal, (ii) a platform 462 ft. long?

(4) How long would a train 360 ft. long going at 54 m.p.h. take to pass a train 300 ft. long going at 36 m.p.h. (i) in the same direction, (ii) in the opposite direction?

(5) A plane is flying at 200 m.p.h. towards a fort. It sees a gun fired from the fort and hears the report 12 sec. afterwards. How far was it from the fort when it saw the gun fired? (Sound travels at 1100 ft. per sec.)

(6) A motor-car uses, on an average, 1 gallon of gasoline for 32 miles and 1 quart of oil for 500 miles. Find the total cost of gasoline and oil for one year (52 weeks) if the average distance traveled weekly is 240 miles; the cost of gasoline is 26¢ a gallon, and the cost of oil is 25¢ a quart. Assume crank case is filled every 500 miles and calculate amount of oil actually bought.

(7) A knot is a speed of 6080 ft. per hour. An airplane, flying at 200 miles an hour, flies over a destroyer steaming in the same direction at 35 knots. After 3 minutes, how many miles will the airplane be ahead of the destroyer?

K. *Percentages.*— Change the following fractions into percentages.

(1) $\frac{1}{2}$, $\frac{1}{3}$, $\frac{2}{3}$, $\frac{1}{4}$, $\frac{3}{4}$, $\frac{1}{5}$, $\frac{2}{5}$, $\frac{3}{5}$, $1\frac{1}{5}$, $\frac{1}{6}$, $\frac{5}{6}$, $\frac{1}{7}$, $\frac{3}{7}$, $\frac{1}{8}$, $\frac{3}{8}$, $3\frac{7}{8}$, $\frac{1}{9}$, $4\frac{4}{9}$, $\frac{1}{10}$, $6\frac{7}{10}$.

(2) Change into percentages and arrange in ascending order of magnitude: $\frac{11}{13}$, $\frac{13}{15}$, $\frac{7}{9}$.

(3) Change into common fractions in their lowest terms: 80%, 16%, $6\frac{1}{4}$%, $87\frac{1}{2}$%, $17\frac{1}{7}$%, $67\frac{7}{9}$%, $\frac{1}{4}$%, $\frac{1}{2}$%, $\frac{1}{8}$%, $114\frac{1}{6}$%, $99\frac{1}{11}$%.

(4) What percentage is the first quantity of the second? $3 of $20; $15.50 of $60; 1 ft. 4 in. of 4 ft.; 352 ft. of 1 mile; $2\frac{2}{7}$ of $14\frac{2}{7}$; 3.04 of 4.56.

(5) Express as percentages:—(a) Discount of 5¢ on the dollar; (b) Commission of $1.50 on $12; (c) Tax of $85 on taxable income of $250; (d) Sale tax of 30¢ on goods worth $2.40; (e) Dividend of $125 on investment of $2500; (f) Rebate of 7¢ on bill for

$1.40; (*g*) Discount of 57¢ on bill for $3.80; (*h*) **15** marks out of a possible 75; (*i*) loss of 6½ lb. weight by a man formerly weighing 130 lb.; (*j*) 38 men in hospital in a camp of 1520 men.

L. *Profit and Loss:*
   (1) I buy an article for $78 and sell it for $97.50. Find my gain per cent.
   (2) Out of 1 cwt. of goods bought at $2.70 per cwt. a quarter are sold at 5¢ per lb. and the rest at 2¢ per lb. Find the gain per cent.
   (3) 360 oranges are bought at 3 for 5¢ and another 360 at 2¢ each. Find actual gain or loss in selling them all at 3 for 7¢ and the gain or loss per cent.
   (4) If 100 lb. of lead are needed for a certain job and if the plumber allows 12% profit, what should he charge for the material used if he buys lead at $120 per ton?
   (5) Find the cost price of an article sold for $31.50 at a loss of 10%.
   (6) An article sold for $140.80 brought in a profit of 6⅔%. What was the cost price of the article?
   (7) A man sells goods for $136.08 and gains 8%. How much profit was this?
   (8) A selling price of 6¢ a lb. yields a profit of 20%. What is the cost price for 1 cwt.?
   (9) A selling price of $6.50 yields a profit of 30%. What price would entail a loss of 25%?
   (10) A selling price of $69 entails a loss of 8%. What will be the gain or loss per cent in selling at $84?
   (11) A book sold for $2.40 gives a profit of 20%. If the price is reduced to $1.80, what is the gain or loss per cent?
   (12) A dealer marks a car which cost him $950 at 20% above the cost. He takes off 5% for a cash sale. What does the customer pay?

M. *Simple Interest:*
   (1) Find the simple interest on $1900 for 3 years at 4%.
   (2)   " $1988 for 3 years at 2%.
   (3)   " $429.60 for 14 weeks at 4%.
   (4)   " $3176.40 for 219 days at 2½%.
   (5) A man was paid $54 as interest on money he lent at 3¾% for a year and a half. How much did he lend?
   (6) At what rate per cent will $15 amount to $20.50 in 10 years?

CHAPTER 18

Averages

Find the average of:
  (1) 7, 2, 9, 14, 3; (2) 7, 9, 0, 5, 2, 10; (3) 15, 16, 17, 18, 19, 20;
      (4) 3.7, 4.2, 1.8, 9.7, 8.2, 1.1, 3.6, .8; (5) $3\frac{1}{2}$, $4\frac{5}{6}$, $7\frac{3}{4}$, $9\frac{3}{8}$, $5\frac{1}{12}$,
      $4\frac{2}{3}$.
  (6) The average weight of 3 boys is 89 lb., and of 2 other boys
      is 99 lb. What is the *total* weight of the five boys and their
      average weight?
  (7) A motor car does the first 76 miles of its journey in 2 hr.
      25 min., and the next 84 miles in 2 hr. 35 min. What is
      the average speed in miles per hour?
  (8) A boy walks for $1\frac{1}{2}$ hours at 4 miles an hour and then 2 hours
      at $3\frac{1}{2}$ miles an hour. What was his average rate of walk-
      ing?
  (9) A car travels 20 miles at 30 m.p.h. and another 20 miles at
      40 m.p.h. Find the average speed for the whole journey.
  (10) A car travels for a quarter of an hour at 50 m.p.h. and then
      for half an hour at 60 m.p.h. Find the average speed for
      the whole journey.
  (11) A racing car travels for $\frac{1}{2}$ mile at 100 miles per hour and for
      $\frac{1}{4}$ mile at 150 m.p.h. What is its average speed for the
      whole distance?
  (12) An airplane flies 200 miles at 150 m.p.h. and another 350
      miles at 120 m.p.h. Find the average speed in miles per
      hour for the whole journey.

CHAPTER 19

Square Root

  (1) Find the square root of the following:
      529; 625; 1225; 3481; 6084; 95481; 15129; 327184; 183184.
  (2) Find the square root of:
      18.49; 15.7609; 41.2164; 5.3824; .0064; 3.7249; 1.522756.
  (3) Find the square root of the following correct to two places:
      2; 3; 5; 13.4; .0051; 45.71.
  (4) A rectangular field of $7\frac{1}{2}$ acres is three times as long as it is
      broad. Find its length. (4840 sq. yds. = 1 acre)
  (5) How long will it take to walk around a square field whose area
      is 160 acres at the rate of 4 miles an hour?

CHAPTER 20

Similar Figures

(1) Give the lengths of the unmarked lines in the following △s
(which are not drawn to scale):

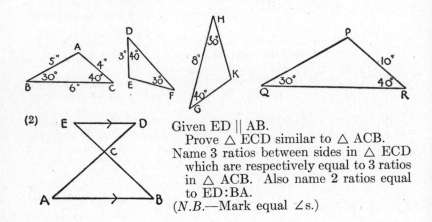

(2)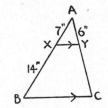

Given ED ∥ AB.
  Prove △ ECD similar to △ ACB.
Name 3 ratios between sides in △ ECD
  which are respectively equal to 3 ratios
  in △ ACB. Also name 2 ratios equal
  to ED:BA.
(*N.B.*—Mark equal ∠s.)

(3) Calculate YC and if XY = 5″ find
  BC.

(4) At 11 A.M. a pole 4 ft. high casts a shadow 5 ft. long. At the
same time a tree's shadow is found to be 52 ft. long. How
high is the tree?

(5) A pyramid on a square base casts a shadow which extends
190 ft. beyond its base, which is 140 ft. each way. At the
same time a stick 6 ft. long casts a shadow 13 ft. long. Make
a rough drawing and calculate the height of the pyramid.

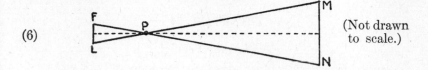

(6)   (Not drawn
                                                            to scale.)

P represents the pin hole in a pin-hole camera.

MN represents a man 5′ 6″ high.

FL represents a film $2\frac{1}{2}$ in. high, in the camera.

P is 5 in. from the film (*i.e.* its perpendicular distance from
FL is 5 in.).

How far from the camera must the man stand in order that a
full-length portrait of him may just be taken?

(7) Suppose the lines FN, LM in Ques. 6 represent a pair of black-
smith's tongs, pivoted at P. If the handles PM and PN are
18 in. long and, when fully open are 6 in. apart at MN and if
each of the shorter arms FP and LP are 4 in. long, find the
greatest thickness of iron bar that can be gripped with the
tongs.

(8) Two trees X and Y are out of sight of
each other because a house stands between them. Lines XP, PY are
marked out on the ground, and their
mid-points joined. The line joining
these mid-points is found to be 35 ft.
long. How far apart are the trees?
(Give reasons for your answer.)

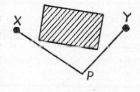

(9) Name all the similar △s you can see in the following figures
(give reasons). Name also three pairs of congruent triangles
in Fig. (*b*).

(*a*)

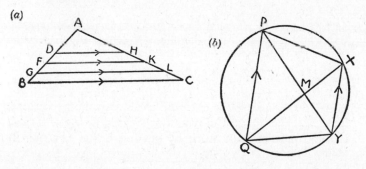

CHAPTER 21

Right-angled Triangles

A. *Theorem of Pythagoras*

(1) The sides of a $\triangle$ enclosing a rt. $\angle$ are 5 cm. and 12 cm. long. Find the length of the third side.

(2) The longest side of a rt. $\angle$ d $\triangle$ is 17″ long. Its shortest side is 8″ long. Find the length of the other side.

(3) Find the value of $(XZ)^2 - (XY)^2$ in sq. in.

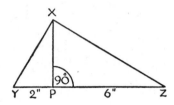

(4) Find the length of YZ.

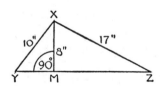

(5) A barrow has to be wheeled up a flight of 3 steps, each with 8″ tread and 6″ rise. Find the shortest plank which may be placed on the steps to enable the barrow to be wheeled up them.

(6) Draw two lines at right angles and make each line 1 inch long. Calculate the length of the line joining their ends [leave answer in square root ($\sqrt{\ }$) form]. Now show how to draw a line $\sqrt{3}$ inches long. Can you now suggest a way of testing the accuracy of your work by getting a line $\sqrt{4}$ (*i.e.* **2**) inches long?

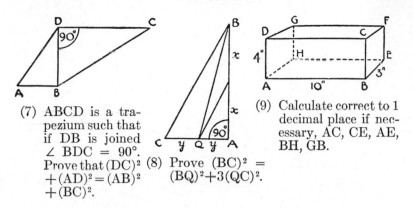

(7) ABCD is a trapezium such that if DB is joined ∠ BDC = 90°. Prove that $(DC)^2 + (AD)^2 = (AB)^2 + (BC)^2$.

(8) Prove $(BC)^2 = (BQ)^2 + 3(QC)^2$.

(9) Calculate correct to 1 decimal place if necessary, AC, CE, AE, BH, GB.

(10) Find the distance from the center of a ⊙ (radius 13 in.) of a chord 10 in. long. (Give answer correct to 1 decimal place.)

(11) A chord 10 in. long is drawn in a ⊙ of radius 6 in. How far is it from the center? (Give answer correct to 1 decimal place.)

B Trigonometrical Ratios

(1) Draw 8 right-angled triangles, naming each by different letters and omitting the guide-letters O, A and H (see Chap. 21). Write down each trigonometrical ratio for each acute angle in each triangle. Check your answers by the key-triangle marked with O, A and H in Chap. 21.

(2) Write down the values of sin A, cos A, tan A, sin B, cos B, tan B in the following triangles:

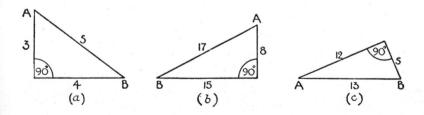

(a)   (b)   (c)

(3) Prove (1) $\sin^2A + \cos^2A = 1$; (2) $\sin^2C + \cos^2C = 1$.

[*Hint:* Use Pythagoras.]

("$\sin^2A$" means "the square of the ratio which is the sine of the $\angle$ A," *i.e.* $\sin^2A$ means $\dfrac{(BC)^2}{(AC)^2}$.)

(4) A telephone wire has to be fixed from the top of tower AB to a point X. The "angle of elevation" at X (*i.e.* angle BXA) is found to be 30°. (*Hint:* What value has sin 30°?) How much wire will be needed? (Ignore fastening and wire inside tower.)

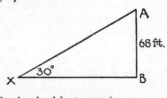

(5) A boat is to be launched down a slip-way 60 yards long which runs at an angle of 30° to the horizontal. Find the height of the boat above the level of the water.

(6) A boy is flying a kite which needs 846 ft. of string. If the string makes an angle of 45° with the horizon, how high is the kite above the ground? (Assume that the string is in a straight line.)

(7) An escalator which runs from one floor of a building to the floor above is inclined at 30° to these floors. If the height between the floors is 24 ft., what is the length of the actual distance the escalator carries a passenger?

(8) When the sun is 60° above the horizon, how long must a vertical post on level ground be to cast a shadow 34.6 ft.? Give answer to nearest whole number.

(9) If C is the rt. $\angle$ in $\triangle$ ABC, and if cot B = 2.4, find the other trigonometrical ratios of B and the six trigonometrical ratios of A.

(*Hint:* Turn 2.4 into an improper fraction. Find third side by Pythagoras. *Note:* these ratios will not give the actual *lengths* of the sides, necessarily.)

(10) If BC (in Question 9) = $2''$, find the lengths of AB and of AC.

CHAPTER 22

A. *Scale Drawing*

(1) On a drawing of scale $\frac{1}{120}$ what is the real length on the ground of these drawn distances: $\frac{7}{8}''$, $1\frac{3}{4}''$, 2.5$''$, $4\frac{1}{6}''$, $\frac{63}{64}''$, 5.3$''$, $1'$, .025$''$, 1.1$''$, $\frac{19}{64}''$.

(2) What are the names commonly applied to the maps to which the following representative fractions give the scale: $\frac{1}{63360}$, $\frac{1}{10560}$, $\frac{1}{2500}$?

(3) Draw, to scale $\frac{1}{120}$, the plan of a hut with three compartments. Length of hut 90 ft., breadth 30 ft. Compartment A, 30 ft. ×24 ft., B, 30 ft. ×42 ft., C, 30 ft. ×24 ft. There is a door 3 ft. 6 in. wide at the W. (left) end of hut, center of door being 12 ft. from the N. (top) side of hut. A door 3 ft. 6 in. wide is at E. end of hut, center of door being 12 ft. from S. side of hut. Interior doors, exactly in middle of the 30-foot walls, lead from A to B and from C to B. These are 3 ft. wide. Measure distance from center of exterior door in A to center of interior door in west wall of C. Also measure diagonal length of whole hut.

B. *Angles of Depression and Elevation*

(1) A man standing on a tower XY observes an object 600 ft. from the foot of the tower. The angle of depression of the object from the top of the tower is 35°. Find the height of the tower by drawing and measurement.

(2) An artillery post is on the top of a hill 500 feet high. Firing at a range of 10,500 ft. on the level the angle of elevation of the guns would normally be 5° 30'. Is the firing angle now one of elevation or depression and what (approx. to 30') is it? (By drawing and measurement.)

(3) If the angle of depression of a clinometer reading from a hill-top to the base of the slope is 37° 14' 20", what is the angle of elevation from the base to the hill-top?

(4) A barrage balloon tethered 1 mile away from an observer bears an angle of elevation of 30°. How high up is it? Answer either by calculation or drawing and measurement.

C. *Bearings.* (*Use any convenient scales*)

(1) A motorist travels for 15 minutes at 40 m.p.h. in the direction 045°, then for 24 minutes at 50 m.p.h. in the direction 160°. Find the distance and bearing he then is from the starting point.

(2) Two men X and Y are at a certain point A. X leaves and travels on 15° for 2 hours at 3 m.p.h.; then on 345° for the same time at the same speed. He then sends signals to Y to

join him. In which direction should Y travel, and how far, to effect a meeting with X?

(3) Draw in this record of a journey made up of distances traveled and bearings taken. Start at A bearing on 45° for 450 ft., B bearing 55° for 300 ft., C bearing 185° for 600 ft., D bearing 270° for 450 ft., E bearing 330° for 300 ft. How far is the end from the beginning? (Scale the drawing to 1 in. to 150 ft.)

(4) Draw this plan of a journey: (*Start*) (1) bearing on 270° for 1 mile, (2) bearing on 190° for $2\frac{1}{4}$ miles, (3) bearing on 150° for $\frac{1}{2}$ mile, (4) bearing on 75° for 3960 ft., (5) back to starting point. State the bearing and the distance from point 5 to point 1 in a direct line. (Scale 4 in. to 1 mile.)

(5) Draw a plan made from the following descriptions of the boundaries of a landing field:
1. 40°; 2160 ft. 2. 90°; 1500 ft. 3. 130°; 1200 ft. 4. 200°; 3000 ft. 5. 290°; 1200 ft. 6. 315°; 2250 ft. (Scale, 1 in. = 600 ft.)

D. *Map-making and Common Scales*

(1) To scale 1 in. = 1 mile draw a map of an area 6 miles E. to W. by 4 miles N. to S. A road runs diagonally across the area and crosses a river flowing N.N.W. to S.S.E. Show a lake of about 3 square miles in area in the S.E. section of the map and a wood $\frac{1}{2}$ mile × 1 mile in area on its E. bank.

(2) Draw the map of a roughly triangular island to the scale $\frac{1}{10560}$ and the same island to the scale $\frac{1}{63360}$. Show 1 river and give 8 compass directions.

(3) On a map whose scale is uncertain and may be either 1 in. = 1 mile or 1 in. = 2 miles the distance between a village and a bridge B is found to be 2 centimeters. What are the two possible distances in miles and feet on the actual country?

(4) On a map scaled as 1 cm. = 5 Km. the distance between two villages is 3.25 cm. What is that distance in miles?

(5) On measuring a contemplated journey on a French map scaled 1 cm. = 1 Km. a traveler finds that the various stages of his journey are:
1. 15.4 cm. 2. 17.3 cm. 3. 14.9 cm. 4. 20.05 cm. 5. 12.1 cm. 6. 10.8 cm. 7. 15.3 cm.
Calculate how many miles he expects to travel in all.

(6) On a map of scale $\frac{1}{10560}$ what distances are represented by (*a*) 3.6 in. (*b*) 2.9 in. (*c*) $4\frac{3}{4}$ in. (*d*) $5\frac{1}{16}$ in.?

CHAPTER 23

Time

(1) Calculate changes in Latitude and Longitude:

	Initial position	Subsequent position
(a)	46° 15′ N; 27° 14′ W	40° 07′ N; 17° 45′ E
(b)	32° 17′ S; 64° 14′ E	3° 06′ N; 65° 13′ E
(c)	43° 32′ N; 102° 20′ E	17° 18′ N; 20° 15′ W
(d)	58° 20′ N; 150° 10′ E	62° 20′ N; 150° 15′ W
(e)	38° 13′ S; 27° 05′ W	15° 12′ S; 137° 20′ W

(2) Find L.M.T. of the following places:
    (a) G.M.T. 1045 hours, place 97° 45′ E.
    (b) G.M.T. 1947 hours, place 33° 15′ W.

(3) Find longitude of the following places:
    (a) G.M.T. 1045 hours, L.M.T. 1915 hours.
    (b) G.M.T. 1330 hours, L.M.T. 1035 hours.

(4) Find L.M.T. at "B" if
    (a) "B" is 80° W and L.M.T. at "A" (33° W) is 1015 hours.
    (b) "B" is 100° E and L.M.T. at "A" (14° E) is 1024 hours.

(5) Find longitude of "B" if
    (a) "A" (12° W) has L.M.T. 0615 hours when L.M.T. at "B" is 1115 hours.
    (b) "A" (172° E) has L.M.T. 1015 hours when L.M.T. at "B" is 0700 hours.

CHAPTER 24

Other Kinds of Equations

A. Solve the following pairs of equations:

(1) $3x+y = 9$
    $4x+y = 11$

(2) $3x+y = 15$
    $4x-y = 13$

(3) $3x+5y = 2$
    $4x+y = 14$

(4) $3x+5y+14 = 0$
    $7x+2y+23 = 0$

(5) $4x-7y = 43$
    $6x+2y = 2$

(6) $8x+9y = 17\frac{1}{2}$
    $5x-4y = -3\frac{1}{2}$

(7) $13x+17y = 109$
    $17x+13y = 221$

(8) $4(x-1)+3(y+1) = 24$
    $x = y+1$

(9) $3(x+2)+5(y-1) = 35$
    $5(x-2)+3(y+1) = 23$

(10) $\dfrac{2x}{3}+\dfrac{4y}{5} = 8$

     $\dfrac{3x}{4}-\dfrac{2y}{5} = 2\frac{1}{2}$

(11) $\frac{1}{2}(x-2) = \frac{1}{3}(y-3)$
     $x+y = 10$

(12) $x-3 = y-5 = 10$

(13) $\dfrac{x+2}{y-3} = 3$

$\dfrac{x-2}{y+3} = -\frac{1}{7}$

(14) $0.4x+0.5y = 3$

$x-2.5y = 0$

(15) $\frac{1}{2}x+\frac{1}{3}y = 1$

$2x+3y+1 = 0$

Quadratic Equations

B. Solve the following equations:

(1) $x^2 = 9$ (2) $x^2-5x = 0$ (3) $x^2 = 4x$ (4) $x^2-4x = 21$

(5) $x^2-5x+6 = 0$ (6) $x^2-7x+12 = 0$ (7) $x^2-x = 0$

(8) $x^2 = 9(x-2)$ (9) $x(x+1) = 72$ (10) $x^2 = 2(5x+12)$

(11) $x-\dfrac{18}{x} = 7$ (12) $x+4 = \dfrac{9}{x+4}$ (13) $\dfrac{x-1}{2x+1} = \dfrac{4}{3x}$

(14) $2x^2+x = 6$ (15) $2x^2+7x+3 = 0$ (16) $6x^2-7x = 3$

(17) $\dfrac{12}{x+5} = 3-x$

CHAPTER 26

Velocity and Acceleration

(1) A body whose initial velocity is 0 has an acceleration of 3 feet-second units. Find its velocity after 18 seconds, and the space it covers in this time.

(2) If a particle with an initial velocity of 20 meters per second moves with uniform acceleration of 5 meters-second units, how long will it take to traverse 1400 meters? Find also the velocity of the particle at the end of this period.

(3) In 6 seconds, a body moving with uniform acceleration of 14 feet-second units, traverses 930 feet. Find its initial velocity.

(4) While increasing his speed from 15 feet per second to 35 feet per second, a cyclist covers a distance of 100 feet. How long would this transition take if the acceleration was uniform; and what would the feet-second units be?

(5) A motor-car, traveling at 60 miles per hour, has a uniform acceleration of -8 feet-second units. In what distance would the car pull up; and how long would it take?

(6) Starting from rest, a train moves with uniform acceleration. If it covers 576 yards in 24 seconds, find its acceleration, and its velocity at the end of the stated distance.

(7) The speed of a wagon increases from 14 feet per second to 80 feet per second in half a minute. What distance does it cover in this time, and what is its uniform acceleration?

CHAPTER 27

Gravity

(1) A particle is precipitated vertically downwards with a velocity of 20 feet per second, and reaches the ground in 5 seconds. From what height did the particle descend?

(2) A body is projected vertically upwards with a velocity of 288 feet per second. How long will it take to reach its highest point? Show that it will require the same length of time to fall as to reach its maximum height.

(3) How long will an object take to reach the ground if it falls from a height of 256 feet?

(4) A stone is thrown vertically upwards with a velocity of 64 feet per second. When and where will its velocity be 48 feet per second?

(5) If a body describes $402\frac{1}{2}$ feet in the 13th second of its fall, what is the value of g?

(6) In its upward vertical flight a body passes a certain point with a velocity of 112 feet per second. How long will the body take to return to the same point in its downward flight?

(7) A particle is projected vertically upwards from the top of a cliff with a velocity of 96 feet per second. If the particle takes 10 seconds to reach the foot of the cliff, find the height of the cliff.

(8) Having dropped for 4 seconds, a body is overtaken by another body dropped 1040 feet above it. How long was the higher body in motion before the lower started falling?

(9) Ascending vertically from the ground, with a certain initial velocity, a body reaches a height of 589 feet; and in 3 seconds returns to this height. Find the highest point reached by the body, and its initial velocity.

(10) A body is thrown vertically upwards from a lighthouse 550 feet above sea-level. If the initial velocity of the

body is 24 feet per second, how far above sea-level is the body after $5\frac{3}{4}$ seconds?

(11) An object, dropped from a bridge 512 feet high, meets another object half way down, which was projected from the ground at the moment it left the bridge. Find the initial velocity of the ascending object, and its velocity in meeting the descending object.

(12) For how much longer will a body ascend, if having been projected vertically upwards, it traverses h feet in t seconds?

CHAPTER 28

Parallelogram and Triangle of Velocities

Complete the following:—

	* Course	† Track	Air Speed	Ground Speed	Wind
(16)	?	092 T	105 kts.	?	026/20 k
(17)	?	275 T	110 kts.	?	195/30 k
(18)	?	192 T	160 m.p.h.	?	005/30
(19)	?	180 T	100 m.p.h.	?	065/28
(20)	?	316 T	140 kts.	?	085/20 k
(21)	150 T	135 T	110 m.p.h.	82 m.p.h.	?
(22)	092 T	084 T	132 kts.	120 kts.	?
(23)	320 T	332 T	146 m.p.h.	123 m.p.h.	?
(24)	130 T	126 T	180 kts.	164 kts.	?
(25)	310 T	305 T	100 m.p.h.	90 m.p.h.	?
(26)	032 T	?	140 m.p.h.	?	140/26
(27)	250 T	?	105 m.p.h.	?	210/12
(28)	048 T	?	140 kts.	?	300/20 k
(29)	340 T	?	90 kts.	?	015/10 k
(30)	237 T	?	98 kts.	?	026/39 k

* Or "Heading."
† Or "Course made good."

(1) In attempting to cross straight over a river 2310 ft. wide, a swimmer lands 5775 ft. below the point directly opposite the place into which he dived. If he crosses the river in $\frac{1}{4}$ of an hour, what is the velocity of the river?

(2) A particle has a vertical velocity of 54 meters per second, and a horizontal velocity of 24 meters per second; find the magnitude and direction of the resultant velocity.

(3) A ship sails westwards at $3\sqrt{3}$ miles per hour, and a sailor crosses the deck in a northerly direction at 3 miles per hour. Find the resultant velocity and direction of the sailor.

(4) To reach a lighthouse, the boatmen pull due west for half an hour at 4 miles an hour. If the current runs due south at 4 miles an hour, how far has the boat moved?

(5) A ship steams at 9 knots due north against a current of 3 knots due east. Find the resultant speed of the ship and the direction in which it moves.

(6) A body has two velocities of 6 centimeters per second and $3\frac{1}{2}$ centimeters per second at 40° to each other. Find the magnitude and direction of the resultant velocity.

(7) After moving westwards for 3 seconds, with a velocity of 2 feet per second, a body acquires an additional southward velocity of 3 feet per second. How far will the body have moved after 5 seconds?

(8) A motorboat, whose bow is directed due west, is propelled at 22 feet per second. Find the strength of the tide which alters the course of the boat to 15° south of west, and reduces its speed to 20 ft./sec.

(9) A balloon, ascending at the rate of 12 feet per second, is 134.16 feet from its starting point after 10 seconds. Find the velocity of the wind.

(10) A steamer steers due east at 10 miles an hour against a tide running due south at $7\frac{1}{2}$ miles an hour. Find the distance traversed by the steamer after steaming for half an hour.

(11) A velocity of 30 miles per hour is resolved into two components each of which makes an angle of 45° with it. Find their magnitude.

(12) From the same harbor, two ships sail eastwards and 30° south of east, at velocities of $4\sqrt{3}$ and 8 miles an hour respectively. How far apart will they be after 5 hours?

(13) Two planes leave their squadron at 5000 feet and, maintaining this altitude, fly at 60° to each other. If their respective speeds are 300 and 200 miles per hour, how far will they be from each other in two hours?

(14) Two equal components of a velocity at 60° to each other are each of $20\sqrt{3}$ miles an hour. Find the velocity, and the angle each component makes with it.

(15) A balloon rises vertically with a velocity of 10 feet per second. If it encounters a wind which gives it a horizontal velocity of 5 feet per second, find the angle the balloon makes with the ground at its starting point after ascending for one minute, and its distance from the starting point.

CHAPTER 29

Center of Gravity

(1) A rod weighing 8 pounds, whose center of gravity is at one-third of its length, is supported at its ends on two spring balances. Find the readings of the balances.

(2) A uniform beam, 12 feet long, and supported at its ends, has a load of 120 lb. at 3 feet from one end. If the loads taken at the respective ends are 155 lb. and 95 lb., what is the weight of the beam?

(3) A meter-stick, weighing 110 grams, has three weights, each 50 grams, at 25, 50, and 75 centimeters from one end. Where must a weight of 100 grams be placed to produce reactions of 210 and 150 grams at the ends of the stick?

(4) The equilateral triangle ABC has sides measuring 2 inches. How far is the center of gravity from the point A?

(5) Find the center of gravity of a triangular lamina, whose sides are 7, 5, and 4 inches respectively, measuring from the intersection of the two latter sides.

(6) A triangular metal sheet of weight W is supported in a horizontal position at its angular points. Prove that the reaction at each support is W/3.

(7) The weight of a lever safety-valve is 180 pounds and is 26 inches from the fulcrum. If the valve is 4 inches from the fulcrum and measures 5 square inches, find the pressure in the boiler when the steam begins to escape.

(8) In lifting the shafts of a wheelbarrow, a man exerts a force of 36 pounds. If the loaded barrow weighs ¾ cwt., and the center of gravity is 18 inches from the line of the center of the wheel, how far from the center of gravity is the point on the shafts where the force is exerted?

(9) A rod of uniform thickness, 20 inches long and weighing 2 ounces, has a weight of 4 ounces on one end, and a weight of 3 ounces at 5 inches from the other end. At what point will the rod balance?

CHAPTER 30

Logarithms

(1) Write down the characteristics of the logarithms of: 4156; 324.9; 6.205; .73; .00567; .6789; 35.7.

(2) Log 45.67 = 1.6597: write down the logs of: 456.7; .04567; 45670; .4567.

(3) 1.4731 = log 29.72: write down the numbers whose logs are 3.4731; $\bar{1}$.4731; 0.4731; $\bar{3}$.4731.

(4) Work out the following examples of addition, subtraction, multiplication and division of logs. Remember always to keep the mantissa (*i.e.* the decimal part) *positive.*

Addition: 1.5678 $\bar{2}$.7359 $\bar{2}$.3792 $\bar{2}$.1049
         $\bar{2}$.7215 $\bar{1}$.4268   4.1568 $\bar{3}$.9672

Subtraction: Subtract the bottom line from the top line in the above examples.

Multiplication: $\bar{1}$.3671×2; $\bar{2}$.7151×2; $\bar{3}$.5671×3; $\bar{2}$.9817×3.

Division: $\bar{1}$.6234÷2; $\bar{5}$.7124÷3.

(5) Find by means of logarithm tables the value (correct to four significant figures) of:

(a) 576×23,   (b) .0438×37.68,   (c) .00329×.04589,

(d) 3.7×2.9×5.2,   (e) 984÷567,   (f) .678÷38.5,

(g) .00279÷49,   (h) $\dfrac{456\times738}{628\times294}$,   (i) $\dfrac{2.36\times5.77}{125.6}$,   (j) (6.78)^2,

(k) (.012)^3,   (l) $\sqrt{5929}$,   (m) $\sqrt[3]{2.744}$.

CHAPTER 31

Solution of Triangles

(1) Given $a = 80'$
        $b = 59'$ } Find A, B, C.
        $c = 50'$

(2) Given A = 52° 40′
        $b = 47$ yds. } Find a, B, C.
        $c = 85$ yds.

(3) Given $a = 46'$
$\quad\quad\quad A = 35°\ 10'$ } Find C, b, c.
$\quad\quad\quad B = 46°\ 15'$

(4) Given $A = 56°\ 10'$
$\quad\quad\quad\quad a = 181'$ } Find c, B, C.
$\quad\quad\quad\quad b = 147'$

(5) Given $B = 42°$
$\quad\quad\quad\quad b = 149$ yds. } Find c, A, C.
$\quad\quad\quad\quad a = 182$ yds.

(6) to (20) Solve the fifteen triangles in Questions (16) to (30), Exercises on Chap. 28.

Chapter 32

Differential Calculus

Differentiate:

(1) $y = x^{12}$.

(2) $y = x^9$.

(3) $y = x$.

(4) $y = x^{\frac{1}{2}}$.

(5) $y = \sqrt{x}$.

(6) $y = x^{\frac{1}{3}}$.

(7) $y = \sqrt[3]{x}$.

(8) $y = x^{-2}$.

(9) $y = \dfrac{1}{x^2}$.

(10) $y = \dfrac{1}{\sqrt[3]{x^5}}$.

(11) $y = x^{-\frac{5}{3}}$.

(12) $y = x^{-\frac{3}{5}}$.

(13) $y = 5x^2 - 14$.

(14) $y = x^2 - 3x + 8$.

(15) $y = 32x - 8x^2$.

(16) $y = 5x^{-1}$.

(17) $y = \dfrac{15}{x^4} + 8$.

(18) $y = 3x^2 + \dfrac{20}{x}$.

(19) $y = (3x^2 + 1)(4x - 3)$.

(20) $y = (28x - 5x^2)(4 + 15x - 3x^3)$.

(21) $y = \dfrac{3x+1}{5x-2}$.

(22) $y = \dfrac{ax+b}{cx+f}$.

(23) $y = \dfrac{1 + x + 2x^2 + 3x^3}{1 + x + 2x^2}$.

(24) $y = \dfrac{x^3}{5} + 2x - 10896$.

Differentiate the following functions of x (Let "y" equal each function in turn, then find $\dfrac{dy}{dx}$):

(25) $.02x^5$.

(26) $\dfrac{6x^{10}}{17}$.

(27) $\dfrac{x^n + a}{x^{-n} + b}$.

Find the second derivative of

(28) $y = x^5 + 3x^4 + 15x.$ (29) $y = 15x - 12x^2.$

CHAPTER 33

Radians and Mils

(1) A side of a hangar 1800 yards away is 90 yards long. How many mils do the ends of the building subtend?

(2) A tank 27 feet long subtends an angle of 3.5 mils. How far away is it?

(3) Change the angle 9° 37′ to mils; to radians.

(4) Change the angle 58.5 mils to degrees and minutes; to radians.

(5) Change the angle 0.187 radians to mils; to degrees and minutes.

(6) An observer 2750 yards away finds the front of a battery to subtend an angle of 55 mils. If he may make an error of 5 mils, between what limits does the length of the battery lie?

(7) What length of arc at 3500 yards will 48 mils intercept?

(8) An angle at the center of a circle 124 yards radius intercepts an arc 46 yards in length. What is the approximate size of the angle in mils if formula (1) is used?

(9) What is the exact size of the angle in Problem 8?

(10) A man on an observation tower 110 feet high notes that the angle of depression of an enemy outpost is 40 mils. What is the distance measured along the ground from the tower to the outpost?

TEST PAPERS

A—EASY TEST PAPERS

(If the questions are easy, practice speed with accuracy.)

I

(1) Express: (*a*) $\frac{5}{8}$ as a decimal; (*b*) .08 as a fraction in its lowest terms.

(2) Simplify $2\frac{1}{5}-1\frac{2}{3}$.   (3) Solve the equation $5x-7 = 4x+1$.

(4) Given that $a = \sqrt{x^2-y^2}$ find the value of a when $x = 13$ and $y = 5$.

(5) The area of a rectangle is 12 sq. cm. and its length is 4 cm. What is its breadth? What is the length of a diagonal?

(6) Two angles of a triangle are 45° and 75°. What is the third angle?

(7) The speeds of A walking at 3 miles an hour and of B cycling at 9 miles an hour are represented on a graph.

The scales are—Horizontal: 1 in. to an hour. Vertical: 1 in. to 5 miles.

How will the speeds be shown for a period of 3 hours?

II

(1) Express: (*a*) $\frac{7}{20}$ as a decimal; (*b*) .075 as a fraction in its lowest terms.

(2) Simplify: $1\frac{1}{6}-\frac{3}{4}$.   (3) Solve the equation $6x-11 = 4x+1$.

(4) Given that $x = \sqrt{a^2+6b^2}$, find the value of x when $a = 5$, $b = 2$.

(5) The sides of a rectangle are 2.1 in. and 2.8 in. What is the length of the diagonal?

(6) The angle opposite the base of an isosceles triangle is 50°. What is the size of each of the other angles?

(7) A train goes at an average speed of 40 miles per hour. This speed is represented on a graph.

The scales are—Horizontal: 1 in. to $\frac{1}{2}$ hour. Vertical: 1 in. to 20 miles.

Describe the graph if the journey lasts three hours.

III

(1) Express: (a) $\frac{17}{40}$ as a decimal; (b) .16 as a common fraction in its lowest terms.

(2) Simplify $2\frac{1}{3}+1\frac{1}{4}-\frac{5}{6}$.   (3) Solve the equation $\frac{3}{4}x-4 = \frac{3}{8}x+5$.

(4) Given that $K = \sqrt{a(a+b)}$, find the value of K when $a = 4$, $b = 5$.

(5) A ship sails 12 miles due North, then 16 miles due East. How far is it from the starting point?

(6) One of the base angles of an isosceles triangle is 70°. What is the size of the angle opposite the base?

(7) The table given below shows the speed of a train at different times between two stations:

| Miles per hour | . | . | 15 | 24 | 32 | 40 | 50 | 50 | 42 | 30 | 15 | 0 |
| Minutes from start | . | . | 12 | 20 | 30 | 42 | 60 | 72 | 85 | 95 | 110 | 120 |

Make a graph showing the changing speed.
The scales are—Horizontal: 1 in. to 20 min. Vertical: 1 in. to 10 m.p.h.
Read off from your graph the two times when the speed was 36 m.p.h.

IV

(1) An aircraft flies at a ground speed of 432 Km. per hour. How far does it fly in 1 minute?

(2) Simplify $3\frac{1}{7}\times8\frac{3}{11}$ and $\frac{13}{4}\div\frac{4}{13}$.

(3) What is the average of the whole numbers from 1 to 20 inclusive?

(4) What is the value of x in the equation: $0.03x = 1.02$?

(5) In rugby football five points are allowed for a goal and three for a try. Give the formula for the score if there are g goals and t tries.

(6) To convert C° Centigrade into F° Fahrenheit, $F = \dfrac{9C}{5} +32$.

Find F when (i) C = 80; (ii) C = −5.
Find C when (i) F = 59; (ii) F = 14.

(7) Convert into True directions—Northeast; N. 10° E.; S. 10° W.

B—HARDER TEST PAPERS

I

(1) Multiply 7.49 by .00358. Give your answer to three significant figures.

(2) Divide 7.49 by .00358. Give your answer to three significant figures.

(3) Express: (a) .0875 as a fraction in its lowest terms; (b) $\frac{7}{16}$ as a decimal.

(4) Given that 1 yard = .9144 meter, express 1 mile 240 yards in meters.

(5) Given that $A = 4\pi r^2$ obtain an expression for r in terms of the other letters.

(6) A train travels for the first 20 min. of its journey at 30 m.p.h. and for the next 30 min. at 50 m.p.h. Find (i) the total distance traveled and (ii) the average speed of the train.

(7) The table below gives the expenses and receipts for a certain newspaper for various numbers of copies produced.

Number of copies . .	1000	2000	3000	4000
Expenses in $ . . .	320	420	520	620
Receipts in $ . . .	240	400	560	720

Draw on the same diagram two graphs:
   (a) Showing the relation between the number of copies and the expenses.
   (b) Showing the relation between the number of copies and the receipts.
What is the smallest number of copies that can be produced to make the paper pay?
Scales—Horizontal: 1 in. to 500 copies. Vertical: 1 in. to $80.

(8) An aircraft travels at 280 m.p.h. for a quarter of an hour on a bearing 40°. It then turns and travels at 180 m.p.h. for 10 min. on a bearing 120°. By means of a scale drawing, find (i) its distance from, and (ii) its bearing from, the starting point.

(9) In a triangle ABC the side BC = 3.9″, the angle ABC = 49°, CA = 5.2″. Construct the triangle and find the length of the side AB.

(10) A map is drawn to the scale of $\frac{1}{126720}$. The distance between two places, as shown on the map, is 3.8″. What is the true distance between these places?

II

(1) If A = 13.09, B = 2.053, C = 9.89, find the value of A ÷ (B×C) correct to three significant figures.

(2) Given that $s = \frac{1}{2}gt^2$, find an expression for t in terms of s and g. Find t if (i) $s = 784$, (ii) $s = 1600$, (iii) $s = 3000$ and $g = 32$ in each case.

(3) Given that 1 in. = 2.54 cm., express in meters and centimeters
    (i) 10 ft., (ii) 150 ft.
(4) An aircraft travels at 220 m.p.h. for 15 min. and then at
    180 m.p.h. for 10 min. Find (i) the total distance traveled,
    (ii) the average speed of the aircraft.
(5) Find by calculation the length of the diagonal of a football
    field 300 ft. long and 150 ft. wide.
    Check your answer by a scale drawing.
(6) (i) Solve $\begin{cases} x+3y = 11 \\ 3x+ y = 9 \end{cases}$ (ii) Solve $x + \dfrac{1}{x} = 4\frac{1}{4}$
(7) Draw a parallelogram ABCD with AB = 5 cm. and BC = 7
    cm. and angle ABC = 65°.
    Find the area of this parallelogram. You will need to make
    one measurement.
(8) Given that 1 Km. = .62 mile, draw a graph that will enable
    you to convert any number of Km. to miles and vice versa.
    Scales—Horizontal: 1″ to 20 miles. Vertical: 1″ to 20 Km.
    Read off the equivalent (i) of 20 miles; (ii) of 20 Km.
(9) A ship is in the position 270°, 120 sea-miles from a point A
    and steams on a course 30° at 20 knots, starting at 1100
    hours and finishing at 1600 hours. Draw a diagram of this
    to a suitable scale and find the distance and bearing of the
    ship from A at 1600 hours.
(10) The Representative Fraction of a map is $\frac{1}{63360}$. Find the
    distance in miles between two places which are shown to
    be 2.7 in. apart on the map.

III

(1) Find, by changing into decimals correct to four significant
    figures, which of these fractions is the greater: $3\frac{1}{7}$ or $\frac{355}{113}$.
(2) Simplify: $\dfrac{2\frac{2}{3} \text{ of } 3\frac{1}{4}-2\frac{1}{2}}{3\frac{3}{4}+5\frac{2}{3}\times 6\frac{1}{7}}$.
(3) Given that 1 in. = 2.54 cm., express in yards, feet and inches
    4 m. 39 cm.; and express 5.28 miles in kilometers.
(4) An aircraft flies at 100 m.p.h. for the first five minutes, then
    at 150 m.p.h. for 10 min. and then at 200 m.p.h. for 15 min.
    Find the average speed of the aircraft.
(5) A boy reckons the number of minutes from 1135 hr. to 1410
    hr. as 165. What is his actual error and what is his per-
    centage error?
(6) A triangular piece of land ABC has the distances AB = 900
    ft., AC = 780 ft., BC = 840 ft. Draw this triangle to
    scale. Find from your drawing the length of a road AX

meeting BC at right angles. What is the distance BX, CX? Verify these measurements by Pythagoras' Theorem.

(7) In Question 6, if C lies 90° from B, find the direction of A from B and C from A.

(8) A car is to be driven from X to Y a distance of 360 miles. It leaves X at 1055 hours and should arrive at Y at 2210 hours. It does the first 150 miles at a speed of 30 m.p.h. What must be the average speed of the remainder of the journey if the car is to arrive at the exact time?

(9) In triangle ABC given $b = 1220.1$ ft., $c = 311.7$ ft., $\angle A = 40° 28'$, find a, $\angle B$, $\angle C$.

(10) (a) Solve by factors: $2x^2 + 5x = 12$. (b) Solve by "completing the square": $x^2 + 6x = 11$. (Answer to three significant figures.)

IV

(1) What is the value of $\frac{S}{3}(P + 3Q + 2R)$ when $S = 1.2$, $P = 2.8$, $Q = 8.4$, $R = 6.4$?

(2) A car travels 70 miles in $1\frac{3}{4}$ hours, and a train travels 30 miles in 50 minutes. Find the ratio of the speed of the car to that of the train.

(3) A boy throws a ball vertically upward with a velocity of 72 ft. per second. What time will elapse before the boy catches the ball?

(4) An aircraft covers in $1\frac{1}{5}$ minutes the distance between two listening posts 3 miles apart. Find its speed in m.p.h.

(5) A plane whose air speed is 280 miles an hour, flies due South against a wind blowing due West at 40 miles an hour. How long will the plane take to cover $100\sqrt{50}$ miles measured on the Earth?

(6) A steel poker 20″ long, and of mass $2\frac{1}{4}$ lb. when suspended from its center requires a force of 12 oz. at one end to keep it horizontal. Find the center of gravity of the poker.

(7) Draw triangle ABC making BC = 1″ and $\angle B = \angle C = 72°$. Now draw CX bisecting angle C and meeting AB at X. Measure AX and XC and tell without measurement the size of angle BXC.

Name two similar triangles in your diagram and hence from equal ratios prove that $(BC)^2 = AB.BX$.

(8) Solve (by factors or by formula): $\frac{x}{3} + \frac{3}{x} = 2\frac{4}{15}$.

(9) A piece of land has four corners A, D, B and C. B lies due
north of A. C lies on the western side and D on the eastern
side of AB. AB = 45 chains. C is 285° from A and 240°
from B while D is 15° from A and 90° from C. Find by
means of an accurately drawn plan the length of CD and
the area of ADBC in sq. chains. (1 chain = 22 yds = 66 ft.)

(10) If the sides of a triangle ABC are $a = 242, b = 323, c = 347$,
find the size of the angles A, B and C.

ANSWERS

CHAPTER 2

A. (1) .7, .08, .007, .13, .079, .73.

(2) $\frac{7}{10}$, $\frac{9}{100}$, $\frac{3}{1000}$, $3\frac{3}{10}$, $3\frac{3}{100}$, $3\frac{333}{1000}$, $7\frac{41}{100}$, $7\frac{41}{1000}$.

(3) 0.099, 0.28, 0.29, 0.92, 1.02.

(4) .2, .15, .76, .34, .475, .412, .026, .375, .875.

(5)
3.5	3.8	2.9	.003	.00043
3.05	308.	.07	.00004	.00027
.07	30340.	.347		
		.0029		

(6) 124.6, 382.8, 28.5, 9.651.
0.073, 0.51, .00028, .0019, .0000017.

B. (1) 37.079. (2) 158.95468. (3) 519.0816. (4) 43.672.
(5) 622.45635. (6) 1214.514412. (7) 15.353 mi. (8) 3.09 in.
(9) 173.8 in. (10) Horizontally: 98.0980, 64.2004,
754.6674, 965.3090. Vertically: 421.5287, 767.8931,
582.4693, 110.3837. Grand total = 1882.2748.

C. (1) 2.23, 4.45, .042, 3.11, 1.329. (2) 92.2170. (3) .3817.
(4) 1.694. (5) .216. (6) .0998. (7) 3.196. (8) 299.97.
(9) 9.92. (10) .05 in.

D. (1) 17.898. (2) 1442.04. (3) .6885. (4) .15533. (5) 187.8602.
(6) .0123697. (7) 92.1700. (8) .028382. (9) 55.95.
(10) 4.06. (11) 5.44. (12) .605. (13) .0103.
(14) 0.00316. (15) .0052. (16) 6 ft. 5 in. (17) 436 m.
(18) 608 m.

E. (1) .13. (2) .0075. (3) .008. (4) .05. (5) .00045. (6) 0.202.
(7) 0.00909. (8) .136. (9) .00325. (10) 0.092.
(11) .0075. (12) .65. (13) .2224. (14) .0715.

F. (1) 4.23. (2) 0.00582. (3) 3122. (4) 15,810. (5) .061.
(6) .0058. (7) 10.625. (8) 139.502. (9) 2.442.
(10) 0.027. (11) .125. (12) 11.204. (13) .01615.
(14) 11.20. (15) 2.364. (16) 6.429.

CHAPTER 3

(1) 150° (supp. ∠s)
(2) $x = 158°$ (supp. ∠s)
$z = 158°$ (vert. opp.)
$y = 22°$
(3) $a = 110°$ (supp.) ⎫
$e = 110°$ (alt.) |
$b = 110°$ (vert. opp.) | Other
$d = 70°$ (corresp.) ⎬reasons
$c = 70°$ (alt.) | valid.
$g = 110°$ (vert. opp.) |
$f = 70°$ (vert. opp.) ⎭
(4) $m = 40°$ (alt.) ⎫
$q = 40°$ (alt.) | Other
$y = 40°$ (corresp.) ⎬reasons
$x = 140°$ (supp.) | valid.
$l = 140°$ (supp.) ⎭
(5) $x = 35°$. Reflex ∠ BMD $= 325°$.
(6) $x = 85°$ (alt.)
$y = 48°$ (corresp.)
$z = 47°$ $(z+85+48 = 180°)$
$x+y+z = 180°$
(7) $a = 25°$ (alt.)
$b = 20°$ (corresp.)
$a+b = 45°$ ext. ∠ = sum
of opp. inter. ∠s.
(8) $x = 70°$ ext. ∠ = sum of
opp. inter. ∠s.
$y = 110°$ (supp.)
(9) $x = 130°$ (supp.)
$y(= x-48) = 130-48$
$= 82°$ (ext. ∠ = sum
of opp. int. ∠s)

(10) $y = 50°$ (vert. opp.)
$z = 70°$ (supp.)
$x = 60°$ (supp.)
$x+y+z = 180°$
(11) $x = 180°-62°-27° = 91°$
(12) $40°+x = 180°$
$40°+y = 180°$
∴ $x = 180°-40° = y$
(13) $a = 81°$ $b = 65°$
(14) $y = 70°$ $z = 40°$
(15) $h = 70°$

CHAPTER 4

(1) $a = 95°, b = 60°, c = 25°, d = 155° = a+b, a+b+c = 180°$.
(2) $a = 74°, c = 74°$.   (3) $x = 38°, y = 38°$.
(4) $p = 60° = q, r = 60°$.
(5) Part 1. $p = 110°$, $q = 95°$, $r = 100°$, $s = 120°$, $t = 115°$,
$c = 70°, b = 85°, a = 80°, e = 60°, d = 65°$. Part 2. 540°.
Part 3. 360°.

(6) (a) 160°.　　(b) S. 75° W.　　(c) 280°.　　(d) 315°.　　(e) 359°.
　　　 (f) 191¼°.
(7) 72°.　(8) (b) 2700 sea-miles.　(c) X.　(d) 1200 sea-miles.

CHAPTER 5

(1) (a) 6.　　　　(b) 12.　　　(c) 8.　　　　(d) 3 rt. ∠s.
(2) (a) 60°.　　　　　　　　　(c) Equal.
(3) (a) 540°.　　(b) 360°.
(4) (a) 1080°.　(b) 360°.　(c) Sum of ∠s at a point always equals
　　　360°.
(5) 108°.　　　　　(6) (a) 540°, 720°, 1080°.　(b) 108°, 120°, 135°.

CHAPTER 6

A. (1) 5324 m., 7037 m., 42.03 m., 3.78 m., .49 m., 50.49 m., .579 m.
　 (2) .427 Km., .0034 Km., 40.225 Km., .0234 Km.
　 (3) 2.3 cm., 100 cm., 5200.4 cm.　　(4) 20 m. 6 dm. 3 cm. 5 mm.
　 (5) 31 Km. 7 Hm. 5 Dm. 2 m.　　(6) 27.5 m., 2750 cm.

B. (1) 7,165,000 sq. mm.　(3) 51,723 sq. m.　(5) 53.92 sq. m.
　 (2) 3,041,709 sq. mm.　(4) 170,302 sq. m.　(6) 3.569008 sq. m.
　　　　　　　　　　　　　　　　　　　　　　(7) .38094 sq. m.

C. (1) 5,235,000 c.c.　　　　　　(6) 9050 mg.
　 (2) 24,057,009 c.c.　　　　　　(7) 8350 g.
　 (3) 17,000,036 c.c.　　　　　　(8) 46.597 Kg.
　 (4) 5.045 g.　　　　　　　　　 (9) 5.498 Kg.
　 (5) 23.008 g.　　　　　　　　　(10) 2.3456 Kg.

D. (1) 22 Kg. 6 Dg. 9 g.　(2) 22.702 m.
　　　　(3) 48 m. 4 dm. 5 cm. 3 mm.
　　　　(4) 23 Km. 4 Hm. 9 Dm. 5 m. 3 dm.　(5) 513.21 Hl.
　　　　(6) 22.62 sq. m. = 2262. sq. dm.　(7) 1.71 Kg.
　　　　(8) 266.84 Kg.

E. (1) 5.195 Kg.　(2) .806 Kg.　(3) 277 mm.　(4) .9606 sq. m.
　　　　(5) 550 c.c.　(6) 6.75 sq. dm.　(7) .6 cm. = 6 mm.
　　　　(8) 14.1 m.　(9) 10.79735 m.　(10) .8 Kg.
　　　　(11) 1.3833 Km.　(12) .3 mm.　(13) 295 g.
　　　　(14) (i) 48 m.; (ii) 52 yards.　(15) 140 sq. Dm.

F. (1) 15.68　(2) 1.71 m.　(3) 12.14 cm.　(4) 26 lengths; rem.
　　　　3.44 cm.　(5) 7.2 Km. per hour.　(6) 306 Km. per hour.
　　　　(7) 105.364 g.　(8) 1.217 g.　(9) .8 cm.

CHAPTER 7

(1) (i) $12a^2$. (ii) a^7. (iii) $12a^7$. (iv) a^2b. (v) $6a^3b^3$. (vi) $30a^3b^3$.
(vii) $15a^6b^3c$. (viii) $8ab^3x^3y$. (ix) $20a^2x^3y^2z^3$.
(x) $21m^6n^4p^3q^5y$.

(2) (i) x^2 sq. cm. (ii) $25p^2$ sq. cm. (iii) $100\,z^2$ sq. cm.
(iv) $144y^2$ sq. cm.

(3) (i) x cm. (ii) $5y$ cm. (iii) $12a$ cm. (iv) $7p$ cm.

(4) Squares: (i) $16a^4$. (ii) $81b^8$. (iii) $256a^{32}$. (iv) a^8x^{24}.

(v) $625p^4q^8r^{20}$. (vi) $\dfrac{256x^{18}}{81y^4}$.

Sq. roots: (i) $\pm 2a$. (This means plus or minus $2a$.) (ii) $\pm 3b^2$.

(iii) $\pm 4a^8$. (iv) $\pm a^2x^6$. (v) $\pm 5pq^2r^5$. (vi) $\dfrac{\pm 4x^{\frac{3}{2}}}{3y}$

(5) (i) 25. (ii) 36. (iii) 30. (iv) 48. (v) 54. (vi) 96.

(6) a^4, x^8, $x^{\frac{1}{2}}$, $x^2y^{\frac{3}{2}}$, $10x^{50}b^{25}$, $\dfrac{11mnp^3}{z^3}$.

(7) (i) x^4 (ii) x^6 (iii) a^6

(iv) ab^2c^3 (v) a^2 (vi) ab

(vii) a^2b (viii) $\dfrac{ab^5}{c}$ (ix) r^3

(x) $2ab$ (xi) $\dfrac{3xy^2}{2z^2}$ (xii) $\frac{3}{4}$

CHAPTER 8

A. (1) 2. (2) -6. (3) $a+5b$. (4) $4a-8b$. (5) $x+y$.
(6) $5a^2-2b^2$. (7) $6a+15b-12c$. (8) $2x-8y$. (9) $4a-b$.
(10) $2a+14b$. (11) $24x$. (12) $4y-4x$.

B. (1) $-2x$ (4) $-x+4y$ (7) 4   (10) $2-x^2$
(2) $-6z$ (5) $x+2y$ (8) $b-a$ (11) $2c-3a$
(3) $x-4y$ (6) $2a^2+7b^2$ (9) $+5$

C. (1) $[x.x.x] \times [x.x.x.x.] = x^7$ (2) $x^6, x^4, x^{10}, x, a^{n+1}$

(3) $\dfrac{x.x.x.x.x.x.}{x.x.} = x^4$ (4) $x^3, x^4, x^4, 8x^3y, x^9, 1$

(5) $p^4, q^6, x^{12}, x^{12}, k^{16}$.

(6) $\pm 5, x, x^5, \pm 5a, \pm 6a^2b, pq^3, \pm 12a^6, x^{\frac{1}{2}}$.

CHAPTER 9

A. (1) 60°, 43°.   (2) 90°; Right-angled and scalene.   (3) 9.3 cm.;
Obtuse-angled.   (4) 3.3″, 2.4″.   (5) 7.5 cm.
(6) 1.5″ (approx.); ∠ Q = ∠ R = 45° (approx.).
B. (1) $x = 55°$.   (2) $a = 75°$, $b = 105°$.   (3) $a = 60°$, $x = 100°$.
(4) $a = 90°$, $b = 35°$.   (5) $x = 45°$, $3x = 135°$, $y = 90°$.
(6) $x = 36°$, $3x = 108°$, $y = 72°$.   (7) $y = 80°$; sum of
∠s of pentagon = 540°, $x = 85°$.
C. (a) Yes; SSS (b) No (equal ∠s not on corresponding side)
(c) Yes; SAS (d) Yes; SAA (e) No.

CHAPTER 10

(2) Paris in Northern Hemisphere; Capetown in Southern Hemisphere.
(5) Outbreak of war.
(6) (i) 43, 29.   (ii) 38, 56.
(7) 1933, No.
(9) (i) 10 miles, $112\frac{1}{2}$ miles.   (ii) 20 miles.
(10) (i) 1630 hr.; 90 miles from starting point.   (ii) 1530 hr.;
1730 hr.
(11) Z 56 m.p.h.; X 51 m.p.h.; Y 45 m.p.h.
(12) 14 miles from P; $3\frac{1}{2}$ hours.
(13) 40 miles from A's starting point at 1300 hr.; 1230 hr.;
1330 hr.
(14) 90 miles.
(15) $2\frac{3}{4}$ lb., 7 lb.; 4.96 in.
(16) 27°; −38°.
(17) (i) 31.4 in.   (ii) 44 ft.   (iii) 4.8 in.   (iv) 5.2 yd.
(18) $\frac{7''}{8}$.
(19) 4.8 hr.; $7\frac{1}{2}$ m.p.h.
(20) 1.3 ft.; 7.4 sec.
(21) 124 ft.; 45°.

CHAPTER 11

A. (1) $6x^2+19x+10$ (4) $24x^2+18x-15$ (7) $15x^2+29xy+12y^2$
(2) $12x^2+7x+1$ (5) $72x^2+20x-8$ (8) $x^2-7xy+12y^2$
(3) $8x^2-2x-15$ (6) $6x^2+7xy+2y^2$ (9) $6x^2-5xy-6y^2$
(10) $8x^2-14xy+5y^2$

B. (1) $x^2+9x+20$ (9) $2x^2-20x+42$ (17) $4x^2+12x+9$
   (2) $x^2+10x+21$ (10) $9x^2-12x+4$ $+12xy+18y+9y^2$
   (3) $3x^2+16x+5$ (11) $4x^2+24x+36$ (18) $25x^2+10xy+y^2$
   (4) $6x^2+26x+28$ (12) $16x^2-32xy+16y^2$ (19) $4x^2+9y^2+16z^2$
   (5) $9x^2+9x-28$ (13) $16x^4+48x^2+36$ $-12xy-16xz+24yz$
   (6) $12x^2-16x-3$ (14) $25x^4-10x^2+1$ (20) $x^2+2xy+y^2-16$
   (7) $6x^2-17x+12$ (15) $4x^4-12x^2y^2+9y^4$. (21) $a^2+2ab+b^2-25$
   (8) $4x^2-16$ (16) $9a^4-30a^2b^2+25b^4$. (22) $4x^2+24x+22$
       (23) $5x^2+8x-22$ (24) a^2-8a+6

C. (1) $3(a+2b)$ (6) $5xy(2x^2-3y^3)$ (11) $a^2(x+a-x) = a^2$
   (2) $4(a-2b)$ (7) $7a(2a^2+3ab+b^2)$ $\times a = a^3$
   (3) $b(a-c)$ (8) $qr(p+s)$ (12) $(a+b)(p-q)$
   (4) $5(a+2b+3c)$ (9) $3x^2y^2(x-2+3y^2)$ (13) $(a+b)(a+2b)$
   (5) $x(x^2+x-1)$ (10) $-x(p+q)$ (14) $2a(a+b)$

D. (1) $(5x+4)(x+1)$ (5) $(x-y)(y-z)$ (9) $(a-b)(x-2y)$
   (2) $(x+2)(x+y)$ (6) $(a^2+1)(a-1)$ (10) $(p+1)(p-q)$
   (3) $(3x+2)(x-1)$ (7) $(5a+3)(a-x)$ (11) $(x-1)(x^4+x^2+1)$
   (4) $(x+z)(x+y)$ (8) $(a^2-1)(a-1)$ (12) $(a-b)(x+y+z)$
       (13) $(a+b)(a-b+3)$

E. (1) $(x+3)(x+4)$ (4) $(x+1)(x+1)$ (7) $(x+12)(x+11)$
   (2) $(x+5)(x+4)$ (5) $(x-2)(x-1)$ (8) $(xy+6)(xy+1)$
   (3) $(x+6)(x+6)$ (6) $(x-7)(x-8)$ (9) $(7-ab)(3-ab)$

F. (1) $(x+6)(x-3)$ (5) $(w-3)(r+1)$ (9) $(x+6)(x-4)$
   (2) $(x-5)(x-1)$ (6) $(x-8)(x-6)$ (10) $(x+9)(x-8)$
   (3) $(x-8)(x+7)$ (7) $(x-12)(x+3)$ (11) $(x+7)(x-3)$
   (4) $(x-5)(x-5)$ (8) $(x-5)(x+4)$ (12) $(x+9)(x+1)$

G. (1) $(x-2)(x+2)$ (10) $(3x^3-5)(3x^3+5)$
   (2) $(y-7)(y+7)$ (11) $(8a-3b^5)(8a+3b^5)$
   (3) $(3-a)(3+a)$ (12) $(7a-6bc^4)(7a+6bc^4)$
   (4) $(ac-6)(ac+6)$ (13) $(x+y-1)(x+y+1)$
   (5) $(3x^2-4)(3x^2+4)$ (14) $(a+b-c)(a+b+c)$
   (6) $(5x-y)(5x+y)$ (15) $(a-b-c)(a-b+c)$
   (7) $(5p^2-4)(5p^2+4)$ (16) $(x+5y-3z)(x+5y+3z)$
   (8) $(9-2ac)(9+2ac)$ (17) $(1-a-3b)(1+a+3b)$
   (9) $(xy-9a^2)(xy+9a^2)$ (18) $(a-b+c)(a+b-c)$
   (19) $(a+b-c-d)(a+b+c+d)$
   (20) $(3x+2y-2z-1)(3x+2y+2z+1)$
   (21) $(a+3b-1-x)(a+3b+1+x)$
   (22) $(x+y-a+b)(x+y+a-b)$

(23) $(2a-b-3x-4y)(2a-b+3x+4y)$
(24) $(x-3y-2a+3c)(x-3y+2a-3c)$
(25) $(x+y-1)(x+y+1)$ (27) $(a-b-c)(a-b+c)$
(26) $(1-a-b)(1+a+b)$ (28) $(3y-a+b)(3y+a-b)$

CHAPTER 12

(1) $1\frac{5}{7}$, $2\frac{3}{5}$, $5\frac{3}{8}$, $5\frac{7}{10}$, $10\frac{3}{14}$, $7\frac{2}{13}$, $8\frac{1}{12}$, $16\frac{11}{17}$.

(2) $\frac{44}{7}$, $\frac{20}{3}$, $\frac{72}{11}$, $\frac{53}{10}$, $\frac{29}{6}$, $\frac{48}{19}$, $\frac{89}{9}$, $\frac{67}{16}$.

(3) $\frac{4}{35}$, $\frac{1}{12}$, $\frac{12}{35}$, $3\frac{3}{4}$, $\frac{5}{21}$, $2\frac{1}{2}$.

(4) $1\frac{2}{7}$, $1\frac{1}{4}$, $1\frac{1}{3}$, $\frac{3}{4}$, $\frac{5}{7}$, $\frac{5}{13}$, 1.

(5) 14, $1\frac{1}{7}$, $\frac{10}{11}$, $2\frac{8}{17}$, 1.

(6) $\dfrac{2x}{a}$, $\dfrac{x}{2a}$, x, $\dfrac{x}{a^2}$, $2x$, ax, $\dfrac{4}{a}$, $\dfrac{4x^2}{3a^3}$, 1, $\dfrac{6q^2}{5p}$, $\dfrac{1}{6a}$, $\dfrac{8x^3}{3z}$.

(7) $\dfrac{x}{2a}$, $\dfrac{2x}{a}$, $\dfrac{x}{a^2}$, $\dfrac{q^3}{p^3}$, $\dfrac{7a}{5b}$, $\dfrac{c}{axy}$.

(8) 12, 35, 42, 21, 78, 55, 125, 563, 102.

(9) b, $5x$, pq, $6a^2b^2$, $7ac$, $11xy^2$, xy.

(10) (1) 36 (2) 30 (3) 1080 (4) 1260 (5) 15840.

(11) (1) $12a$ (2) $6a^3$ (3) $20a^2b^2$ (4) x^5 (5) abc (6) $120abc$
   (7) $a^2b^2c^2$.

(12) (1) $\frac{7}{9}$, $\frac{5}{9}$, $\frac{11}{16}$, $\frac{9}{13}$;   (2) $\frac{1}{5}$, $\frac{1}{4}$, $\frac{1}{3}$; $\frac{2}{3}$, $\frac{3}{4}$, $\frac{4}{5}$; $\frac{2}{9}$, $\frac{3}{10}$, $\frac{5}{12}$, $\frac{1}{2}$.

(13) $2\frac{13}{60}$, $1\frac{29}{220}$, $4\frac{88}{105}$, $4\frac{61}{72}$.

(14) $\frac{1}{2}$, $\frac{1}{12}$, $\frac{1}{63}$, $1\frac{5}{42}$, $\frac{2}{3}$.

(15) $1\frac{29}{180}$, $\frac{1}{4}$, $1\frac{7}{12}$, $4\frac{3}{8}$.

(16) (1) $\dfrac{9}{a}$ (2) $\dfrac{13a}{12}$ (3) $\dfrac{b+a}{ab}$ (4) $\dfrac{4a+3b+5}{ab}$ (5) $\dfrac{3b+2a}{6ab}$ (6) $\dfrac{17}{12a}$

   (7) $\dfrac{pbc+qac+rab}{abc}$ (8) $\dfrac{v+u}{vu}$ (9) $\dfrac{a+b+c}{abc}$ (10) $\dfrac{3a+4}{a^2}$

   (11) $\dfrac{b-a}{ab}$ (12) $\frac{1}{6}x$ (13) $\dfrac{xy+x}{y}$ (14) $\dfrac{19x}{30}$ (15) $\dfrac{a^2-1}{a}$

   (16) $\dfrac{x}{10}$ (17) $\dfrac{2x^2+3y^2+xy}{xy}$ (18) $\dfrac{az+bx+cy}{xyz}$

(17) (1) $\frac{7}{12}$ (2) $\frac{1}{21}$ (3) $1\frac{7}{12}$ (4) $1\frac{2}{15}$ (5) $1\frac{29}{48}$ (6) $1\frac{37}{48}$ (7) 126
   (8) $2\frac{1}{12}$ (9) $23\frac{4}{27}$ (10) $\frac{33}{40}$ (11) $6\frac{2}{3}$.

(18) (1) $.5$, $.333$, $.25$, $.2$, $.167$, $.143$, $.125$, $.111$, $.1$.
   (2) $.05$, $.0625$, $.04$, $.025$, $.02$, $.37$, $.019$.
   (3) $.667$, $.8$, $.833$, $.571$, $.625$, $.444$, $.455$, 2.308, 7.233, 4.444,
   8.889.

(19) $\frac{3}{4}$, $\frac{3}{5}$, $\frac{7}{8}$, $\frac{7}{10}$, $\frac{19}{20}$. $6\frac{7}{20}$, $17\frac{1}{25}$, $9\frac{5}{8}$, $8\frac{1}{20}$, $3\frac{6}{25}$.

CHAPTER 13

(1) $x = 1$ (6) $x = 0$ (11) $x = -2$ (16) $x = 7$
(2) $x = -2\frac{1}{9}$ (7) $x = \frac{2}{3}$ (12) $x = 7$ (17) $x = .029$
(3) $x = -3$ (8) $x = -12$ (13) $x - 3$ (18) $x = .5$
(4) $x = -28$ (9) $x = 20$ (14) $x = 9$ (19) $x = +3.5$
(5) $x = -5$ (10) $x = 2$ (15) $x = 11$ (20) $x = 1$

CHAPTER 14

A. (1) $2n+1$ or $2n-1$.   (2) $C = \dfrac{22d}{7}$.   (3) $(180-2x)$ degrees.

(4) $\dfrac{180-v}{2}$ degrees.   (5) $\dfrac{n}{2}-1$ or $\dfrac{n-2}{2}$.   (6) Charge $= \dfrac{3x+6y}{100}$.

(7) Floor space $= (300+5p)$ sq. ft.   (8) Area $= 2(l+b)h$.

(9) x ft. per sec. $= \dfrac{15x}{22}$ m.p.h., x m.p.h. $= \dfrac{22x}{15}$ ft. per sec.

(10) $H = \sqrt{(a^2+b^2)}$.   (11) $d = \dfrac{4l}{\pi}$.   (12) $A = \dfrac{4l^2}{\pi}$.

(13) $D = n(p+q)$ miles.   (14) $\dfrac{ax+by}{a+b}$.   (15) $g = (100p-q)\cancel{c}$.

(16) $t = \dfrac{rp}{r+p}$.   (17) $A = 2d(l+b-2d)$.   (18) $A = 2d(l+b+2d)$.

B. (1) $a = X-b$

(2) $a = X+b$, $b = a-X$

(3) $a = \dfrac{X}{b}$

(4) $a = bX$, $b = \dfrac{a}{X}$

(5) $a = \sqrt{X}$

(6) $a = X^2$

(7) $r = \dfrac{c}{2\pi}$

(8) $v = \dfrac{s}{t}$

(9) $h = \dfrac{A}{2(l+b)}$

(10) $h = \dfrac{2T}{a+b}$

(11) $b = \dfrac{2A}{h}$, $h = \dfrac{2A}{b}$

(12) $r = \sqrt{\dfrac{A}{\pi}}$

(13) $l = \dfrac{gt^2}{4\pi^2}$

(14) $l = \dfrac{s}{2\pi r}$, $r = \dfrac{s}{2\pi l}$

(15) $v = \dfrac{gt^2 + 2s}{2t}$

(19) $y = \dfrac{2x}{P} - 5$

(16) $h = \dfrac{33}{50}D^2$

(20) $h = \dfrac{3V}{A}$

(17) $F = \dfrac{9}{5}C + 32$

(21) $y = \dfrac{5x}{S} - 4$

(18) $f = \dfrac{uv}{u+v}$, $u = \dfrac{vf}{v-f}$

(22) $L = \dfrac{188T + .6B^3}{B^2}$

C. (1) 3.6, 1.2. (2) $r = 14$ in. (3) $r = 1.5$ ft. (4) $V = 523\frac{1}{3}$ cu.
cm., $h = 3$ in. (5) 66. (6) 1.1 sq. cm. (7) 1203 tons
(app.). (8) 30. (9) 96 ft. (10) 30. (11) $653\frac{1}{3}$. (12) 161
(app.).

D. (1) 24
   (2) 3 quarters, 24 dimes
   (3) $800
   (4) 120 yd., 40 yd.
   (5) $A = 90°$, $B = 60°$
          $C = 30°$

(6) $4\frac{1}{2}$ in., 6 in.
(7) 130
(8) $1800
(9) 16 hits; 17 hits
(10) 4 m.p.h.

(11) $\frac{8}{15}$
(12) 400, 500,
     340

CHAPTER 15

(2) PQ $\perp$ AB, PQ bisects AB.
(5) They cut the other side into the same number of equal parts.
(6) Edge of protractor makes equal corresponding $\angle$s with edge of
ruler.

CHAPTER 16

A (3) ABDC is a $\square$
   (4) 75°, 15°, 15°, 15°

B

(1) 24 sq. ft.
(2) $31\frac{1}{2}$ sq. ft.
(3) 25 sq. ft.
(4) 44 sq. ft.
(5) 384 sq. ft.
(6) $(p^2 + 2pq + p^2)$
    sq. ft.
(7) $42\frac{1}{2}$ sq. ft.
(8) 7 sq. ft.
(9) 12 sq. ft.
(10) 8 sq. ft.
(11) 10 sq. ft.

C

(1) $\triangle$ ADB = $\triangle$ AEB.
    $\triangle$ DEA = $\triangle$ DEB.
    $\triangle$ CEA = $\triangle$ CBD.
(2) $\triangle$ PXY = $\triangle$ YPZ =
    $\triangle$ ZPM.
(3) $\triangle$ XBC = $\triangle$ XCD.
    $\triangle$ BDX = $\triangle$ BDC.
    $\triangle$ ADX (add each of last
    pair to $\triangle$ ADB).
    $\triangle$ ADX (add each of last
    pair to $\triangle$ ADB).

D

(1) $326\frac{1}{2}$ sq. yds.
(2) 595 sq. yds.
(3) $\frac{1}{2}ah + \frac{1}{2}bh$.
(4) $1778\frac{1}{2}$ sq. yds.
(5) Area $= 6$ sq. yds.
$x = 2\frac{2}{5}$ yds.

CHAPTER 17

A. (1) $\frac{3}{4}$, $\frac{4}{3}$. (2) $\frac{3}{2}$, $\frac{2}{3}$. (3) $\frac{5}{3}$, $\frac{3}{5}$. (4) $\frac{5}{6}$, $\frac{6}{5}$. (5) $\frac{1}{2}$, $\frac{2}{1}$. (6) $\frac{1}{25}$, $\frac{25}{1}$.
(7) $\frac{20}{17}$, $\frac{17}{20}$. (8) $\frac{5}{8}$, $\frac{8}{5}$. (9) $\frac{3}{4}$, $\frac{4}{3}$.

B. (1) $\frac{3}{4}$, $\frac{4}{7}$. (2) $\frac{2}{3}$, $\frac{4}{9}$. (3) $\frac{3}{3}$, $\frac{4}{4}$. (4) $\frac{1}{2}$. (5) $\frac{5}{6}$.

C. (1) $2:1$. (2) $3:1$. (3) $\frac{1}{3}:1$. (4) $1\frac{1}{2}:1$. (5) $2\frac{1}{6}:1$. (6) $\frac{5}{12}:1$.
(7) $8:1$. (8) $8.8:1$. (9) $1\frac{1}{3}:1$.

D. (1) 4. (2) 4. (3) 6. (4) $6\frac{2}{7}$. (5) $6.30. (6) $2\frac{1}{13}$. (7) 30 francs.
(8) 12 in.

E. (1) $\frac{1}{1800}$. (2) $\frac{1}{10000}$. (3) 1250 ft. (4) 4 Km. (5) $\frac{1}{21120}$, $1\frac{5}{16}$ in.
(6) (a) 1 in. to 1 mile; 1 mile to 1 in.
(b) 1 in. to 7.89 ($= 8$) miles; 1 mile to .12672 ($= .13$) in.
(c) 1 in. to 15.78 ($= 16$) miles; 1 mile to .06336 ($= .06$) in.
(d) 1 in. to 2 miles; 1 mile to .5 in.
(e) 1 in. to 39.45 mile; 1 mile to .025 in.
(f) 1 in. to 3 miles; 1 mile to .33 in.
(7) (1) is twice as large a scale as (4) and three times as
large a scale as (6). (2) is twice as large a scale as (3)
and five times as large a scale as (5).
(8) $6\frac{1}{3}$ inches. (9) 59.96 miles.

F. (1) $2\frac{1}{2}$ hr. (2) $25. (3) 7 ft. (4) $34\frac{2}{3}$. (5) $9.75.

G. (1) 18. (2) 4 hr. (3) 36 days. (4) $1.87. (5) 15 m.p.h.
(6) $16\frac{2}{3}$ days. (7) $9\frac{1}{3}$. (8) 5. (9) 120. (10) 30 extra
copies.

H. (1) 24. (2) $56. (3) 18. (4) 1280. (5) 6 more men.

J. (1) $164. (2) $12,375. (3) (i) 6 sec., (ii) 13 sec. (4) (i) 25 sec.,
(ii) 5 sec. (5) $3\frac{1}{6}$ miles. (6) $107.65. (7) $7\frac{65}{66}$ m. $= 8$ m.
(approx.).

K. (1) 50, $33\frac{1}{3}$, $66\frac{2}{3}$, 25, 75, 20, 40, 60, 120, $16\frac{2}{3}$, $83\frac{1}{3}$, $14\frac{2}{7}$, $42\frac{6}{7}$, $12\frac{1}{2}$,
$37\frac{1}{2}$, $387\frac{1}{2}$, $11\frac{1}{9}$, $444\frac{4}{9}$, 10, 670.
(2) $\frac{7}{9} = 77\frac{7}{9}\%$, $\frac{11}{13} = 84\frac{8}{13}\%$, $\frac{13}{15} = 86\frac{2}{3}\%$.
(3) $\frac{4}{5}$, $\frac{4}{25}$, $\frac{1}{16}$, $\frac{7}{8}$, $\frac{6}{35}$, $\frac{61}{90}$, $\frac{1}{400}$, $\frac{1}{200}$, $\frac{1}{800}$, $1\frac{17}{120}$, $\frac{109}{110}$.
(4) 15%, $25\frac{5}{6}\%$, $33\frac{1}{3}\%$, $6\frac{2}{3}\%$, 20%, $66\frac{2}{3}\%$.

(5) (a) 5%   (b) 12½%   (c) 34%
    (d) 12½%   (e) 5%   (f) 5%
    (g) 15%   (h) 20%   (i) 5%
    (j) 2½%.
L. (1) 25%   (2) 1.85%   (3) $3.60 gain, $27\tfrac{3}{11}\%$ gain
    (4) $6.72   (5) $35   (6) $132
    (7) $10.08   (8) $5   (9) $3.75
    (10) 12% gain (11) 10% loss (12) $1083
M. (1) $228   (2) $119.28   (3) $4.62
    (4) $47.64   (5) $960   (6) $3\tfrac{2}{3}$

CHAPTER 18

(1) 7. (2) $5\tfrac{1}{2}$. (3) $17\tfrac{1}{2}$. (4) 4.1375. (5) $5\tfrac{125}{144}$. (6) 465 lb.; 93 lb. (7) 32 m.p.h. (8) $3\tfrac{5}{7}$ m.p.h. (9) $34\tfrac{2}{7}$ m.p.h. (10) $56\tfrac{2}{3}$ m.p.h. (11) $112\tfrac{1}{2}$ m.p.h. (12) $129\tfrac{7}{17}$ m.p.h.

CHAPTER 19

(1) 23, 25, 35, 59, 78, 309, 123, 572, 428.   (4) 330 yd.
(2) 4.3, 3.97, 6.42, 2.32, .08, 1.93, 1.234.   (5) ½ hour.
(3) 1.41, 1.73, 2.24, 3.66, .07, 6.76.

CHAPTER 20

(1) EF = 3.75 in., DF = 4.5 in.   (4) 41.6 ft.
    GK = 5.33 in., HK = 6.67 in.   (5) 120 ft.
    PQ = 12.5 in., QR = 15 in.   (6) 11 ft.
(2) ED:EC = AB:BC   ED:DC = AB:AC   (7) $1\tfrac{1}{3}$ in.
    EC:CD = BC:AC   EC:CB = DC:AC   (8) 70 ft.
(3) YC = 12 in., BC = 15 in.
    (9) (a) ADH, AFK, AGL, ABC; (b) PMQ, YMX
        (parallels); PMX ≡ QMY, PXY ≡ QYX, PXQ
        ≡ QYP.

CHAPTER 21

A. (1) 13 cm.   (9) AC = 10.8 in.
    (2) 15 in.   CE = 5 in.
    (3) 32 sq. in.   AE = 10.4 in.
    (4) YM = 6 in., MZ = 15 in.   BH = 10.4 in.
        ∴ YZ = 21 in.   GB = 11.2 in.
    (5) 30 in.   (10) 12 in.
    (6) $\sqrt{2}$ in.   (11) 3.3 in.

	(a)	(b)	(c)
B. (2) Sin A	$\frac{4}{5}$	$\frac{15}{17}$	$\frac{5}{13}$
Cos A	$\frac{3}{5}$	$\frac{8}{17}$	$\frac{12}{13}$
Tan A	$\frac{4}{3}$	$\frac{15}{8}$	$\frac{5}{12}$
Sin B	$\frac{3}{5}$	$\frac{8}{17}$	$\frac{12}{13}$
Cos B	$\frac{4}{5}$	$\frac{15}{17}$	$\frac{5}{13}$
Tan B	$\frac{3}{4}$	$\frac{8}{15}$	$\frac{13}{12}$

(5) 30 yd.

(6) 200 yd. (approx.).

(7) 48 ft.

(8) 60 ft.

(9) Sin B $= \frac{5}{13}$ Sin A $= \frac{12}{13}$
Cos B $= \frac{12}{13}$ Cos A $= \frac{5}{13}$
Tan B $= \frac{5}{12}$ Tan A $= \frac{12}{5}$
Csc B $= \frac{13}{5}$ Csc A $= \frac{13}{12}$
Sec B $= \frac{13}{12}$ Sec A $= \frac{13}{5}$
Cot A $= \frac{5}{12}$

(10) AB $= 2\frac{1}{6}$ in.
AC $= \frac{5}{6}$ in.

(3) Sin A $= \dfrac{BC}{AC}$, Cos A $= \dfrac{AB}{AC}$.

$$\therefore \text{Sin}^2 A + \text{Cos}^2 A = \frac{(BC)^2}{(AC)^2} + \frac{(AB)^2}{(AC)^2} = \frac{(BC)^2 + (AB)^2}{(AC)^2}$$

$$= \frac{(AC)^2}{(AC)^2} = 1.$$

Similarly $\text{Sin}^2 C + \text{Cos}^2 C = 1$.

(4) Sin $30° = \frac{1}{2} = \dfrac{AB}{AX}$. $\therefore \dfrac{68}{AX} = \frac{1}{2}$. $\therefore AX = 136$ ft.

(5) 30 yds.,   (6) 598 ft. (approx.),   (7) 48 ft.,   (8) 60 ft.,
(9) sin B $= \frac{5}{13}$, cos B $= \frac{12}{13}$, tan B $= \frac{5}{12}$, cosec B $= \frac{13}{5}$,
sec B $= \frac{13}{12}$,   sin A $= \frac{12}{13}$,   cos A $= \frac{5}{13}$,   tan A $= \frac{12}{5}$,
cosec A $= \frac{13}{12}$, sec A $= \frac{13}{5}$, cot A $= \frac{5}{12}$, (10) AB $= 2\frac{1}{6}''$,
AC $= \frac{5}{6}''$.

CHAPTER 22

A. (1) 8' 9", 17' 6", 25', 41' 8", 9' 10", 53', 120', 3", 11', 2' 11$\frac{5}{8}$"
(2) 1 in. = 1 mile, 6 in. = 1 mile, 25 in. = 1 mile.
(3) 66 ft., 94.86 ft.

B. (1) 420 ft. (2) $+2° 30'$ (see if tan 3° = .05 approx.).
(3) 37° 14' 20". (4) 3000 ft. approx.

C. (1) 18$\frac{1}{2}$ miles 131°.   (2) 11.6 miles due North.   (3) 165 ft.
(4) 2$\frac{1}{2}$ miles, 010°.

D. (3) 4155 ft. or 1 mile 3030 ft.   (4) 10.1 miles (approx.).
(5) 65.7 miles.   (6) $\frac{3}{5}$ mile, 2552 ft., 5180 ft.,
4455 ft.

CHAPTER 23

(1). (a) 06° 08′ S.; 45° 01′ E.
    (b) 35° 23′ N.; 00° 59′ E.
    (c) 26° 14′ S.; 122° 35′ W.
    (d) 04° N.; 59° 35′ E.
    (e) 23° 01′ N.; 110° 15′ W.
(2). (a) 1716 hours.   (b) 1734 hours.
(3). (a) 127° 30′ E.   (b) 43° 45′ W.
(4). (a) 0707 hours.   (b) 1608 hours.
(5). (a) 108° E.   (b) 123° 15′ E.

CHAPTER 24

A. (1) 2, 3.   (5) 2, −5.   (9) 3, 5.   (13) 1, 4.
   (2) 4, 3.   (6) $\frac{1}{2}$, $1\frac{1}{2}$.   (10) 6, 5.   (14) 5, 2.
   (3) 4, −2.   (7) $19\frac{1}{2}$, $−8\frac{1}{2}$.   (11) 4, 6.   (15) 4, −3.
   (4) −3, −1.   (8) 4, 3.   (12) 13, 15.
B. (1) $x = 3$, or −3.   (6) 3, 4.   (11) 9 or −2.
   (2) 5, 0.   (7) 1, 0.   (12) −1, −7.
   (3) 0, 4.   (8) 6, 3.   (13) 4, $−\frac{1}{3}$.
   (4) 7, −3.   (9) 8, 9.   (14) −2, $+1\frac{1}{2}$.
   (5) 2, 3.   (10) 12, −2.   (15) −3, $−\frac{1}{2}$.
        (16) $1\frac{1}{2}$, $−\frac{1}{3}$.   (17) $+1$, $−3$.

CHAPTER 26

(1) 54 ft./sec.   (3) 113 ft./sec.   (5) 484 ft.   (7) 1410 ft.
   486 ft.   11 secs.   2.2 ft./sec.²
(2) 20 secs.   (4) 4 secs.   (6) 6 ft./sec.²
   120 m./sec.   5 ft./sec.²   144 ft./sec.

CHAPTER 27

(1) 500 ft.   (7) 640 ft.
(2) 9 secs.   (8) 5 secs.
(3) 4 secs.   (9) 625 ft.; 200 ft./sec.
(4) After $\frac{1}{2}$ sec. $\Big\}$ 28 ft. up.   (10) 159 ft.
   After $3\frac{1}{2}$ sec.   (11) (a) 128 ft./sec. (b) 0 ft./sec.
(5) 32.2 ft./sec.²
(6) 7 secs.   (12) $\left(\dfrac{h}{gt} - \dfrac{t}{2}\right)$ secs.

CHAPTER 28

(1) $4\frac{3}{8}$ miles per hour.
(2) 59.1 meters per sec.; 66°
(3) 6 miles per hour, 300°.
(4) 2.8 miles (approx.).
(5) $3\sqrt{10}$ knots = 9.486, 18° 30'.
(6) 9 cm.per sec.(approx.),14°32'.
(7) 11.66 ft.
(8) 5.8 ft. per sec.

(9) 6 ft. per sec.
(10) $6\frac{1}{4}$ miles.
(11) 21.2 miles per hour.
(12) 20 miles.
(13) $200\sqrt{7}$ miles = 529 miles.
(14) 34.6 m.p.h., 30°.
(15) $63\frac{1}{2}$° (approx.)
         671 ft. (approx.)

(16) Co. 082 T   G/S   95 Kts.

(17) Co. 259 T   G/S   101 Kts.
(18) Co. 193 T   G/S   190 m.p.h.
(19) Co. 165 T   G/S   108 m.p.h.
(20) Co. 322 T   G/S   152 Kts.

(21) $\boxed{185/37}$

(22) $\boxed{145/21 \text{ k}}$

(23) $\boxed{275/36}$

(24) $\boxed{165/20 \text{ k}}$

(25) $\boxed{347/13}$

(26) Tr. 023 T   G/S   150 m.p.h.
(27) Tr. 255 T   G/S   96 m.p.h.
(28) Tr. 055 T   G/S   147 Kts.
(29) Tr. 336 T   G/S   82 Kts.
(30) Tr. 226 T   G/S   133 Kts.

CHAPTER 29

(1) $5\frac{1}{3}$ lb., $2\frac{2}{3}$ lb.
(2) 130 lb.
(3) 20 cm. from one end.
(4) 1.16 in. from A.

(5) 1.9 in.
(7) 234 lb. per sq. in.
(8) 2 ft.
(9) $7\frac{2}{9}$ from one end.

CHAPTER 30

(1) 3, 2, 0, $\bar{1}$, $\bar{3}$, $\bar{1}$, 1.
(2) 2.6597; $\bar{2}$.6597; 4.6597; $\bar{1}$.6597.
(3) 2972; .2972; 2.972; .002972.

(4) $0.2893; \overline{2}.1627; 2.5360; \overline{4}.0721; 2.8463; \overline{1}.3091; \overline{6}.2224; 0.1377;$
  $\overline{2}.7342, \overline{3}.4302; \overline{8}.7013; \overline{4}.9451, \overline{1}.8117; \overline{2}.5708.$

(5) (a) 13248   (d) 55.80   (g) .00005694   (j) 45.96
   (b) 1.65   (e) 1.736   (h) 1.823   (k) .000001728
   (c) .000151   (f) .01761   (i) .1084   (l) 77.   (m) 1.4.

CHAPTER 31

(1) A $= 94° 4'$.
   B $= 47° 22'$.
   C $= 38° 34'$.

(2) $a = 67.734$ yds.
   B $= 33° 29'$.
   C $= 93° 51'$.

(3) C $= 98° 35'$.
   $b = 57.69$ ft.
   $c = 78.977$ ft.

(4) $c = 215.48$ ft.
   B $= 42° 25.6'$.
   C $= 81° 24.4'$.

(5) Either $\begin{cases} c = 221.11 \text{ yd.} \\ A = 54° 49'. \\ C = 83° 11'. \end{cases}$

or $\begin{cases} c = 49.397 \text{ yd.} \\ A = 125° 11'. \\ C = 12° 49'. \end{cases}$

CHAPTER 32

(1) $12x^{11}$.   (2) $9x^8$.   (3) 1.   (4) $\frac{1}{2}x^{-\frac{1}{2}}\left(\text{or } \frac{1}{2\sqrt{x}}\right)$.   (5) see (4).

(6) $\frac{1}{3}x^{-\frac{2}{3}}\left(\text{or } \frac{1}{3\sqrt[3]{x^2}}\right)$.   (7) see (6).   (8) $-2x^{-3}\left(\text{or } -\frac{2}{x^3}\right)$.

(9) see (8).   (10) $-\frac{5}{3}x^{-\frac{8}{3}}\left(\text{or } -\frac{5}{3\sqrt[3]{x^8}}\right)$.   (11) see (10).

(12) $-\dfrac{3}{5\sqrt[5]{x^6}}$.   (13) $10x$.   (14) $2x-3$.   (15) $32x-16x$.

(16) $\dfrac{-5}{x^2}$.   (17) $\dfrac{-60}{x^5}$.   (18) $6x+\dfrac{20}{x^2}$.   (19) $36x^2-18x+4$.

(20) $75x^4-336x^3-225x^2+800x+112$.   (21) $\dfrac{-11}{(5x-2)^2}$.

(22) $\dfrac{2\,acx+af+bc}{(cx+f)^2}$.   (23) $\dfrac{3x^2(3+2x+2x^2)}{(1+x+2x^2)^2}$.   (24) $\frac{3}{5}x^2+2$.

(25) $\dfrac{x^4}{10}$. (26) $\dfrac{60x^9}{17}$. (27) $\dfrac{2nx^{-1}+anx^{-n-1}+bnx^{n-1}}{(x^{-n}+b)^2}$.

(28) $\dfrac{d^2y}{dx^2} = 20x^9+30x^2$. (29) $\dfrac{d^2y}{dx^2}-24$.

CHAPTER 33

(1) 50 mils. (2) 7714 ft. (3) 171 mils; 0.168 radians.
(4) 3° 17.4′; 0.0574 radians.
(5) 190.5 mils; 10° 42.8′.
(6) Between 137.5 yards and 165 yards.
(7) 165 yards. (8) 371 mils. (9) 378 mils.
(10) 2750 feet.

A—EASY TEST PAPERS

I

(1) (a) .625; (b) $\frac{2}{25}$. (2) $\frac{8}{15}$. (3) $x = 8$. (4) $a = 12$.
(5) 3 cm., 5 cm. (6) 60°. (7) Two straight lines.

II

(1) (a) .35; (b) $\frac{9}{40}$. (2) $\frac{5}{12}$. (3) $x - 6$. (4) 7. (5) 3.5. (6) 65°.
(7) A straight line making 45° with the horizontal.

III

(1) (a) .425; (b) $\frac{4}{25}$. (2) $2\frac{3}{4}$. (3) $x = 24$. (4) 6. (5) 20 miles.
(6) 40°. (7) $35\frac{1}{2}$ min. and 90 min. from the start.

IV

(1) 7.2 Km. (2) 26, $10\frac{9}{16}$. (3) $10\frac{1}{2}$. (4) 34. (5) $5g+3t$.
(6) F = 176, 23; C = 15, −10. (7) 45°; 010°; 190°.

B—HARDER TEST PAPERS

I

(1) .0268.　(2) 2090.　(3) (a) $\frac{7}{80}$; (b) .4375.　(4) 1828.8 meters.

(5) $r = \frac{1}{2}\sqrt{\dfrac{A}{\pi}}.$　(6) 35 miles; 42 m.p.h.　(7) 2350 copies.

(8) 81 (i) miles; (ii) 62°.　(9) 6.9″.　(10) 7.6 miles.

II

(1) .644.　(2) $t = \sqrt{\dfrac{2s}{g}}$; (i) 7; (ii) 10; (iii) 13.7.

(3) (i) 3.048 meters; (ii) 45.72 meters.　(4) (i) 85 miles;
(ii) 204 m.p.h.　(5) 336 ft. approximately.　(6) (i) $x = 2$,
$y = 3$; (ii) $x = 4$ or $\frac{1}{4}$.　(7) 31.5 sq. in.　(8) (i) 32 Km.;
(ii) $12\frac{1}{2}$ miles.　(9) 321.5°, 111 sea-miles.　(10) 2.7 miles.

III

(1) $3\frac{1}{7} = 3.1428$; $\frac{355}{113} = 3.1416$.　(2) $\frac{74}{457}$.　(3) 14 ft. 4.8 in.;
8.497 Km.　(4) $166\frac{2}{3}$ m.p.h.　(5) 10 min.; $6\frac{14}{31}\%$.
(6) AX = 720 ft.; BX = 540 ft.; CX = 300 ft.　(7) 37°;
157°.　(8) $33\frac{3}{5}$ m.p.h.　(9) $a = 1003.8$ ft.; B = 127° 54′;
C = 11° 38′.　(10) (a) $1\frac{1}{2}$, -4; (b) 1.47, -7.47.

IV

(1) 16.32.　(2) 10:9.　(3) $4\frac{1}{2}$ sec.　(4) 150 m.p.h.　(5) $2\frac{1}{2}$ hours.
(6) $3\frac{1}{3}″$ from center.　(7) AX = XC = 1″; 72°; $\triangle$s ABC,
CBX; $\dfrac{AB}{BC} = \dfrac{BC}{BX}$ ∴ (BC)^2 = AB.BX.　(8) 5, $1\frac{4}{5}$.

(9) CD = $57\frac{1}{2}$ ch.; ADBC = $1293\frac{3}{4}$ sq. ch.
(10) A = 42° 10′; B = 63° 36′; C = 74° 14′.

TABLES OF WEIGHTS AND MEASURES

Length

12 inches (in.) or ('')	= 1 foot (ft.) or (')
3 ft.	= 1 yard (yd.)
22 yds.	= 1 chain (ch.)
10 ch.	= 1 furlong (fur.)
8 fur.	= 1 mile

220 yds. = 1 furlong   100 links = 1 ch.
1760 yds. = 1 mile $5\frac{1}{2}$ yds. = 1 pole or rod or perch
5280 ft.   = 1 mile   40 poles (etc.) = 1 furlong

Nautical Measures

6 ft. = 1 fathom (depth)
600 ft. = 1 cable
6080 ft. = 1 sea-mile
69 land miles = 60 sea-miles (approximately)
1 knot is a *speed* of 1 nautical mile per hour
(*Never* say "so many knots per hour.")

Area

144 (= $(12)^2$) sq. ins. = 1 sq. ft.   10 sq. ch. = 1 acre
9 (= $(3)^2$) sq. ft.   = 1 sq. yd.   640 acres = 1 sq. mile
484 (= $(22)^2$) sq. yds. = 1 sq. ch.   *i.e.* 4840 sq. yds. = 1 acre
$30\frac{1}{4}$ (= $5\frac{1}{2}$ squared) sq. yds. = 1 sq. pole
40 sq. poles = 1 rood
4 roods = 1 acre

Avoirdupois Weight

16 ounces (oz.) = 1 pound (lb.)
100 pounds = 1 hundredweight (cwt.)
20 hundredweight, or 2000 pounds = 1 ton (T.)

Volume

1728 (= $(12)^3$) cu. ins. = 1 cu. ft.
27 (= $(3)^3$) cu. ft.   = 1 cu. yd.

Capacity

4 gills = 1 pint (pt.)	2 gall. = 1 peck (pk.)
2 pts. = 1 quart (qt.)	4 pks. = 1 bushel (bush.)
4 qts. = 1 gallon (gall.)	8 bush. = 1 quarter (qr.)

Time

(Used in all countries)

60 seconds = 1 minute	365 days = 1 year
(sec.) or (″) (min.) or (′)	366 days = 1 leap year
60 min. = 1 hour (hr.)	12 months = 1 year
24 hrs. = 1 day	52 weeks = 1 year
7 days = 1 week	
2 weeks or 14 days = 1 fortnight	

[Although not used in this book, the following may be of interest and value]

BRITISH MONEY

Farthing. (Anglo-Saxon "feorthing"—a fourth part.) The smallest coin in value. $\frac{1}{4}$ penny.

Halfpenny. (Pronounced "hay-pny.") = $\frac{1}{2}$ penny or 2 farthings.

Penny. (Written "d" for Latin "denarius". Plural, "pence," also written "d.")

Threepenny piece. (Pronounced "thrupny" piece.) The smallest silver coin, = 3d.

Sixpence. Silver coin worth 6d or $\frac{1}{2}$ a shilling.

Shilling. Silver coin worth 12d. (Written "s.")

Florin. Silver coin with cross on one side, value two shillings. (Originally, in Middle Ages, a gold coin bearing a lily—Latin "flos, floris.")

Half-crown. Silver coin slightly larger than florin (no cross on it). 2s 6d.

Crown. (Now practically obsolete.) Silver coin, value 5 shillings.

Half-sovereign. Gold coin (not in circulation since 1914). Value 10 shillings. Now replaced by "10-shilling" Treasury note.

Sovereign (Pound). Gold coin (not in circulation since 1914). Value, 20 shillings. Now replaced by "one-pound" Treasury note. Also called "one pound" and written with £ on left-hand side of number (as dollar sign). In the Middle Ages a pound weight of silver was worth "one pound" in money also. This explains the £ sign, being a glorified capital L, standing for the Latin "libra," a pound. Hence also the abbreviation, "lb." for pound-weight. Hence also the reason why "pounds" (weight) should be abbreviated "lb.," not "lbs."

Guinea. Originally a gold coin made from gold from the Guinea coast of West Africa. Now obsolete as a coin, but professional men usually charge their clients in guineas. Value, 21 shillings.

4 farthings or	
2 ha'pence	= 1 penny (d)
12 pence	= 1 shilling (s)
20 shillings	= 1 pound (£)

Farthings and ha'pence are written as fractions of a penny, *e.g.* 3 farthings = $\frac{3}{4}$ d; 1 ha'penny = $\frac{1}{2}$ d.

£. s. d are written either £3. 5s. 6d or £3.5.6 or £3/5/6.
In addition to 10/– and £1 Treasury notes, the Bank of England
issues £5, £10 Bank of England notes.

The American equivalents of British money given below are
approximate only and are based on a rate of exchange of $4.04 to £1.

Penny	1d	= a little more than 1 cent
Threepenny piece	3d	= 5 cents
Sixpence	6d	= 10 cents
Shilling	1/–	= 20 cents
Florin	2/–	= 40 cents
Half-crown	2/6	= 50 cents
Crown	5/–	= $1.01
Half-sovereign	10/–	= $2.02
Sovereign (pound)	£1	= $4.04
Guinea	£1/1/0	= $4.24

INDEX

Abacus, 1
Abscissa, 236
Acceleration, 204, 207, 257
Addition, decimals, 5
    fractions, 93
    mixed numbers, 93
Air speed, 212
Algebraic factors, 78
    manipulation, 54
    signs, 45
"Allsintancos," 237
Ambiguous case, 245
"Amount" (Interest), 138
Angle, 11
    bisector, 111
Angles, acute, 12
    adjacent, 13, 58
    alternate, 14, 15, 59
    bisector of, 111
    complementary, 12, 167
    construction of, 112
    corresponding, 14, 15
    equal, 111–112
    in opposite segment, 203
    in semi-circle, 202
    measurement of, 182
    obtuse, 12
    of depression, 170
    of elevation, 170
    reflex, 12
    right, 12
    supplementary, 12, 239
    vertically opposite, 13, 15, 58
Angular measurement
    mil, 259–260
    radian, 259–260
Approximation, 9
Arc, 55
Area, of parallelograms, 115
    of rectangles, 31
    of triangles, 116
Averages, 140–145
Axis, 64
Azimuth, 212

Base line, 150, 178
Bearing, 174, 212

Binomial, 75
Bisection, of angle, 111
    of line, 111
    of parallelogram, 114
Bracket, common, 79
Brackets, algebraic, 50, 75, 78
    arithmetical, 94
British money, 337

Calculus, differential, 248
Capacity, table of, 336
Center, of circle, 220
Center of gravity, 218
Centroid, 220
Change of latitude and longitude, 182, 183
Characteristic, 225–226
Chord, 55, 162, 200
Circle, area, 104
    definitions, 55
    facts about, 200–203
    great, 20
Circumference, 55, 103
Clock, twenty-four-hour, 69
Coinage, decimal, 36
Common bracket, 79
    factor, 89
    fraction, 84
    multiple, 89
    term, 79
Compass, 24
Complementary angles, 12, 167
Compound interest, 139
    proportion, 132
Cone, volume, 104
Congruent triangles, 58, 60
Consecutive numbers (algebraic representation), 109
Conversion, fractions to decimals and vice versa, 94
Corresponding angles, 14, 59
Cosecant (csc), 168, 236
Cosine (cos), 164, 236
Cotangent (cot), 168, 236
Course, 212
Cross multiplication (factors), 80
Cube, 34

Cube root, 231
Cuboid, 34, 105
Curve, 67, 68, 70, 72, 73, 74
Cyclic quadrilateral, 202
Cylinder, volume, 104
  hollow, volume, 107

Decimal coinage, 36
Decimals, 4
  recurring, 9
Degree, angular, 16, 182
  temperature, 283
Denominator, 84
Depression, angle of, 170
Derivative, first, 252, 256
  second, 257
Deviation, 212
Diagonal, 114
Diameter, 55, 103
Difference of two squares (factors), 82
Differential calculus, 248
Direct variation, 129
Direction, 16, 17, 18, 19
  in algebra, 45, 47, 48
  of wind, 212
Dividend, 7
Division, 4
  of decimals, 7
  of fractions, 85
  of line, 113
  of mixed numbers, 88
Divisor, 7
Drift, 212

Elevation, angle of, 170
Equations, graphical solution, 189, 197
  involving brackets, 100
    decimals, 100
    fractions, 99
  quadratic, 192
  simple, 95
  simultaneous, 187
Equator, 20, 181, 206
Equilateral triangle, 26
Even numbers, algebraic representation, 109
Exterior angle (of triangle), 59

Factor, 7
  algebraic, 78
  arithmetic, 7
  common, 89

Factor, highest common, 89, 90
  prime, 41, 88
First derivative, 252, 256
Force, moment of, 221
Formula, 102
  change of subject, 106
Fraction, representative, 128, 169, 176
Fractions, common, 84
  improper, 84
  proper, 84

Galileo, 206
Geometrical constructions, 56, 111
  facts, 58
Gram, 34
Graphs, 63
  proportion, 72
  speed, 67
Gravity, 206–208
  center of, 218
Great circle, 20
Greenwich Mean Time (G.M.T.), 184
Ground speed, 212
Growth, relative, 248

Haversine, 243
Heading, 212
Hexagon, 27
Highest common factor, 88, 89, 90
Hypotenuse, 56, 156, 158, 164

Improper fraction, 84
Indices, 38
  law of, 38, 42
"Infinity," 238
Interest, compound, 139
  simple, 138
Interpolation, 229
Inverse variation, 129
Isosceles triangle, 26, 58, 161
  construction of, 61

Kilometers, conversion of, 127
Knot, 127, 212

Latitude, 20, 181
Length, table of, 335
Line, bisector of, 111
  division of, 113
Lines, parallel, 13
  perpendicular, 111
Liter, 34
Local Mean Time (L.M.T.), 184

Logarithms, 225
Longitude, 20
  and time, 183
Lowest common multiple, 88, 90, 91

Magnetic North, 23
Mantissa, 225, 227
Map-making, 150, 177
Mass, 28, 207
Measure, metric, 30
Medians, 220
Meridian, 20, 181
Meter, 29
Metric system, 29
Mil, 259–260
Minute (angular), 182
Mixed number, 85
Moment of force, 221
Money, British, table of, 337
Multiple, 89
  common, 89
  lowest common, 90, 91
Multiplicand, 6
Multiplication, by 10, 100, 1000, 4
  "diagonal," 124
  of decimals, 6
  of fractions, 85
  of mixed numbers, 88

Nautical measures, table of, 335
Nautical mile, 182
Newton, 206
North, compass, 212
  magnetic, 23, 212
  true, 212
Number, mixed, 85
Numerator, 84

Obtuse angle, 12
Obtuse-angled triangle, 27
Octagon, 27
Odd number (algebraic representa-
  tion), 109
Ordinate, 236
Origin, 64
Oscillation, 72–73

Parallel lines, 13, 114
  quick method of drawing, 113
Parallelogram, 25, 114
  area of, 115
  of velocities, 210
Parallels of latitude, 21

Pentagon, 27
Percentage, 134
  profit and loss, 137
Perpendicular, 112, 113
π, 103
Plane, 21
Plane figure, 25
Plane surface, 25
Plans, 171
Plough, 19
Pole star, 19
Polygon, 28, 59
Port, 212
Principal, 138
Product, 10
Profit and loss, 136
Projection, 234
Proper fractions, 84
Proportion, 123
  compound, 132
  direct, 125, 129
  four numbers in, 119
  graphs, 72, 126
  inverse, 129
  unitary method, 125
Proportional parts, 230
Protractor, 16
Pyramid, 26
Pythagoras, 158

Quadrant, 64
Quadratic equation, 192
Quadrilateral, 25
  cyclic, 202
Quotient, 8, 85

Radian, 259-260
Radius, 55, 103
Rate (interest), 138
Ratio, 118–139
Reciprocals, 150
Rectangle, 25, 115
Recurring decimals, 9
Reflex angle, 12
Relative bearing, 212
Relative velocity, 209
Representative fraction, 128, 169
Resultant velocity, 210
Retardation (Gravity), 207
Rhombus, 114
Right angle, 12
Right-angled triangle, 27, 157
Root, cube, 231
  square, 39, 146, 231

Scale, 64, 128, 169
Scale drawing, 169
Scalene triangle, 26
Scales (map), 128
Secant, 168, 236
Second (angular), 182
Second derivative, 257
Sector, 55
Segment, 55, 201
Semi-circle, 55
Significant figures, 9
Signs, algebraic, 45
 rule of, 50
Similar figures, 120, 149
 triangles, 119, 156
Simple equations, 95
 interest, 138
Simultaneous equations, 187
Sine, 164, 236
Solid figures, 25
Solution of triangles, 240
Speed, 67, 68, 69, 70, 71, 130
Sphere (vol. of), 233
Square, 25, 39, 114
Square root, 40, 146, 231
Squares, difference of two, 82
Starboard, 212
Statute miles (conversion of), 127
Substitution, 190, 197
Subtraction, algebraic rule, 50
 decimals, 5
 fractions, 93
 mixed numbers, 93
Supplementary angles, 12

Tables of weights and measures, 335
Tangent (geometric), 203
 (trigonometric), 164, 236
Tests of accuracy
 equations, 97
 simplifications, 78
Theorem of Pythagoras, 158
Time, 181–186
 table of, 336

Track ("Course made good"), 212
Transversal, 13
Trapezium, 25
Triangle, 26, 56
 of velocities, 211
Triangles, acute-angled, 27
 area of, 116
 congruent, 58
 construction of, 56
 equiangular, 149
 equilateral, 26
 isosceles, 27, 61
 obtuse-angled, 27
 right-angled, 157
 scalene, 26
 similar, 118, 150
 solution of, 234
Trigonometry, 164, 234
True Bearing, 212
True North, 212
Twenty-four-hour clock, 69

Unitary method, 125

Variation, direct, 125, 129
 inverse, 129
Vector, 212
Velocities, parallelogram of, 209
 triangle of, 211, 212
Velocity, 204, 207
 relative, 209
 resultant, 210
Vertically opposite angles, 13, 58
Volume, of cone, 104
 of cube, 33
 of cuboid, 33
 of cylinder, 104
 of metal in pipes, 107
 table of, 335

Weight, 28, 207
 avoirdupois, table of, 335
Weights and measures, tables of, 335

TABLES

I. FOUR-PLACE LOGARITHMS . . . . . iii-iv

II. FOUR-PLACE VALUES OF FUNCTIONS AND RA-
DIANS . . . . v-ix

III. LOGARITHMS OF TRIGONOMETRIC FUNCTIONS . x-xiv

Notes

Those who will have to use Five-Place Tables (e.g., prospective air navigators) are advised to purchase them and become familiar with them from the outset (see specimen on p. 228).

For the convenience of the general reader the less bulky Four-Place Tables are printed on the pages which follow. Those anxious to learn how to use Tables but not concerned with minute accuracy will find these sufficient for their needs. The same general principles of interpolation (see p 230) apply to Four-Place Tables, but with considerable less accuracy of course.

In Chapter 31 (Solution of Triangles) the correct results may be obtained by the use of Table II. If one desires to solve the problems by means of logarithms, Table III should be used.

In Tables II and III to find the value or the logarithm of the trigonometrical functions of angles from 0° to 45°, locate the required angle in *left-hand* column and read value or logarithm of function from the *top* of the page.

For angles between 45° and 90°, find required angle in *right-hand* column and read value or logarithm of function from the *bottom* of the page (working upwards).

I. FOUR-PLACE LOGARITHMS

n	0	1	2	3	4	5	6	7	8	9
10	0000	0043	0086	0128	0170	0212	0253	0294	0334	0374
11	0414	0453	0492	0531	0569	0607	0645	0682	0719	0755
12	0792	0828	0864	0899	0934	0969	1004	1038	1072	1106
13	1139	1173	1206	1239	1271	1303	1335	1367	1399	1430
14	1461	1492	1523	1553	1584	1614	1644	1673	1703	1732
15	1761	1790	1818	1847	1875	1903	1931	1959	1987	2014
16	2041	2068	2095	2122	2148	2175	2201	2227	2253	2279
17	2304	2330	2355	2380	2405	2430	2455	2480	2504	2529
18	2553	2577	2601	2625	2648	2672	2695	2718	2742	2765
19	2788	2810	2833	2856	2878	2900	2923	2945	2967	2989
20	3010	3032	3054	3075	3096	3118	3139	3160	3181	3201
21	3222	3243	3263	3284	3304	3324	3345	3365	3385	3404
22	3424	3444	3464	3483	3502	3522	3541	3560	3579	3598
23	3617	3636	3655	3674	3692	3711	3729	3747	3766	3784
24	3802	3820	3838	3856	3874	3892	3909	3927	3945	3962
25	3979	3997	4014	4031	4048	4065	4082	4099	4116	4133
26	4150	4166	4183	4200	4216	4232	4249	4265	4281	4298
27	4314	4330	4346	4362	4378	4393	4409	4425	4440	4456
28	4472	4487	4502	4518	4533	4548	4564	4579	4594	4609
29	4624	4639	4654	4669	4683	4698	4713	4728	4742	4757
30	4771	4786	4800	4814	4829	4843	4857	4871	4886	4900
31	4914	4928	4942	4955	4969	4983	4997	5011	5024	5038
32	5051	5065	5079	5092	5105	5119	5132	5145	5159	5172
33	5185	5198	5211	5224	5237	5250	5263	5276	5289	5302
34	5315	5328	5340	5353	5366	5378	5391	5403	5416	5428
35	5441	5453	5465	5478	5490	5502	5514	5527	5539	5551
36	5563	5575	5587	5599	5611	5623	5635	5647	5658	5670
37	5682	5694	5705	5717	5729	5740	5752	5763	5775	5786
38	5798	5809	5821	5832	5843	5855	5866	5877	5888	5899
39	5911	5922	5933	5944	5955	5966	5977	5988	5999	6010
40	6021	6031	6042	6053	6064	6075	6085	6096	6107	6117
41	6128	6138	6149	6160	6170	6180	6191	6201	6212	6222
42	6232	6243	6253	6263	6274	6284	6294	6304	6314	6325
43	6335	6345	6355	6365	6375	6385	6395	6405	6415	6425
44	6435	6444	6454	6464	6474	6484	6493	6503	6513	6522
45	6532	6542	6551	6561	6571	6580	6590	6599	6609	6618
46	6628	6637	6646	6656	6665	6675	6684	6693	6702	6712
47	6721	6730	6739	6749	6758	6767	6776	6785	6794	6803
48	6812	6821	6830	6839	6848	6857	6866	6875	6884	6893
49	6902	6911	6920	6928	6937	6946	6955	6964	6972	6981
50	6990	6998	7007	7016	7024	7033	7042	7050	7059	7067
51	7076	7084	7093	7101	7110	7118	7126	7135	7143	7152
52	7160	7168	7177	7185	7193	7202	7210	7218	7226	7235
53	7243	7251	7259	7267	7275	7284	7292	7300	7308	7316
54	7324	7332	7340	7348	7356	7364	7372	7380	7388	7396

n	0	1	2	3	4	5	6	7	8	9
55	7404	7412	7419	7427	7435	7443	7451	7459	7466	7474
56	7482	7490	7497	7505	7513	7520	7528	7536	7543	7551
57	7559	7566	7574	7582	7589	7597	7604	7612	7619	7627
58	7634	7642	7649	7657	7664	7672	7679	7686	7694	7701
59	7709	7716	7723	7731	7738	7745	7752	7760	7767	7774
60	7782	7789	7796	7803	7810	7818	7825	7832	7839	7846
61	7853	7860	7868	7875	7882	7889	7896	7903	7910	7917
62	7924	7931	7938	7945	7952	7959	7966	7973	7980	7987
63	7993	8000	8007	8014	8021	8028	8035	8041	8048	8055
64	8062	8069	8075	8082	8089	8096	8102	8109	8116	8122
65	8129	8136	8142	8149	8156	8162	8169	8176	8182	8189
66	8195	8202	8209	8215	8222	8228	8235	8241	8248	8254
67	8261	8267	8274	8280	8287	8293	8299	8306	8312	8319
68	8325	8331	8338	8344	8351	8357	8363	8370	8376	8382
69	8388	8395	8401	8407	8414	8420	8426	8432	8439	8445
70	8451	8457	8463	8470	8476	8482	8488	8494	8500	8506
71	8513	8519	8525	8531	8537	8543	8549	8555	8561	8567
72	8573	8579	8585	8591	8597	8603	8609	8615	8621	8627
73	8633	8639	8645	8651	8657	8663	8669	8675	8681	8686
74	8692	8698	8704	8710	8716	8722	8727	8733	8739	8745
75	8751	8756	8762	8768	8774	8779	8785	8791	8797	8802
76	8808	8814	8820	8825	8831	8837	8842	8848	8854	8859
77	8865	8871	8876	8882	8887	8893	8899	8904	8910	8915
78	8921	8927	8932	8938	8943	8949	8954	8960	8965	8971
79	8976	8982	8987	8993	8998	9004	9009	9015	9020	9025
80	9031	9036	9042	9047	9053	9058	9063	9069	9074	9079
81	9085	9090	9096	9101	9106	9112	9117	9122	9128	9133
82	9138	9143	9149	9154	9159	9165	9170	9175	9180	9186
83	9191	9196	9201	9206	9212	9217	9222	9227	9232	9238
84	9243	9248	9253	9258	9263	9269	9274	9279	9284	9289
85	9294	9299	9304	9309	9315	9320	9325	9330	9335	9340
86	9345	9350	9355	9360	9365	9370	9375	9380	9385	9390
87	9395	9400	9405	9410	9415	9420	9425	9430	9435	9440
88	9445	9450	9455	9460	9465	9469	9474	9479	9484	9489
89	9494	9499	9504	9509	9513	9518	9523	9528	9533	9538
90	9542	9547	9552	9557	9562	9566	9571	9576	9581	9586
91	9590	9595	9600	9605	9609	9614	9619	9624	9628	9633
92	9638	9643	9647	9652	9657	9661	9666	9671	9675	9680
93	9685	9689	9694	9699	9703	9708	9713	9717	9722	9727
94	9731	9736	9741	9745	9750	9754	9759	9763	9768	9773
95	9777	9782	9786	9791	9795	9800	9805	9809	9814	9818
96	9823	9827	9832	9836	9841	9845	9850	9854	9859	9863
97	9868	9872	9877	9881	9886	9890	9894	9899	9903	9908
98	9912	9917	9921	9926	9930	9934	9939	9943	9948	9952
99	9956	9961	9965	9969	9974	9978	9983	9987	9991	9996

Degrees	Radians	Sin	Csc	Tan	Cot	Sec	Cos		
0° 0′	.0000	.0000	——	.0000	——	1.000	1.0000	1.5708	90° 0′
10′	029	029	343.8	029	343.8	000	000	679	50′
20′	058	058	171.9	058	171.9	000	000	650	40′
30′	.0087	.0087	114.6	.0087	114.6	1.000	1.0000	1.5621	30′
40′	116	116	85.95	116	85.94	000	.9999	592	20′
50′	145	145	68.76	145	68.75	000	999	563	10′
1° 0′	.0175	.0175	57.30	.0175	57.29	1.000	.9998	1.5533	89° 0′
10′	204	204	49.11	204	49.10	000	998	504	50′
20′	233	233	42.98	233	42.96	000	997	475	40′
30′	.0262	.0262	38.20	.0262	38.19	1.000	.9997	1.5446	30′
40′	291	291	34.38	291	34.37	000	996	417	20′
50′	320	320	31.26	320	31.24	001	995	388	10′
2° 0′	.0349	.0349	28.65	.0349	28.64	1.001	.9994	1.5359	88° 0′
10′	378	378	26.45	378	26.43	001	993	330	50′
20′	407	407	24.56	407	24.54	001	992	301	40′
30′	.0436	.0436	22.93	.0437	22.90	1.001	.9990	1.5272	30′
40′	465	465	21.49	466	21.47	001	989	243	20′
50′	495	494	20.23	495	20.21	001	988	213	10′
3° 0′	.0524	.0523	19.11	.0524	19.08	1.001	.9986	1.5184	87° 0′
10′	553	552	18.10	553	18.07	002	985	155	50′
20′	582	581	17.20	582	17.17	002	983	126	40′
30′	.0611	.0610	16.38	.0612	16.35	1.002	.9981	1.5097	30′
40′	640	640	15.64	641	15.60	002	980	068	20′
50′	669	669	14.96	670	14.92	002	978	039	10′
4° 0′	.0698	.0698	14.34	.0699	14.30	1.002	.9976	1.5010	86° 0′
10′	727	727	13.76	729	13.73	003	974	981	50′
20′	756	756	13.23	758	13.20	003	971	952	40′
30′	.0785	.0785	12.75	.0787	12.71	1.003	.9969	1.4923	30′
40′	814	814	12.29	816	12.25	003	967	893	20′
50′	844	843	11.87	846	11.83	004	964	864	10′
5° 0′	.0873	.0872	11.47	.0875	11.43	1.004	.9962	1.4835	85° 0′
10′	902	901	11.10	904	11.06	004	959	806	50′
20′	931	929	10.76	934	10.71	004	957	777	40′
30′	.0960	.0958	10.43	.0963	10.39	1.005	.9954	1.4748	30′
40′	989	987	10.13	992	10.08	005	951	719	20′
50′	.1018	.1016	9.839	.1022	9.788	005	948	690	10′
6° 0′	.1047	.1045	9.567	.1051	9.514	1.006	.9945	1.4661	84° 0′
10′	076	074	9.309	080	9.255	006	942	632	50′
20′	105	103	9.065	110	9.010	006	939	603	40′
30′	.1134	.1132	8.834	.1139	8.777	1.006	.9936	1.4573	30′
40′	164	161	8.614	169	8.556	007	932	544	20′
50′	193	190	8.405	198	8.345	007	929	515	10′
7° 0′	.1222	.1219	8.206	.1228	8.144	1.008	.9925	1.4486	83° 0′
10′	251	248	8.016	257	7.953	008	922	457	50′
20′	280	276	7.834	287	7.770	008	918	428	40′
30′	.1309	.1305	7.661	.1317	7.596	1.009	.9914	1.4399	30′
40′	338	334	7.496	346	7.429	009	911	370	20′
50′	367	363	7.337	376	7.269	009	907	341	10′
8° 0′	.1396	.1392	7.185	.1405	7.115	1.010	.9903	1.4312	82° 0′
10′	425	421	7.040	435	6.968	010	899	283	50′
20′	454	449	6.900	465	6.827	011	894	254	40′
30′	.1484	.1478	6.765	.1495	6.691	1.011	.9890	1.4224	30′
40′	513	507	6.636	524	6.561	012	886	195	20′
50′	542	536	6.512	554	6.435	012	881	166	10′
9° 0′	.1571	.1564	6.392	.1584	6.314	1.012	.9877	1.4137	81° 0′
		Cos	Sec	Cot	Tan	Csc	Sin	Radians	Degrees

II. FOUR-PLACE VALUES OF FUNCTIONS AND RADIANS (*Cont.*)

Degrees	Radians	Sin	Csc	Tan	Cot	Sec	Cos		
9° 0'	.1571	.1564	6.392	.1584	6.314	1.012	.9877	1.4137	81° 0'
10'	600	593	277	614	197	013	872	108	50'
20'	629	622	166	644	084	013	868	079	40'
30'	.1658	.1650	6.059	.1673	5.976	1.014	.9863	1.4050	30'
40'	687	679	5.955	703	871	014	858	1.4021	20'
50'	716	708	855	733	769	015	853	992	10'
10° 0'	.1745	.1736	5.759	.1763	5.671	1.015	.9848	1.3963	80° 0'
10'	774	765	665	793	576	016	843	934	50'
20'	804	794	575	823	485	016	838	904	40'
30'	.1833	.1822	5.487	.1853	5.396	1.017	.9833	1.3875	30'
40'	862	851	403	883	309	018	827	846	20'
50'	891	880	320	914	226	018	822	817	10'
11° 0'	.1920	.1908	5.241	.1944	5.145	1.019	.9816	1.3788	79° 0'
10'	949	937	164	974	066	019	811	759	50'
20'	978	965	089	2004	4.989	020	805	730	40'
30'	.2007	.1994	5.016	.2035	4.915	1.020	.9799	1.3701	30'
40'	036	.2022	4.945	065	843	021	793	672	20'
50'	065	051	876	095	773	022	787	643	10'
12° 0'	.2094	.2079	4.810	.2126	4.705	1.022	.9781	1.3614	78° 0'
10'	123	108	745	156	638	023	775	584	50'
20'	153	136	682	186	574	024	769	555	40'
30'	.2182	.2164	4.620	.2217	4.511	1.024	.9763	1.3526	30'
40'	211	193	560	247	449	025	757	497	20'
50'	240	221	502	278	390	026	750	468	10'
13° 0'	.2269	.2250	4.445	.2309	4.331	1.026	.9744	1.3439	77° 0'
10'	298	278	390	339	275	027	737	410	50'
20'	327	306	336	370	219	028	730	381	40'
30'	.2356	.2334	4.284	.2401	4.165	1.028	.9724	1.3352	30'
40'	385	363	232	432	113	029	717	323	20'
50'	414	391	182	462	061	030	710	294	10'
14° 0'	.2443	.2419	4.134	.2493	4.011	1.031	.9703	1.3265	76° 0'
10'	473	447	086	524	3.962	031	696	235	50'
20'	502	476	039	555	914	032	689	206	40'
30'	.2531	.2504	3.994	.2586	3.867	1.033	.9681	1.3177	30'
40'	560	532	950	617	821	034	674	148	20'
50'	589	560	906	648	776	034	667	119	10'
15° 0'	.2618	.2588	3.864	.2679	3.732	1.035	.9659	1.3090	75° 0'
10'	647	616	822	711	689	036	652	061	50'
20'	676	644	782	742	647	037	644	032	40'
30'	.2705	.2672	3.742	.2773	3.606	1.038	.9636	1.3003	30'
40'	734	700	703	805	566	039	628	974	20'
50'	763	728	665	836	526	039	621	945	10'
16° 0'	.2793	.2756	3.628	.2867	3.487	1.040	.9613	1.2915	74° 0'
10'	822	784	592	899	450	041	605	886	50'
20'	851	812	556	931	412	042	596	857	40'
30'	.2880	.2840	3.521	.2962	3.376	1.043	.9588	1.2828	30'
40'	909	868	487	994	340	044	580	799	20'
50'	938	896	453	.3026	305	045	572	770	10'
17° 0'	.2967	.2924	3.420	.3057	3.271	1.046	.9563	1.2741	73° 0'
10'	996	952	388	089	237	047	555	712	50'
20'	.3025	979	357	121	204	048	546	683	40'
30'	.3054	.3007	3.326	.3153	3.172	1.048	.9537	1.2654	30'
40'	083	035	295	185	140	049	528	625	20'
50'	113	062	265	217	108	050	520	595	10'
18° 0'	.3142	.3090	3.236	.3249	3.078	1.051	.9511	1.2566	72° 0'
		Cos	Sec	Cot	Tan	Csc	Sin	Radians	Degrees

Degrees	Radians	Sin	Csc	Tan	Cot	Sec	Cos		
18° 0'	.3142	.3090	3.236	.3249	3.078	1.051	.9511	1.2566	72° 0'
10'	171	118	207	281	047	052	502	537	50'
20'	200	145	179	314	018	053	492	508	40'
30'	.3229	.3173	3.152	.3346	2.989	1.054	.9483	1.2479	30'
40'	258	201	124	378	960	056	474	450	20'
50'	287	228	098	411	932	057	465	421	10'
19° 0'	.3316	.3256	3.072	.3443	2.904	1.058	.9455	1.2392	71° 0'
10'	345	283	046	476	877	059	446	363	50'
20'	374	311	021	508	850	060	436	334	40'
30'	.3403	.3338	2.996	.3541	2.824	1.061	.9426	1.2305	30'
40'	432	365	971	574	798	062	417	275	20'
50'	462	393	947	607	773	063	407	246	10'
20° 0'	.3491	.3420	2.924	.3640	2.747	1.064	.9397	1.2217	70° 0'
10'	520	448	901	673	723	065	387	188	50'
20'	549	475	878	706	699	066	377	159	40'
30'	.3578	.3502	2.855	.3739	2.675	1.068	.9367	1.2130	30'
40'	607	529	833	772	651	069	356	101	20'
50'	636	557	812	805	628	070	346	072	10'
21° 0'	.3665	.3584	2.790	.3839	2.605	1.071	.9336	1.2043	69° 0'
10'	694	611	769	872	583	072	325	1.2014	50'
20'	723	638	749	906	560	074	315	985	40'
30'	.3752	.3665	2.729	.3939	2.539	1.075	.9304	1.1956	30'
40'	782	692	709	973	517	076	293	926	20'
50'	811	719	689	.4006	496	077	283	897	10'
22° 0'	.3840	.3746	2.669	.4040	2.475	1.079	.9272	1.1868	68° 0'
10'	869	773	650	074	455	080	261	839	50'
20'	898	800	632	108	434	081	250	810	40'
30'	.3927	.3827	2.613	.4142	2.414	1.082	.9239	1.1781	30'
40'	956	854	595	176	394	084	228	752	20'
50'	985	881	577	210	375	085	216	723	10'
23° 0'	.4014	.3907	2.559	.4245	2.356	1.086	.9205	1.1694	67° 0'
10'	043	934	542	279	337	088	194	665	50'
20'	072	961	525	314	318	089	182	636	40'
30'	.4102	.3987	2.508	.4348	2.300	1.090	.9171	1.1606	30'
40'	131	.4014	491	383	282	092	159	577	20'
50'	160	041	475	417	264	093	147	548	10'
24° 0'	.4189	.4067	2.459	.4452	2.246	1.095	.9135	1.1519	66° 0'
10'	218	094	443	487	229	096	124	490	50'
20'	247	120.	427	522	211	097	112	461	40'
30'	.4276	.4147	2.411	.4557	2.194	1.099	.9100	1.1432	30'
40'	305	173	396	592	177	100	088	403	20'
50'	334	200	381	628	161	102	075	374	10'
25° 0'	.4363	.4226	2.366	.4663	2.145	1.103	.9063	1.1345	65° 0'
10'	392	253	352	699	128	105	051	316	50'
20'	422	279	337	734	112	106	038	286	40'
30'	.4451	.4305	2.323	.4770	2.097	1.108	.9026	1.1257	30'
40'	480	331	309	806	081	109	013	228	20'
50'	509	358	295	841	066	111	001	199	10'
26° 0'	.4538	.4384	2.281	.4877	2.050	1.113	.8988	1.1170	64° 0'
10'	567	410	268	913	035	114	975	141	50'
20'	596	436	254	950	020	116	962	112	40'
30'	.4625	.4462	2.241	.4986	2.006	1.117	.8949	1.1083	30'
40'	654	488	228	.5022	1.991	119	936	054	20'
50'	683	514	215	059	977	121	923	1.1025	10'
27° 0'	.4712	.4540	2.203	.5095	1.963	1.122	.8910	1.0996	63° 0'
		Cos	Sec	Cot	Tan	Csc	Sin	Radians	Degrees

Degrees	Radians	Sin	Csc	Tan	Cot	Sec	Cos		
27° 0'	.4712	.4540	2.203	.5095	1.963	1.122	.8910	1.0996	63° 0'
10'	741	566	190	132	949	124	897	966	50'
20'	771	592	178	169	935	126	884	937	40'
30'	.4800	.4617	2.166	.5206	1.921	1.127	.8870	1.0908	30'
40'	829	643	154	243	907	129	857	879	20'
50'	858	669	142	280	894	131	843	850	10'
28° 0'	.4887	.4695	2.130	.5317	1.881	1.133	.8829	1.0821	62° 0'
10'	916	720	118	354	868	134	816	792	50'
20'	945	746	107	392	855	136	802	763	40'
30'	.4974	.4772	2.096	.5430	1.842	1.138	.8788	1.0734	30'
40'	.5003	797	085	467	829	140	774	705	20'
50'	032	823	074	505	816	142	760	676	10'
29° 0'	.5061	.4848	2.063	.5543	1.804	1.143	.8746	1.0647	61° 0'
10'	091	874	052	581	792	145	732	617	50'
20'	120	899	041	619	780	147	718	588	40'
30'	.5149	.4924	2.031	.5658	1.767	1.149	.8704	1.0559	30'
40'	178	950	020	696	756	151	689	530	20'
50'	207	975	010	735	744	153	675	501	10'
30° 0'	.5236	.5000	2.000	.5774	1.732	1.155	.8660	1.0472	60° 0'
10'	265	025	1.990	812	720	157	646	443	50'
20'	294	050	980	851	709	159	631	414	40'
30'	.5323	.5075	1.970	.5890	1.698	1.161	.8616	1.0385	30'
40'	352	100	961	930	686	163	601	356	20'
50'	381	125	951	969	675	165	587	327	10'
31° 0'	.5411	.5150	1.942	.6009	1.664	1.167	.8572	1.0297	59° 0'
10'	440	175	932	048	653	169	557	268	50'
20'	469	200	923	088	643	171	542	239	40'
30'	.5498	.5225	1.914	.6128	1.632	1.173	.8526	1.0210	30'
40'	527	250	905	168	621	175	511	181	20'
50'	556	275	896	208	611	177	496	152	10'
32° 0'	.5585	.5299	1.887	.6249	1.600	1.179	.8480	1.0123	58° 0'
10'	614	324	878	289	590	181	465	094	50'
20'	643	348	870	330	580	184	450	065	40'
30'	.5672	.5373	1.861	.6371	1.570	1.186	.8434	1.0036	30'
40'	701	398	853	412	560	188	418	1.0007	20'
50'	730	422	844	453	550	190	403	977	10'
33° 0'	.5760	.5446	1.836	.6494	1.540	1.192	.8387	.9948	57° 0'
10'	789	471	828	536	530	195	371	919	50'
20'	818	495	820	577	520	197	355	890	40'
30'	.5847	.5519	1.812	.6619	1.511	1.199	.8339	.9861	30'
40'	876	544	804	661	501	202	323	832	20'
50'	905	568	796	703	1.492	204	307	803	10'
34° 0'	.5934	.5592	1.788	.6745	1.483	1.206	.8290	.9774	56° 0'
10'	963	616	781	787	473	209	274	745	50'
20'	992	640	773	830	464	211	258	716	40'
30'	.6021	.5664	1.766	.6873	1.455	1.213	.8241	.9687	30'
40'	050	688	758	916	446	216	225	657	20'
50'	080	712	751	959	437	218	208	628	10'
35° 0'	.6109	.5736	1.743	.7002	1.428	1.221	.8192	.9599	55° 0'
10'	138	760	736	046	419	223	175	570	50'
20'	167	783	729	089	411	226	158	541	40'
30'	.6196	.5807	1.722	.7133	1.402	1.228	.8141	.9512	30'
40'	225	831	715	177	393	231	124	483	20'
50'	254	854	708	221	385	233	107	454	10'
36° 0'	.6283	.5878	1.701	.7265	1.376	1.236	.8090	.9425	54° 0'
		Cos	Sec	Cot	Tan	Csc	Sin	Radians	Degrees

Degrees	Radians	Sin	Csc	Tan	Cot	Sec	Cos		Degrees
36° 0'	.6283	.5878	1.701	.7265	1.376	1.236	.8090	.9425	54° 0'
10'	312	901	695	310	368	239	073	396	50'
20'	341	925	688	355	360	241	056	367	40'
30'	.6370	.5948	1.681	.7400	1.351	1.244	.8039	.9338	30'
40'	400	972	675	445	343	247	021	308	20'
50'	429	995	668	490	335	249	004	279	10'
37° 0'	.6458	.6018	1.662	.7536	1.327	1.252	.7986	.9250	53° 0'
10'	487	041	655	581	319	255	969	221	50'
20'	516	065	649	627	311	258	951	192	40'
30'	.6545	.6088	1.643	.7673	1.303	1.260	.7934	.9163	30'
40'	574	111	636	720	295	263	916	134	20'
50'	603	134	630	766	288	266	898	105	10'
38° 0'	.6632	.6157	1 624	.7813	1.280	1.269	.7880	.9076	52° 0'
10'	661	180	618	860	272	272	862	047	50'
20'	690	202	612	907	265	275	844	.9018	40'
30'	.6720	.6225	1.606	.7954	1.257	1.278	.7826	.8988	30'
40'	749	248	601	.8002	250	281	808	959	20'
50'	778	271	595	050	242	284	790	930	10'
39° 0'	.6807	.6293	1.589	.8098	1.235	1.287	.7771	.8901	51° 0'
10'	836	316	583	146	228	290	753	872	50'
20'	865	338	578	195	220	293	735	843	40'
30'	.6894	.6361	1.572	.8243	1.213	1.296	.7716	.8814	30'
40'	923	383	567	292	206	299	698	785	20'
50'	952	406	561	342	199	302	679	756	10'
40° 0'	.6981	.6428	1.556	.8391	1.192	1.305	.7660	.8727	50° 0'
10'	.7010	450	550	441	185	309	642	698	50'
20'	039	472	545	491	178	312	623	668	40'
30'	.7069	.6494	1.540	.8541	1.171	1.315	.7604	.8639	30'
40'	098	517	535	591	164	318	585	610	20'
50'	127	539	529	642	157	322	566	581	10'
41° 0'	.7156	.6561	1.524	.8693	1.150	1.325	.7547	.8552	49° 0'
10'	185	583	519	744	144	328	528	523	50'
20'	214	604	514	796	137	332	509	494	40'
30'	.7243	.6626	1.509	.8847	1.130	1.335	.7490	.8465	30'
40'	272	648	504	899	124	339	470	436	20'
50'	301	670	499	952	117	342	451	407	10'
42° 0'	.7330	.6691	1.494	.9004	1.111	1.346	.7431	.8378	48° 0'
10'	359	713	490	057	104	349	412	348	50'
20'	389	734	485	110	098	353	392	319	40'
30'	.7418	.6756	1.480	.9163	1.091	1.356	.7373	.8290	30
40'	447	777	476	217	085	360	353	261	20'
50'	476	799	471	271	079	364	333	232	10'
43° 0'	.7505	.6820	1.466	.9325	1.072	1.367	.7314	.8203	47° 0'
10'	534	841	462	380	066	371	294	174	50'
20'	563	862	457	435	060	375	274	145	40'
30'	.7592	.6884	1.453	.9490	1.054	1.379	.7254	.8116	30'
40'	621	905	448	545	048	382	234	087	20'
50'	650	926	444	601	042	386	214	058	10'
44° 0'	.7679	.6947	1.440	.9657	1.036	1.390	.7193	.8029	46° 0'
10'	709	967	435	713	030	394	173	999	50'
20'	738	988	431	770	024	398	153	970	40'
30'	.7767	.7009	1.427	.9827	1.018	1.402	.7133	.7941	30'
40'	796	030	423	884	012	406	112	912	20'
50'	825	050	418	942	006	410	092	883	10'
45° 0'	.7854	.7071	1.414	1.000	1.000	1.414	.7071	.7854	45° 0'
		Cos	Sec	Cot	Tan	Csc	Sin	Radians	Degrees

III. LOGARITHMS OF TRIGONOMETRIC FUNCTIONS*

Angle	L Sin	d 1'	L Tan	cd 1'	L Cot	d 1'	L Cos	Angle
0° 0'					12.5363	.0	10.0000	90° 0'
10'	7.4637	301.1	7.4637	301.1	.2352	.0	.0000	50'
20'	.7648	176.0	.7648	176.1		.0	.0000	40'
30'	.9408	125.0	.9409	124.9	.0591	.0	.0000	30'
40'	8.0658	96.9	8.0658	96.9	11.9342	.0	.0000	20'
50'	.1627	79.2	.1627	79.2	.8373	.0	.0000	10'
1° 0'	8.2419	66.9	8.2419	67.0	11.7581	.1	9.9999	89° 0'
10'	.3088	58.0	.3089	58.0	.6911	.0	.9999	50'
20'	.3668	51.0	.3669	51.2	.6331	.0	.9999	40'
30'	.4179	45.8	.4181	45.7	.5819	.0	.9999	30'
40'	.4637	41.3	.4638	41.5	.5362	.1	.9998	20'
50'	.5050	37.8	.5053	37.8	.4947	.0	.9998	10'
2° 0'	8.5428	34.8	8.5431	34.8	11.4569	.1	9.9997	88° 0'
10'	.5776	32.1	.5779	32.2	.4221	.0	.9997	50'
20'	.6097	30.0	.6101	30.0	.3899	.1	.9996	40'
30'	.6397	28.0	.6401	28.1	.3599	.0	.9996	30'
40'	.6677	26.3	.6682	26.3	.3318	.1	.9995	20'
50'	.6940	24.8	.6945	24.9	.3055	.0	.9995	10'
3° 0'	8.7188	23.5	8.7194	23.5	11.2806	.1	9.9994	87° 0'
10'	.7423	22.2	.7429	22.3	.2571	.1	.9993	50'
20'	.7645	21.2	.7652	21.3	.2348	.0	.9993	40'
30'	.7857	20.2	.7865	20.2	.2135	.1	.9992	30'
40'	.8059	19.2	.8067	19.4	.1933	.1	.9991	20'
50'	.8251	18.5	.8261	18.5	.1739	.1	.9990	10'
4° 0'	8.8436	17.7	8.8446	17.8	11.1554	.1	9.9989	86° 0'
10'	.8613	17.0	.8624	17.1	.1376	.0	.9989	50'
20'	.8783	16.3	.8795	16.5	.1205	.1	.9988	40'
30'	.8946	15.8	.8960	15.8	.1040	.1	.9987	30'
40'	.9104	15.2	.9118	15.4	.0882	.1	.9986	20'
50'	.9256	14.7	.9272	14.8	.0728	.1	.9985	10'
5° 0'	8.9403	14.2	8.9420	14.3	11.0580	.2	9.9983	85° 0'
10'	.9545	13.7	.9563	13.8	.0437	.1	.9982	50'
20'	.9682	13.4	.9701	13.5	.0299	.1	.9981	40'
30'	.9816	12.9	.9836	13.0	.0164	.1	.9980	30'
40'	.9945	12.5	.9966	12.7	.0034	.1	.9979	20'
50'	9.0070	12.2	9.0093	12.3	10.9907	.2	.9977	10'
6° 0'	9.0192	11.9	9.0216	12.0	10.9784	.1	9.9976	84° 0'
10'	.0311	11.5	.0336	11.7	.9664	.1	.9975	50'
20'	.0426	11.3	.0453	11.4	.9547	.2	.9973	40'
30'	.0539	10.9	.0567	11.1	.9433	.1	.9972	30'
40'	.0648	10.7	.0678	10.8	.9322	.1	.9971	20'
50'	.0755	10.4	.0786	10.5	.9214	.2	.9969	10'
7° 0'	9.0859	10.2	9.0891	10.4	10.9109	.1	9.9968	83° 0'
10'	.0961	9.9	.0995	10.1	.9005	.2	.9966	50'
20'	.1060	9.7	.1096	9.8	.8904	.2	.9964	40'
30'	.1157	9.5	.1194	9.7	.8806	.1	.9963	30'
40'	.1252	9.3	.1291	9.4	.8709	.2	.9961	20'
50'	.1345	9.1	.1385	9.3	.8615	.2	.9959	10'
8° 0'	9.1436	8.9	9.1478	9.1	10.8522	.1	9.9958	82° 0'
10'	.1525	8.7	.1569	8.9	.8431	.2	.9956	50'
20'	.1612	8.5	.1658	8.7	.8342	.2	.9954	40'
30'	.1697	8.4	.1745	8.6	.8255	.2	.9952	30'
40'	.1781	8.2	.1831	8.4	.8169	.2	.9950	20'
50'	.1863	8.0	.1915	8.2	.8085	.2	.9948	10'
9° 0'	9.1943		9.1997		10.8003	.2	9.9946	81° 0'
	L Cos	d 1'	L Cot	cd 1'	L Tan	d 1'	L Sin	Angle

For simplicity, − 10 has been omitted after each entry.

— x —

Angle	L Sin	d 1'	L Tan	cd 1'	L Cot	d 1'	L Cos	
9° 0'	9.1943		9.1997		10.8003		9.9946	81° 0'
10'	.2022	7.9	.2078	8.1	.7922	.2	.9944	50'
20'	.2100	7.8	.2158	8.0	.7842	.2	.9942	40'
30'	.2176	7.6	.2236	7.8	.7764	.2	.9940	30'
40'	.2251	7.5	.2313	7.7	.7687	.2	.9938	20'
50'	.2324	7.3	.2389	7.6	.7611	.2	.9936	10'
10° 0'	9.2397	7.3	9.2463	7.4	10.7537	.2	9.9934	80° 0'
10'	.2468	7.1	.2536	7.3	.7464	.3	.9931	50'
20'	.2538	7.0	.2609	7.3	.7391	.2	.9929	40'
30'	.2606	6.8	.2680	7.1	.7320	.2	.9927	30'
40'	.2674	6.8	.2750	7.0	.7250	.3	.9924	20'
50'	.2740	6.6	.2819	6.9	.7181	.2	.9922	10'
11° 0'	9.2806	6.6	9.2887	6.8	10.7113	.3	9.9919	79° 0'
10'	.2870	6.4	.2953	6.6	.7047	.2	.9917	50'
20'	.2934	6.4	.3020	6.7	.6980	.3	.9914	40'
30'	.2997	6.3	.3085	6.5	.6915	.2	.9912	30'
40'	.3058	6.1	.3149	6.4	.6851	.3	.9909	20'
50'	.3119	6.1	.3212	6.3	.6788	.2	.9907	10'
12° 0'	9.3179	6.0	9.3275	6.3	10.6725	.3	9.9904	78° 0'
10'	.3238	5.9	.3336	6.1	.6664	.3	.9901	50'
20'	.3296	5.8	.3397	6.1	.6603	.2	.9899	40'
30'	.3353	5.7	.3458	6.1	.6542	.3	.9896	30'
40'	.3410	5.7	.3517	5.9	.6483	.3	.9893	20'
50'	.3466	5.6	.3576	5.9	.6424	.3	.9890	10'
13° 0'	9.3521	5.5	9.3634	5.8	10.6366	.3	9.9887	77° 0'
10'	.3575	5.4	.3691	5.7	.6309	.3	.9884	50'
20'	.3629	5.4	.3748	5.7	.6252	.3	.9881	40'
30'	.3682	5.3	.3804	5.6	.6196	.3	.9878	30'
40'	.3734	5.2	.3859	5.5	.6141	.3	.9875	20'
50'	.3786	5.2	.3914	5.5	.6086	.3	.9872	10'
14° 0'	9.3837	5.1	9.3968	5.4	10.6032	.3	9.9869	76° 0'
10'	.3887	5.0	.4021	5.3	.5979	.3	.9866	50'
20'	.3937	5.0	.4074	5.3	.5926	.3	.9863	40'
30'	.3986	4.9	.4127	5.3	.5873	.4	.9859	30'
40'	.4035	4.9	.4178	5.1	.5822	.3	.9856	20'
50'	.4083	4.8	.4230	5.2	.5770	.3	.9853	10'
15° 0'	9.4130	4.7	9.4281	5.1	10.5719	.4	9.9849	75° 0'
10'	.4177	4.7	.4331	5.0	.5669	.3	.9846	50'
20'	.4223	4.6	.4381	5.0	.5619	.3	.9843	40'
30'	.4269	4.6	.4430	4.9	.5570	.4	.9839	30'
40'	.4314	4.5	.4479	4.9	.5521	.3	.9836	20'
50'	.4359	4.5	.4527	4.8	.5473	.4	.9832	10'
16° 0'	9.4403	4.4	9.4575	4.8	10.5425	.4	9.9828	74° 0'
10'	.4447	4.4	.4622	4.7	.5378	.3	.9825	50'
20'	.4491	4.4	.4669	4.7	.5331	.4	.9821	40'
30'	.4533	4.2	.4716	4.7	.5284	.4	.9817	30'
40'	.4576	4.3	.4762	4.6	.5238	.3	.9814	20'
50'	.4618	4.2	.4808	4.6	.5192	.4	.9810	10'
17° 0'	9.4659	4.1	9.4853	4.5	10.5147	.4	9.9806	73° 0'
10'	.4700	4.1	.4898	4.5	.5102	.4	.9802	50'
20'	.4741	4.1	.4943	4.5	.5057	.4	.9798	40'
30'	.4781	4.0	.4987	4.4	.5013	.4	.9794	30'
40'	.4821	4.0	.5031	4.4	.4969	.4	.9790	20'
50'	.4861	4.0	.5075	4.4	.4925	.4	.9786	10'
18° 0'	9.4900	3.9	9.5118	4.3	10.4882	.4	9.9782	72° 0'
	L Cos	d 1'	L Cot	cd 1'	L Tan	d 1'	L Sin	Angle

III. LOGARITHMS OF TRIGONOMETRIC FUNCTIONS (*Cont.*)

Angle	L Sin	d 1'	L Tan	cd 1'	L Cot	d 1'	L Cos	Angle
18° 0'	9.4900		9.5118		10.4882		9.9782	72° 0'
10'	.4939	3.9	.5161	4.3	.4839	.4	.9778	50'
20'	.4977	3.8	.5203	4.2	.4797	.4	.9774	40'
		3.8		4.2		.4		
30'	.5015		.5245		.4755		.9770	30'
40'	.5052	3.7	.5287	4.2	.4713	.5	.9765	20'
50'	.5090	3.8	.5329	4.2	.4671	.4	.9761	10'
		3.6		4.1		.4		
19° 0'	9.5126		9.5370		10.4630		9.9757	71° 0'
10'	.5163	3.7	.5411	4.1	.4589	.5	.9752	50'
20'	.5199	3.6	.5451	4.0	.4549	.4	.9748	40'
		3.6		4.0		.5		
30'	.5235		.5491		.4509		.9743	30'
40'	.5270	3.5	.5531	4.0	.4469	.4	.9739	20'
50'	.5306	3.6	.5571	4.0	.4429	.5	.9734	10'
		3.5		4.0		.4		
20° 0'	9.5341		9.5611		10.4389		9.9730	70° 0'
10'	.5375	3.4	.5650	3.9	.4350	.5	.9725	50'
20'	.5409	3.4	.5689	3.9	.4311	.4	.9721	40'
		3.4		3.8		.5		
30'	.5443		.5727		.4273		.9716	30'
40'	.5477	3.4	.5766	3.9	.4234	.5	.9711	20'
50'	.5510	3.3	.5804	3.8	.4196	.5	.9706	10'
		3.3		3.8		.4		
21° 0'	9.5543		9.5842		10.4158		9.9702	69° 0'
10'	.5576	3.3	.5879	3.7	.4121	.5	.9697	50'
20'	.5609	3.3	.5917	3.8	.4083	.5	.9692	40'
		3.2		3.7		.5		
30'	.5641		.5954		.4046		.9687	30'
40'	.5673	3.2	.5991	3.7	.4009	.5	.9682	20'
50'	.5704	3.1	.6028	3.7	.3972	.5	.9677	10'
		3.2		3.6		.5		
22° 0'	9.5736		9.6064		10.3936		9.9672	68° 0'
10'	.5767	3.1	.6100	3.6	.3900	.5	.9667	50'
20'	.5798	3.1	.6136	3.6	.3864	.6	.9661	40'
		3.0		3.6		.5		
30'	.5828		.6172		.3828		.9656	30'
40'	.5859	3.1	.6208	3.6	.3792	.5	.9651	20'
50'	.5889	3.0	.6243	3.5	.3757	.5	.9646	10'
		3.0		3.6		.6		
23° 0'	9.5919		9.6279		10.3721		9.9640	67° 0'
10'	.5948	2.9	.6314	3.5	.3686	.5	.9635	50'
20'	.5978	3.0	.6348	3.4	.3652	.6	.9629	40'
		2.9		3.5		.5		
30'	.6007		.6383		.3617		.9624	30'
40'	.6036	2.9	.6417	3.4	.3583	.6	.9618	20'
50'	.6065	2.9	.6452	3.5	.3548	.5	.9613	10'
		2.8		3.4		.6		
24° 0'	9.6093		9.6486		10.3514		9.9607	66° 0'
10'	.6121	2.8	.6520	3.4	.3480	.5	.9602	50'
20'	.6149	2.8	.6553	3.3	.3447	.6	.9596	40'
		2.8		3.4		.6		
30'	.6177		.6587		.3413		.9590	30'
40'	.6205	2.8	.6620	3.3	.3380	.6	.9584	20'
50'	.6232	2.7	.6654	3.4	.3346	.5	.9579	10'
		2.7		3.3		.6		
25° 0'	9.6259		9.6687		10.3313		9.9573	65° 0'
10'	.6286	2.7	.6720	3.3	.3280	.6	.9567	50'
20'	.6313	2.7	.6752	3.2	.3248	.6	.9561	40'
		2.7		3.3		.6		
30'	.6340		.6785		.3215		.9555	30'
40'	.6366	2.6	.6817	3.2	.3183	.6	.9549	20'
50'	.6392	2.6	.6850	3.3	.3150	.6	.9543	10'
		2.6		3.2		.6		
26° 0'	9.6418		9.6882		10.3118		9.9537	64° 0'
10'	.6444	2.6	.6914	3.2	.3086	.7	.9530	50'
20'	.6470	2.6	.6946	3.2	.3054	.6	.9524	40'
		2.5		3.1		.6		
30'	.6495		.6977		.3023		.9518	30'
40'	.6521	2.6	.7009	3.2	.2991	.6	.9512	20'
50'	.6546	2.5	.7040	3.1	.2960	.7	.9505	10'
		2.4		3.2		.6		
27° 0'	9.6570		9.7072		10.2928		9.9499	63° 0'
	L Cos	d 1'	L Cot	c d 1'	L Tan	d 1'	L Sin	Angle

III. LOGARITHMS OF TRIGONOMETRIC FUNCTIONS (*Cont.*)

Angle	L Sin	d 1'	L Tan	cd 1'	L Cot	d 1'	L Cos	
27° 0'	9.6570		9.7072		10.2928		9.9499	63° 0'
10'	.6595	2.5	.7103	3.1	.2897	.7	.9492	50'
20'	.6620	2.5	.7134	3.1	.2866	.6	.9486	40'
		2.4		3.1		.7		
30'	.6644	2.4	.7165	3.1	.2835	.6	.9479	30'
40'	.6668	2.4	.7196	3.0	.2804	.7	.9473	20'
50'	.6692	2.4	:7226	3.1	.2774	.7	.9466	10'
		2.4				.7		
28° 0'	9.6716	2.4	9.7257	3.0	10.2743	.6	9.9459	62° 0'
10'	.6740	2.3	.7287	3.0	.2713	.7	.9453	50'
20'	.6763	2.4	.7317	3.1	.2683	.7	.9446	40'
30'	.6787	2.3	.7348	3.0	.2652	.7	.9439	30'
40'	.6810	2.3	.7378	3.0	.2622	.7	.9432	20'
50'	.6833	2.3	.7408	3.0	.2592	.7	.9425	10'
29° 0'	9.6856	2.2	9.7438	2.9	10.2562	.7	9.9418	61° 0'
10'	.6878	2.3	.7467	3.0	.2533	.7	.9411	50'
20'	.6901	2.2	.7497	2.9	.2503	.7	.9404	40'
30'	.6923	2.3	.7526	3.0	.2474	.7	.9397	30'
40'	.6946	2.2	.7556	2.9	.2444	.7	.9390	20'
50'	.6968	2.2	.7585	2.9	.2415	.8	.9383	10'
30° 0'	9.6990	2.2	9.7614	3.0	10.2386	.7	9.9375	60° 0'
10'	.7012	2.1	.7644	2.9	.2356	.7	.9368	50'
20'	.7033	2.2	.7673	2.8	.2327	.8	.9361	40'
30'	.7055	2.1	.7701	2.9	.2299	.7	.9353	30'
40'	.7076	2.1	.7730	2.9	.2270	.8	.9346	20'
50'	.7097	2.1	.7759	2.9	.2241	.7	.9338	10'
31° 0'	9.7118	2.1	9.7788	2.8	10.2212	.8	9.9331	59° 0'
10'	.7139	2.1	.7816	2.9	.2184	.8	.9323	50'
20'	.7160	2.1	.7845	2.8	.2155	.7	.9315	40'
30'	.7181	2.0	.7873	2.9	.2127	.8	.9308	30'
40'	.7201	2.1	.7902	2.8	.2098	.8	.9300	20'
50'	.7222	2.0	.7930	2.8	.2070	.8	.9292	10'
32° 0'	9.7242	2.0	9.7958	2.8	10.2042	.8	9.9284	58° 0'
10'	.7262	2.0	.7986	2.8	.2014	.8	.9276	50'
20'	.7282	2.0	.8014	2.8	.1986	.8	.9268	40'
30'	.7301	2.0	.8042	2.8	.1958	.8	.9260	30'
40'	.7322	2.0	.8070	2.7	.1930	.8	.9252	20'
50'	.7342	1.9	.8097	2.8	.1903	.8	.9244	10'
33° 0'	9.7361	1.9	9.8125	2.8	10.1875	.8	9.9236	57° 0'
10'	.7380	1.9	.8153	2.7	.1847	.8	.9228	50'
20'	.7400	2.0	.8180	2.8	.1820	.9	.9219	40'
30'	.7419	1.9	.8208	2.7	.1792	.8	.9211	30'
40'	.7438	1.9	.8235	2.8	.1765	.8	.9203	20'
50'	.7457	1.9	.8263	2.7	.1737	.9	.9191	10'
34° 0'	9.7476	1.8	9.8290	2.7	10.1710	.8	9.9186	56° 0'
10'	.7494	1.9	.8317	2.7	.1683	.9	.9177	50'
20'	.7513	1.8	.8344	2.7	.1656	.8	.9169	40'
30'	.7531	1.9	.8371	2.7	.1629	.9	.9160	30'
40'	.7550	1.8	.8398	2.7	.1602	.9	.9151	20'
50'	.7568	1.8	.8425	2.7	.1575	.9	.9142	10'
35° 0'	9.7586	1.8	9.8452	2.7	10.1548	.8	9.9134	55° 0'
10'	.7604	1.8	.8479	2.7	.1521	.9	.9125	50'
20'	.7622	1.8	.8506	2.7	.1494	.9	.9116	40'
30'	.7640	1.8	.8533	2.7	.1467	.9	.9107	30'
40'	.7657	1.7	.8559	2.6	.1441	.9	.9098	20'
50'	.7675	1.8	.8586	2.7	.1414	.9	.9089	10'
36° 0'	9.7692	1.7	9.8613	2.7	10.1387	.9	9.9080	54° 0'
	L Cos	d 1'	L Cot	cd 1'	L Tan	d 1'	L Sin	Angle

Angle	L Sin	d 1'	L Tan	cd 1'	L Cot	d 1'	L Cos	
36° 0'	9.7692		9.8613		10.1387		9.9080	54° 0'
10'	.7710	1.8	.8639	2.6	.1361	1.0	.9070	50'
20'	.7727	1.7	.8666	2.7	.1334	.9	.9061	40'
30'	.7744	1.7	.8692	2.6	.1308	.9	.9052	30'
40'	.7761	1.7	.8718	2.6	.1282	1.0	.9042	20'
50'	.7778	1.7	.8745	2.7	.1255	.9	.9033	10'
37° 0'	9.7795	1.7	9.8771	2.6	10.1229	1.0	9.9023	53° 0'
10'	.7811	1.6	.8797	2.6	.1203	.9	.9014	50'
20'	.7828	1.7	.8824	2.7	.1176	1.0	.9004	40'
30'	.7844	1.6	.8850	2.6	.1150	.9	.8995	30'
40'	.7861	1.7	.8876	2.6	.1124	1.0	.8985	20'
50'	.7877	1.6	.8902	2.6	.1098	1.0	.8975	10'
38° 0'	9.7893	1.6	9.8928	2.6	10.1072	1.0	9.8965	52° 0'
10'	.7910	1.7	.8954	2.6	.1046	1.0	.8955	50'
20'	.7926	1.6	.8980	2.6	.1020	1.0	.8945	40'
30'	.7941	1.5	.9006	2.6	.0994	1.0	.8935	30'
40'	.7957	1.6	.9032	2.6	.0968	1.0	.8925	20'
50'	.7973	1.6	.9058	2.6	.0942	1.0	.8915	10'
39° 0'	9.7989	1.6	9.9084	2.6	10.0916	1.0	9.8905	51° 0'
10'	.8004	1.5	.9110	2.6	.0890	1.0	.8895	50'
20'	.8020	1.6	.9135	2.5	.0865	1.1	.8884	40'
30'	.8035	1.5	.9161	2.6	.0839	1.0	.8874	30'
40'	.8050	1.5	.9187	2.6	.0813	1.0	.8864	20'
50'	.8066	1.6	.9212	2.5	.0788	1.1	.8853	10'
40° 0'	9.8081	1.5	9.9238	2.6	10.0762	1.0	9.8843	50° 0'
10'	.8096	1.5	.9264	2.6	.0736	1.1	.8832	50'
20'	.8111	1.5	.9289	2.5	.0711	1.1	.8821	40'
30'	.8125	1.4	.9315	2.6	.0685	1.1	.8810	30'
40'	.8140	1.5	.9341	2.6	.0659	1.0	.8800	20'
50'	.8155	1.5	.9366	2.5	.0634	1.1	.8789	10'
41° 0'	9.8169	1.4	9.9392	2.6	10.0608	1.1	9.8778	49° 0'
10'	.8184	1.5	.9417	2.5	.0583	1.1	.8767	50'
20'	.8198	1.4	.9443	2.6	.0557	1.1	.8756	40'
30'	.8213	1.5	.9468	2.5	.0532	1.1	.8745	30'
40'	.8227	1.4	.9494	2.6	.0506	1.2	.8733	20'
50'	.8241	1.4	.9519	2.5	.0481	1.1	.8722	10'
42° 0'	9.8255	1.4	9.9544	2.5	10.0456	1.1	9.8711	48° 0'
10'	.8269	1.4	.9570	2.6	.0430	1.2	.8699	50'
20'	.8283	1.4	.9595	2.5	.0405	1.1	.8688	40'
30'	.8297	1.4	.9621	2.6	.0379	1.2	.8676	30'
40'	.8311	1.4	.9646	2.5	.0354	1.1	.8665	20'
50'	.8324	1.3	.9671	2.5	.0329	1.2	.8653	10'
43° 0'	9.8338	1.4	9.9697	2.6	10.0303	1.2	9.8641	47° 0'
10'	.8351	1.3	.9722	2.5	.0278	1.2	.8629	50'
20'	.8365	1.4	.9747	2.5	.0253	1.1	.8618	40'
30'	.8378	1.3	.9772	2.5	.0228	1.2	.8606	30'
40'	.8391	1.3	.9798	2.6	.0202	1.2	.8594	20'
50'	.8405	1.4	.9823	2.5	.0177	1.2	.8582	10'
44° 0'	9.8418	1.3	9.9848	2.5	10.0152	1.3	9.8569	46° 0'
10'	.8431	1.3	.9874	2.6	.0126	1.2	.8557	50'
20'	.8444	1.3	.9899	2.5	.0101	1.2	.8545	40'
30'	.8457	1.3	.9924	2.5	.0076	1.3	.8532	30'
40'	.8469	1.2	.9949	2.5	.0051	1.2	.8520	20'
50'	.8482	1.3	.9975	2.6	.0025	1.3	.8507	10'
45° 0'	9.8495	1.3	10.0000	2.5	10.0000	1.2	9.8495	45° 0'
	L Cos	d 1'	L Cot	cd 1'	L Tan	d 1'	L Sin	Angle